S204 Biology: uniformity and diversity
Science: Level 2

The Open U

Generating Diversity

Edited by Michael Gillman

This publication forms part of an Open University course S204 *Biology: uniformity and diversity*. The complete list of texts which make up this course can be found at the back. Details of this and other Open University courses can be obtained from the Student Registration and Enquiry Service, The Open University, PO Box 197, Milton Keynes MK7 6BJ, United Kingdom: tel. +44 (0)845 300 60 90, email general-enquiries@open.ac.uk

Alternatively, you may visit the Open University website at http://www.open.ac.uk where you can learn more about the wide range of courses and packs offered at all levels by The Open University.

To purchase a selection of Open University course materials visit http://www.ouw.co.uk, or contact Open University Worldwide, Walton Hall, Milton Keynes MK7 6AA, United Kingdom for a brochure. tel. +44 (0)1908 858793; fax +44 (0)1908 858787; email ouw-customer-services@open.ac.uk

The Open University
Walton Hall, Milton Keynes
MK7 6AA

First published 2001. Second edition 2007

Edited and designed by The Open University.

Typeset by The Open University.

Printed and bound in the United Kingdom at the University Press, Cambridge.

ISBN 978 0 7492 1449 4

2.1

The S204 Course Team

Course Team Chair
Hilary MacQueen

Maintenance Course Team Chair
Colin Walker

Academic Editor
Caroline Pond

Course Managers
Vivien Bacigalupo
Chris Edwards
Alastair Ewing
Christine Gardener

Course Secretary
Dawn Partner

Authors
Mary Bell (Book 5)
Eric Bowers (Book 6)
John Burnett (Book 4)
Alan Cann (Book 4)
Melanie Clements (Book 3)
Basiro Davey (Book 2)
Hilary Denny (Book 5)
Sue Downs (Book 5)
Mandy Dyson (Books 2 and 6)
Anna Furth (Books 3 and 4)
Michael Gillman (Book 2)
Tim Halliday (Book 2)
Jane Loughlin (Book 3)
David Male (Book 4)
Hilary MacQueen (Book 4)
Judith Metcalfe (Book 3)
Paul O'Shea (Book 3)
Phil Parker (Book 5)
Caroline Pond (Books 1, 2 and 6)
Irene Ridge (Books 1, 4 and 5)
Jerry Roberts (Book 5)
David Robinson (Book 6)
Jill Saffrey (Book 3)
Robert Saunders (Book 6)
Ayona Silva-Fletcher (Book 3)
Valda Stevens (Book 2)
Margaret Swithenby (Books 3 and 4)
Colin Walker (Books 3 and 4)

GLO Editor
Peggy Varley

Editors
Pat Forster
Ian Nuttall
Gillian Riley
Bina Sharma
Margaret Swithenby
Peter Twomey

OU Graphic Design
Sue Dobson
Ruth Drage
Sara Hack
Jenny Nockles
Pam Owen
Howard Twiner
Andrew Whitehead
Liz Yeomans

Library
Lydia Eaton
Judy Thomas

Picture Research
Lydia Eaton

Book Assessors
Gianfranco Novarino (Book 1)
Aubrey Manning (Book 2)
Karl Swann and David Harris (Book 3)
Peter White (Book 4)
David Clarkson and Rachel Leech (Book 5)
John Currey and Brian James (Book 6)

External Course Assessor
Professor Sir David Smith

Consultants
Patricia Ash
Sue Downs
Christine Gardener
Jean Macqueen
Terry Whatson

Skills
Patricia Ash
Hilary Denny

CD-ROM AND VIDEO PRODUCTION

PHOTO ON COVER

MITOCHONDRIA

False-colour transmission electron micrograph of mitochondria (green) shown in cross-section.

In eukaryotic organisms mitochondria are the sites of respiration, the chemical process that uses molecular oxygen to oxidise sugars and fats to release energy. The energy is stored as adenosine triphosphate (ATP) and is used by the cell to drive chemical reactions such as protein synthesis. Mitochondria are bound by a double membrane; the inner membrane is folded to produce ingrowths (red lines) called cristae, which are where the chemical reactions of respiration occur.

Mitochondria occur in virtually all eukaryotic cells, although this particular example is taken from a mammal. In contrast, bacterial cells (prokaryotic) do not contain mitochondria. However, mitochondria are widely believed to have originated as free-living prokaryotic cells that were 'captured' within eukaryotic cells. Consequently there are many structural and functional similarities between mitochondria and bacterial cells. Mitochondria therefore illustrate the theme of uniformity across the diverse range of living organisms: plants, animals and microbes.

The micrograph also includes other cellular organelles, visible in the surrounding cytosol.

Courtesy of Dr Gopal Murti/Science Photo Library.

CONTENTS

SURVIVING THE WINTER

1.1 LIVING IN A FLUCTUATING ENVIRONMENT

The great majority of organisms live in environments that fluctuate extensively and cyclically. For example, an animal such as a limpet living on a sea-shore experiences a 12-hour cycle in which it is alternately exposed, first to the air, the wind and the heat of the Sun, then to pounding by the sea. Life in the natural world exposes organisms to a diversity of environmental cycles, acting on a variety of time-scales. The most obvious cycles are night and day, with a period of 24 hours, and winter and summer or wet and dry seasons over a year; less obvious, but important for many organisms, is the lunar cycle (28 days). Even organisms that live deep in the oceans or under the ground may be exposed to cyclic variations in their environment.

In this chapter, we study one aspect of the fluctuating nature of an organism's environment. We consider how organisms living in a temperate climate, such as that in Britain, are adapted to cope with winter. You will see that there is much diversity of adaptations among organisms, with different species coping with the demands of a fluctuating environment in quite different ways. As cyclic variations are a widespread feature of environments, the range of adaptations to them is an important source of biological diversity.

1.1.1 A DIVERSITY OF STRATEGIES

Faced with an environment that becomes relatively hostile with the onset of winter, an adult organism can, broadly speaking, do one of four things:

1   It can maintain an active lifestyle, adapting in various ways to the prevailing conditions. The robin (*Erithacus rubecula*) is an example of such a species; so are evergreen trees.

2   It can abandon an active lifestyle, adopting an inactive existence for the duration of winter. The hedgehog (*Erinaceus europaeus*) spends the winter in hibernation. Many plants remain dormant below ground during the winter.

3   It can die before the onset of winter, as many adult insects do, but their offspring can survive the winter, for example as an egg or a pupa. Some plants survive the winter as seeds.

4   It can leave, migrating to a part of the world where conditions are favourable during the winter months. Each year, swallows (*Hirundo rustica*) leave Britain in autumn and migrate to Africa, whilst other birds such as barnacle and pink-footed geese migrate to Britain from further north.

Each of these four strategies is more applicable to some kinds of organisms than others. Long-distance migration, for example, is only an option for species that can store energy or can feed continuously (e.g. reindeer, *Rangifer tarandus*). For each of the three groups of species in Table 1.1 there is one strategy that is not an option. Later in this chapter, we will focus on each strategy in turn, examining how it is manifested in different groups of organisms. Table 1.1 summarizes these alternative strategies and gives some examples of organisms that use each of them. This table provides a conceptual framework for much of the chapter.

Table 1.1   A framework for considering the diverse ways in which selected groups of organisms have adapted to winter in a temperate region, such as Britain.

Strategy	Plants	Insects	Vertebrates
1 *'Tough it out'* Maintain an active adult existence by altering behaviour and physiology with changing conditions.	Plants that continue to photosynthesize, e.g. evergreen trees	Not an option for most insects	Mammals that remain active, e.g. fox Birds that remain active, e.g. robin
2 *'Opt out'* Maintain an inactive existence as adults for the duration of the hostile period.	Perennial plants that survive the winter by dying down or going dormant above-ground and/or forming subterranean storage organs, e.g. bulbs and rhizomes	Survive the hostile period in a state of torpor, e.g. certain wasps, bees and butterflies.	True hibernation in small mammals Not an option for most birds Winter torpor in amphibians and reptiles Freeze-tolerance in amphibians
3 *Juvenile survival* Survive the hostile period as some non-adult phase of the life cycle.	Survive the hostile period only in the form of seeds.	Survive the hostile period in the form of eggs, larvae or pupae.	Not an option for vertebrates
4 *'Go away'* Migrate as adults to a location where conditions are favourable.	Not an option for plants	Some butterflies migrate north each spring and summer.	Migration in some birds and mammals

Each of the four strategies can be discussed at different *levels of explanation*. For example, with migration of birds we can consider the molecular and cellular processes involved in energy storage and its utilization for long-distance flight. We can discuss the physiological and structural features of birds' wings that allow long distance flight. Alternatively, we can consider migration in an evolutionary context, discussing the selection pressures that favour migration. This approach leads us into the ideas of *types* of explanation. We will see firstly that organisms carry out certain activities, such as breeding, at those times of year when it is most adaptive for them to do so (i.e. to maximize their fitness, detailed further in Chapter 3) and, secondly, that those activities are performed in response to appropriate environmental cues. For example, many animals whose food is available mainly in summer ensure their survival in winter by building up fat reserves in the autumn.

It is important to separate arguments about adaptation during evolution, referred to as *ultimate* types of explanation, from the analysis of causal mechanisms, referred to as *proximate* types of explanation. To this end, a distinction is made between proximate and ultimate factors. **Ultimate factors** are those features of the environment that have favoured the evolution of particular adaptations; for example, many small mammals have evolved hibernation as an adaptation for coping with adverse winter conditions. **Proximate factors** are those specific features of the environment that elicit specific responses by organisms; long nights elicit a variety of responses in many small mammals, such as increased foraging, laying down fat and hoarding food. Thus proximate factors may operate at several levels. We will see that uniformity and diversity can only be fully understood with reference to both types of factors (ultimate and proximate) as well as several different levels of explanation.

1.2 RESPONSE TO WINTER: UNDERSTANDING AT DIFFERENT LEVELS

Winter in a temperate region poses a number of environmental problems for organisms. Most obviously, average temperatures are lower than at other times of year and there are frequent frosts. Frost is highly significant for living organisms because water forms such a large proportion of their body tissues; for the great majority of organisms, freezing of their tissues leads to death. Secondly, because, as shown in Table 1.1, many adult organisms die, go into hiding or migrate in winter, many of those animals that remain have a greatly reduced supply of food (i.e. plants for herbivores and prey for carnivores). A third significant factor in winter is that the daylight period becomes markedly shorter than at other times of the year. For plants that require light for photosynthesis and for animals that use daylight vision to find food, shorter days in winter severely restrict their ability to acquire the energy and nutrients that they need to support life. Finally, a major problem for plants in winter is shortage of water, which arises for two reasons. Firstly, when water becomes frozen in the ground, it is no longer available for plants to take up through their roots. Secondly, low temperatures greatly reduce the capacity of plant roots to take up water that is available, because their physiological processes are slowed down and, often, the transport tubes (xylem) become blocked by air bubbles, so are unable to function. Here we will introduce these problems at a number of levels: Sections 1.2.1–1.2.3 invoke proximate types of explanation whilst Section 1.2.4 considers ultimate types of explanation.

1.2.1 THE MOLECULAR LEVEL

It is common knowledge that the freezing point of pure water is $0\,°C$. Often, however, the temperature of water can fall below $0\,°C$ without it freezing, for two reasons:

1   Any solvent containing a dissolved substance has a lower freezing point than when pure, which is why the sea freezes at a lower temperature than clean freshwater.

2   The occurrence of **supercooling**, the phenomenon by which a fluid remains liquid at a temperature below its normal freezing point. Freezing occurs when

water molecules become aligned in a particular pattern that leads to the formation of ice crystals. It begins when two molecules become aligned, a process called nucleation, and ice grows from a *nucleation point*. Whether or not water molecules become appropriately aligned depends on the conditions, so the temperature at which freezing occurs varies within a narrow range. Supercooled water freezes abruptly if an ice crystal is added to it. Small objects such as microbes also act as nucleation points, including certain bacteria on the surfaces of plant leaves. For example, *Pseudomonas syringae* cells act as ice-nucleation points, causing ice to start forming at −1 °C. In the absence of these bacteria, ice does not form on plants until about −5 °C. Genetically engineered strains of *P. syringae*, called 'ice-minus', have been produced which lack ice-nucleating characteristics. When these bacteria are sprayed onto the leaves of crop plants, they make them more frost-resistant.

Fishes living in temperate and arctic habitats remain active through the winter (strategy 1 in Table 1.1), swimming about in very cold water. The winter flounder (*Pseudopleuronectes americanus*), for example, swims actively in water at a temperature well below the freezing point of its blood. What prevents its tissues from freezing? Two hypotheses, both of which invoke molecular levels of explanation, have been proposed. The ice-prevention hypothesis is that the tissues of fishes contain compounds that act as antifreeze, lowering the overall freezing point of their cells and body fluids. A number of such compounds have been identified, but they do not occur in some body fluids, such as urine and the fluid in the eye, suggesting that freezing is only prevented in some parts of the body. The alternative hypothesis, proposed by Valerio *et al.* (1992) is that ice is excluded from the body by a surface barrier. The skin of the winter flounder contains peptides (short chains of amino acids) which prevent ice formation. These molecules act in two ways: by lowering the freezing point of water in the skin and by binding to water molecules and so preventing them from binding to each other to form ice crystals. As described above, ice grows from nucleation points and the skin prevents ice formation at the fish's interface with very cold water.

1.2.2 THE CELLULAR LEVEL

The water in plant and animal tissues has two major components: the intracellular fluid (within cells) and the extracellular fluid, which fills the spaces between cells. When a tissue freezes, ice typically forms first in the extracellular fluid. Ice formation has two harmful effects:

1 It disrupts cell walls and cellular membranes.

2 The formation of ice in extracellular fluid effectively removes water from solution, thereby increasing its solute concentration. The gradient in solute concentration between the extracellular fluid and the cells it surrounds causes water to move out of the cells into the extracellular spaces (a process called osmosis), so that the cells collapse.

The destructive effect of frost on plants is a familiar consequence of these forms of cellular dysfunction. Frosted foliage collapses and turns brown, a result of the destruction of tissues in which ice has formed. These effects are especially obvious in some non-native plants, which are not adapted to survive frost.

1.2.3 THE PHYSIOLOGICAL AND BEHAVIOURAL LEVELS

ANTICIPATION OF WINTER

If organisms are to survive winter, they must be well prepared for cold weather and sometimes for reduced supply of food. Physiological changes such as shedding leaves and building up fat reserves, and behaviours such as hoarding food, must be completed before winter begins. In order to be prepared, organisms need to anticipate the onset of winter, which is done in two ways, each of which has its own associated physiological mechanisms. First, they could respond to environmental cues that predict that winter is imminent, e.g. lower temperatures and shorter day lengths.

○ Which of these cues is the more reliable?

● Changes in day length, which follow an identical pattern every year. We know from personal experience that temperature is very variable and that cold weather comes earlier in some years than others.

Secondly, animals could have an internal clock which tells them what time of year it is, just as a calendar tells us the date.

PHOTOPERIODISM

A great deal of research has been carried out into the way that organisms respond to changes in day length, i.e. the relative durations of light and darkness in a 24-hour period. This relationship is expressed as the ratio of the number of hours of light (L) to the number of hours of darkness (D), i.e. L : D. **Photoperiodism** is defined as the responses of organisms to changes in the L : D ratio. For example, flowering plants can be divided into three categories on the basis of the effect of photoperiodism on the onset of flowering:

* *Short-day plants* flower in early spring (e.g. primrose, *Primula vulgaris*) or in the autumn (e.g. *Chrysanthemum* spp.), when L is small relative to D.

* *Long-day plants* flower in the summer (e.g. potato, *Solanum tuberosum*, or lettuce, *Lactuca sativa*), when L is large relative to D.

* *Day-neutral plants* are not affected, in terms of flowering, by changes in the L : D ratio (e.g. groundsel, *Senecio vulgaris*).

Horticulturalists have long been familiar with these effects and exploit them to get plants to flower at times that suit them. If you go to the Chelsea Flower Show, which takes place in May, you see spring, summer and autumn plants, raised under artificial conditions, all in bloom at the same time.

○ How can chrysanthemums be made to flower later in the year than normal?

● By keeping them under high L : D conditions during the spring, using artificial lights, and transferring them to low L : D conditions just before they are required to bloom.

Simply observing that primroses, for example, flower in early spring is consistent with the hypothesis that they flower in response to short light periods, but it does not preclude alternative hypotheses, such as that they flower in response to increased temperature. However, primroses kept indoors under consistently long light periods and a variety of temperatures do not flower, confirming that onset of flowering is indeed a response to short light periods. Photoperiodism can only be revealed by means of experimental manipulations in which plants are kept under different L : D regimes, and in which other environmental cues to which they might respond are held constant. Variations on this kind of experiment tell us other things about photoperiodism. For example, some plants flower in response to a single exposure to an appropriate L : D ratio. Others flower only if an appropriate L : D ratio is sustained for several days. A pigment, called phytochrome, which switches between 'dark' and 'light' forms, is involved in sensing the length of the light and dark periods.

For a specific physiological response, there is typically a particular L : D ratio at which the response starts to occur. The **critical photoperiod** is defined as that L : D ratio at which 50% of the population being studied switches from one state to another. There is considerable variation in the preciseness of a particular organism's response to a critical photoperiod. Figure 1.1 shows two examples of critical photoperiods for animals. Whereas *all* aphids switch from sexual to asexual reproduction at an L : D ratio of 10 : 14, male sparrows start to show testicular development at an L : D ratio of about 8 : 16, but all do not mature unless the ratio is about 16 : 8.

In some animals, the physiological basis of this effect is known. The hormone melatonin is secreted by the brain during the dark period, with the result that in winter blood levels of melatonin are much higher.

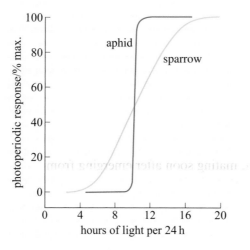

Figure 1.1 Critical photoperiodic responses in two species: transition from sexual to asexual reproduction in the vetch aphid (*Megoura viciae*) and testicular development in the white-crowned sparrow (*Zonotrichia leucophrys*).

CIRCANNUAL CLOCKS

The physiology and behaviour of microbes, plants and animals show cyclical changes on a diversity of time-scales. Most familiar to humans are circadian rhythms, which determine patterns of sleep and wakefulness and of changes in body temperature over a 24-hour period. There is also evidence that certain annual rhythms are controlled by internal clock mechanisms, called **circannual clocks** (circannual means 'about a year').

Whatever the time-scale over which they operate, the existence of endogenous clocks can only be determined by experimental investigation. Simply observing that an animal or a plant shows a daily or an annual cycle of activity or physiology does not preclude the possibility that it is responding to rhythmic changes in the environment. The crucial experiment is called a **free-running** experiment, in which organisms are kept under conditions in which they are unable to detect normal cycles in external features of their environment. For example, captive alpine marmots (*Marmota marmota*, a member of the squirrel family) have been kept for long periods under constant temperatures and constant L : D ratios. Despite having no known cues that winter was approaching, they showed a 100% increase in food intake in the autumn, just as they do in nature, in preparation for hibernation. Kenagy (1981) found that chipmunks (*Eutamias minimus* and *E. amoenus*, also in the squirrel family) kept under combinations of three photoperiods (L : D ratios 8 : 16, 12 : 12 and 16 : 8) and two temperatures (5 and 23 °C) maintained normal cyclical patterns of testis growth, body mass, water consumption, locomotion and winter torpor.

LINKAGE OF ANIMAL REPRODUCTIVE CYCLES TO WINTER

The reproductive success of organisms is crucially determined by the time of year when they breed. Many birds living in Britain breed in the spring, with the result that they are able to feed their young at that time of year when there is most suitable food available. For many kinds of animal, all parts of the reproductive process, from mating to birth, follow the end of the winter. A complication for some larger mammals, however, is that there is a long gestation period (the interval between conception and birth, nine months in humans). A long gestation period and giving birth early in the spring are not easily reconciled with being inactive in winter. Figure 1.2 shows how the reproductive cycles of four mammals native to Britain are related to the winter.

The hedgehog (*Erinaceus europaeus*) has a short reproductive cycle and so can complete the entire process in the spring, mating soon after emerging from hibernation. The red deer (*Cervus elaphus*), with a long gestation period, mates in the autumn (the rut) and gives birth in spring, remaining active through the winter. The other two species shown in Figure 1.2 have gestation periods that are too long for the entire reproductive cycle to be completed in the spring, but too short to occupy the whole winter. Badgers (*Meles meles*) mate in the autumn and the eggs are fertilized immediately. Implantation of the zygote into the wall of the uterus is, however, delayed for several months, during which the female spends short cold spells in a state of torpor in an underground den. The noctule bat (*Nyctalus noctula*) mates in the autumn but the eggs are not fertilized. Instead,

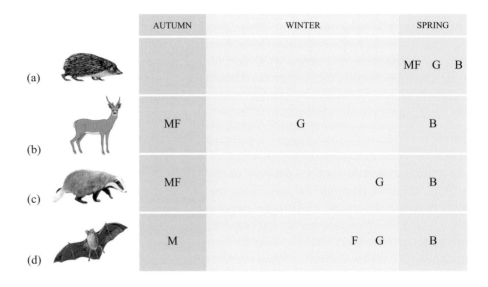

	AUTUMN	WINTER	SPRING
(a)			MF G B
(b)	MF	G	B
(c)	MF	G	B
(d)	M	F G	B

Figure 1.2   Reproductive cycles of (a) hedgehog, (b) red deer, (c) badger and (d) noctule bat, in relation to the winter. M = mating; F = fertilization of the egg(s); G = gestation; B = birth. In the badger, implantation occurs 3–9 months after fertilization. In the noctule bat, fertilization is delayed for up to 7 months following mating.

females store sperm in their reproductive tract until late winter, when fertilization occurs and gestation begins. Throughout this time, they are hibernating.

These different reproductive patterns are controlled by environmental cues in much the same way as the flowering of plants. Red deer, badgers and bats are called *short-day breeders*; the development of their gonads and their sexual behaviour is stimulated by the lengthening dark period characteristic of autumn. Hedgehogs and many other small mammals are *long-day breeders*; their gonad development and sexual behaviour are triggered by a decrease in the dark period.

Figure 1.2 illustrates how diverse are the reproductive cycles of a single group of animals, the mammals. Deer, badgers and hedgehogs are very different animals, however, and before we leave this brief account of seasonal breeding, it is important to emphasize that there is enormous diversity, even among closely related species. Figure 1.3 shows the breeding seasons of members of a single genus, *Peromyscus*, in North America. *Peromyscus* is a genus of small American rodents that includes a variety of mice, such as the deermouse, white-footed mouse and cactus mouse.

○   How does the breeding season in *Peromyscus* species change with latitude?

●   The breeding season of *Peromyscus* is limited to a single, three-month period in northerly latitudes, but is continuous through the year in Mexico. In between, there is considerable variation in the duration of the breeding season; in some regions at intermediate latitudes, there are two peaks in breeding activity.

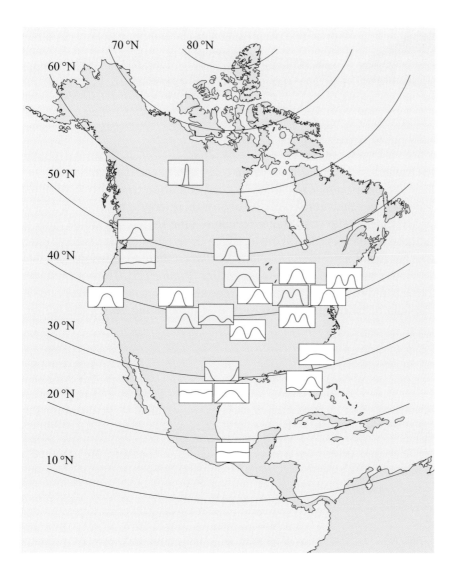

Figure 1.3 The breeding seasons (expressed as the relative proportion of females pregnant in each month) of several populations of *Peromyscus* species in North America. Each box represents a 12-month period from January (left) to December (right). The yellow boxes are all for a single species, the deermouse (*P. maniculatus*). Data from Bronson (1987).

WINTER FAT RESERVES AND REPRODUCTION

For some animals in which breeding begins as soon as the winter has finished, energy reserves accumulated in the previous autumn may be important, not only for winter survival but also for reproductive success in the following spring. In newts, for example, as in other temperate amphibians, nutrient reserves are built up in the late summer and autumn, in both the liver and the abdominal fat stores. These reserves are only partly used up in the winter, when newts are largely torpid underground, and the remainder plays a key role in reproduction. Female newts use their fat reserves to produce yolk for their eggs; males use theirs to develop a large dorsal crest, which is crucial in mating, females responding positively only to males with large crests (Figure 1.4). A population of great crested newts (*Triturus cristatus*) on the Open University campus has been studied in detail by John Baker. He weighed and measured males as they

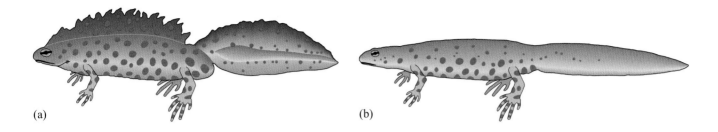

(a)   (b)

Figure 1.4 (a) Male and (b) female great crested newts (*Triturus cristatus*) in breeding condition.

migrated towards their breeding pond in early spring and, for each male, he calculated a 'condition index'. Males in good condition (i.e. with a condition index value greater than zero) were heavy for their length, because of their larger fat reserves. Later in the year, Baker recaptured the same individuals, now in the pond, and measured their dorsal crest, which develops after newts have entered the water. He found a positive correlation between their crest height and their condition index measured a few weeks earlier (Figure 1.5). Thus, a male newt's attractiveness to females, and hence his reproductive success, is partly determined by the amount of fat that he has left over after hibernating during the winter.

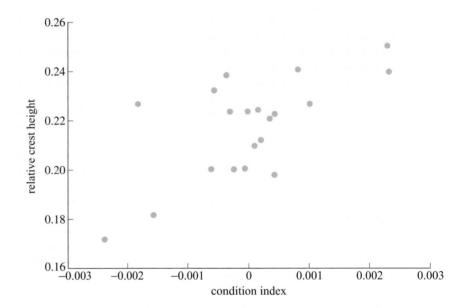

Figure 1.5 The relationship between a male great crested newt's condition index when he arrives at a pond and the size of the dorsal crest which he develops a few weeks later. Data from Baker (1992).

1.2.4 THE EVOLUTIONARY LEVEL

LIFE HISTORIES AND TRADE-OFFS

In this section, the emphasis switches from proximate (molecular, cellular, physiological and behavioural) types of explanation to ultimate types of explanation. In order to proceed, we need to understand two key concepts: **life history** and **trade-off**. Both of these concepts are important tools in organizing thoughts about why organisms are so diverse. An organism's life history is the set of key biological events in its life, including birth, growth, reproduction, sometimes migration, and death. Life histories are distinguished from life cycles, which are a detailed description of the sequence of stages in an organism's life. Life histories can be subjected to quantitative analysis. A familiar example of a life history is that of an annual plant which, following birth (germination), grows, flowers (reproduces), sets many seed and then dies. A contrasting life history is that of large-bodied mammals such as African elephants or blue whales. Following birth, these animals grow to a very large size before giving birth to (usually) one offspring at a time. There is then a period of recovery before new young can be produced. Death may follow 20–30 years after the first birth, during which time perhaps 8–10 young may have been born.

Between the extremes of an elephant and an annual plant lie the life histories of many species. If these life histories are subjected to quantitative analysis, for example by plotting fecundity (number of offspring) against chances of survival, the results indicate that trade-offs are at work. For instance, organisms with a high fecundity have a lower chance of future survival. What are the reasons for these results? The patterns between species reflect processes that have occurred within species and can be given proximate explanations. In proximate terms, each behavioural, physiological or biochemical activity has an energetic cost. For a given energy input (food or light intake) an organism cannot afford to indulge in many different costly activities. Therefore trade-offs have to occur. Let us take the example of a short-lived plant in which there is genetic variation in the amount of photosynthetic product (e.g. starch) that can be stored in the root. Some individuals can store more in the roots than others. Those individuals that store less in the roots divert the energy into seed production. The probability of plants surviving after flowering is inversely related to the amount of seed produced. Thus plants that put less stores into roots have a higher probability of dying after flowering, in contrast to plants that store more in the roots. The latter produce fewer or smaller seeds and hence have a higher probability of survival after flowering.

Natural selection can operate on this genetic variation. It may be that under certain environmental conditions the storers are favoured, and under other environmental conditions, those that produce many seeds are favoured. It may also be that both strategies are favoured by the same environmental conditions. Thus both seed producers and storers do well in winter, i.e. there are two equally adaptive solutions to the same environmental problem. Hence we can see how genetic variation underpinning life history variation due to trade-offs in individuals can, through natural selection and subsequent speciation, be represented as life history variation between species. (Genetic variation and natural selection are reviewed in Chapter 3.) In conclusion, it is possible to move from proximate explanations of trade-offs and life history variation in individuals, to ultimate explanations of life history variation between species. This book will cover many examples of trade-offs, which act as important constraints on organism structure.

PLANT LIFE HISTORIES

To review ideas on life histories, let us consider some plant examples. Among plants, there are three broad categories of life history, each of which has different implications for how they respond to the onset of winter:

1 *Annuals* As described above, these plants complete their life cycle in a single year. Most annuals in temperate regions set seed during the summer and then die before winter (Table 1.1, strategy 3). They represent the extreme version of the high seed-producers discussed above.

2 *Biennials or short-lived herbaceous perennials* These plants have the capacity for storage of photosynthetic product(s). In this particular category are plants that live for two or a few years, flowering and setting seed only in the second or final year. Since biennials that did not survive their first winter would fail to reproduce, they must be adapted for winter survival. They allocate some of their resources to growth in the first year, and some to accumulating stored reserves in their roots. Their foliage may die back with the onset of winter (strategy 2) but their stored nutrients and energy enable them to grow quickly in the second year, prior to flowering. Thus, whereas growth (vegetative) and reproductive phases of the life history occur in the same year in annuals, they are separated into different years in biennials.

3 *Long-lived perennials* These plants may persist for many years, typically reproducing many times. Perennial plants include herbaceous plants that die back each year (strategy 2), and woody plants, which possess a number of adaptations for surviving the winter (strategies 1 and 2). There may be a long juvenile period before the first reproduction event.

For smaller biennials and perennials, the typical overwintering strategy is for those parts of the plant above ground to die back, leaving an underground storage organ, such as a tap root, a bulb or a rhizome, to survive the winter. For larger plants such as trees, this option is not viable, because reconstructing the above-ground parts of the plant every year would preclude any long-term growth. Trees have two main strategies for surviving the winter, belonging to either the **deciduous** or the **evergreen** category (strategies 2 and 1 respectively). Deciduous trees are those that shed all their leaves in a particular season, usually the autumn. Evergreen trees retain leaves all year round; they do drop and replace their leaves, but only some at a time. While trees do not possess discrete storage organs, they store energy-releasing compounds and other nutrients during the winter, in their trunks and roots.

Storage during the winter involves risks because, among temperate animals, there are herbivores that follow strategy 1, remaining active through the winter. Plant storage organs are a vital food source for such animals and many individual plants fail to survive the winter because their storage materials have been consumed by animals or fungi.

We will now discuss in more detail the means by which selected groups of organisms survive the winter, with reference to the four strategies in Table 1.1. Throughout the discussion of these strategies, we will move between different types and levels of explanation. It will also be clear that certain strategies are only open to certain taxonomic groups.

SUMMARY OF SECTIONS 1.1 AND 1.2

1 The majority of organisms are exposed to environmental fluctuations, including seasonal change in climate. In this chapter, we focus on the effects of winter.

2   Organisms have evolved a range of strategies to cope with winter. Thus this common environmental variable has led to a diversity of responses.

3   The strategies for coping with winter can be considered with respect to different levels and types of explanation.

4   Molecular and cellular level responses to winter include the prevention of freezing through the production of antifreeze molecules such as peptides.

5   Physiological and behavioural responses include detecting the onset of winter through changes in the L : D ratio which prompts alteration of sexual behaviour. The reproductive cycles of many organisms are linked to the L : D ratio. Many of these effects can be investigated by experiment.

6   The life histories of organisms can be viewed as the products of trade-offs in biological processes.

1.3 STRATEGY 1: REMAINING ACTIVE THROUGH THE WINTER ('TOUGH IT OUT')

1.3.1 EVERGREEN PLANTS

In temperate regions, the most prominent evergreen plants are coniferous trees, or conifers (phylum Coniferophyta). Conifers dominate large portions of the Earth's land area, particularly at northern latitudes and high altitudes. This distribution reflects their ability to withstand long periods of cold weather. The major problem faced by conifers in winter is lack of water. Water that has turned into ice is not available to plants and, at freezing temperatures, plant roots are able to absorb such water as is available only very slowly. If conifers are not to die of desiccation they must, therefore, reduce the rate at which they lose water. The needle-like shape of conifer leaves reduces the rate at which water is lost from their surfaces and so reduces a tree's requirement for water.

Though very small compared to the leaves of most deciduous trees, pine needles are relatively thick, in comparison to the broad, flat leaves of deciduous trees. Consequently, their surface area is small relative to their volume, reducing water loss. Evaporation is further reduced by a thick, waxy cuticle that forms the outer surface of needles and by the stomata (pores through which leaves exchange gases with the air) being positioned in sunken pits.

Not all conifers are evergreens, and not all evergreens are conifers. There are some ten species of larches (genus *Larix*) that live mostly at high altitude in the Northern Hemisphere; all are deciduous, dropping their needles at the onset of winter. The holm oak (*Quercus ilex*), also known as the evergreen oak, is not a conifer, but retains its leaves through the winter. The holm oak is a native of continental Europe, from the Mediterranean to Brittany, that has been introduced into Britain.

As explained in Section 1.2.4, life histories involve trade-offs between many factors and this principle is well illustrated by a comparison between deciduous and evergreen trees. By retaining their leaves through the winter, evergreens do not bear the cost, as deciduous trees do, of reconstructing their entire photosynthetic apparatus each spring. However, the adaptations that enable their leaves to survive the winter make them less efficient in the spring and summer than those of deciduous trees. Another trade-off is that conifers have a simpler system of water-conducting cells which is less efficient when water is plentiful, but better (because it is less likely to block) when water is scarce and freezing occurs.

1.3.2 BIRDS AND MAMMALS

Birds and mammals are **endotherms**, meaning that they produce and retain a lot of heat within their own tissues, rather than absorb heat from their environment, as **ectotherms**, such as insects and reptiles, do. The terms endotherm and endothermy are now often used in preference to homeotherm and homeothermy, which refer to the ability of birds and mammals to maintain a more or less constant body temperature. Some endotherms, as you will see later, do not maintain a high body temperature at all times, and some ectotherms, such as larger reptiles, maintain a constant body temperature for long periods, even though the temperature of their environment changes.

Whilst endothermy allows some birds and mammals to remain active during winter, it also places formidable demands on those animals. Reduced environmental temperatures increase the amount of heat that they need to generate internally to maintain a constant temperature, at a time when the amount of food available to them is much reduced. For birds and many mammals, shorter day length in winter reduces the time available for finding food. It has been estimated that a small bird, such as a great tit, which feeds on seeds and small insects, has to find food items at an average rate of one every ten seconds during daylight hours through the winter. The extreme challenge posed to birds by the shortage of food in winter is illustrated by the impact of bird-tables in urban areas, which supplement their natural diet. Studies by the RSPB (Royal Society for the Protection of Birds) suggest that, in urban areas of Britain, the provision of food at bird-tables significantly increases the winter survival rate of several garden bird species.

MAINTAINING BODY HEAT

Mammals that remain active in winter maintain a core body temperature of around 37–38 °C; that of most birds is a little higher. In temperate habitats, thermal constancy is achieved despite the temperature of the environment varying between −20 and +20 °C. For animals in polar regions, the problem is even more severe, their environment varying between −60 and +20 °C. There are three principal ways in which endotherms can respond adaptively to cold conditions:

1   They can raise their metabolic rate so as to produce more heat to offset the increased heat loss.

2   They can improve external insulation between their body and the external environment, so as to reduce the rate of heat loss.

3   They can alter the pattern of blood circulation around their body so as to minimize the extent to which warm blood comes close to the skin (i.e. another form of insulation).

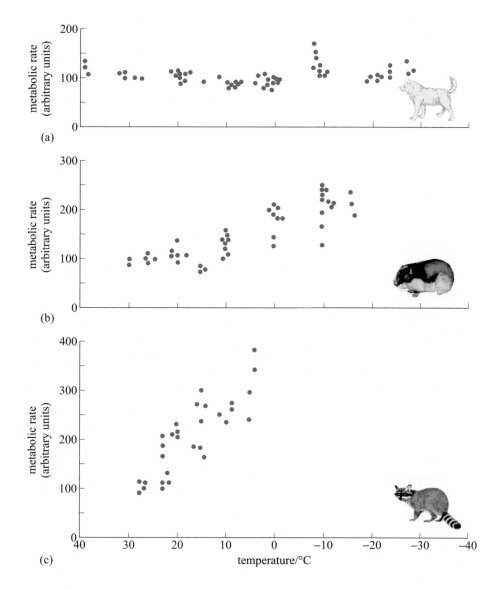

Figure 1.6 The effect of declining temperatures on the metabolic rate of (a) an Eskimo dog, (b) an arctic lemming and (c) a tropical raccoon. Note that temperature decreases from left to right along the horizontal axis. Data from Irving (1966).

Considering the first of these processes, Figure 1.6 shows data from experiments in which three mammalian species, two from the Arctic and one from the tropics, were exposed to declining temperatures.

○ In what way does the response to reduced temperature of (a) the Eskimo dog and (b) the arctic lemming differ from that of the tropical raccoon?

● (a) The metabolic rate of the Eskimo dog shows no clear pattern of change (except possibly increasing at very low temperatures), whereas that of the raccoon increases almost linearly as the temperature decreases from 28 to 5 °C. (b) The metabolic rate of the arctic lemming begins increasing at about 15 °C, but more gradually than that of the tropical raccoon.

Mammals and birds living at high latitudes generally rely on processes 2 and 3, rather than 1, though, as we have seen from Figure 1.6b, there are arctic species, such as the lemming, in which process 1 does play a major role.

Maintaining a high metabolic rate through a long winter requires that mammals and birds either maintain a high rate of food intake, or carry substantial energy reserves within their body, or show some combination of the two. They must also reduce heat loss during the winter. Many species maintain larger energy reserves, in the form of adipose tissue. The adipose tissue beneath the skin (subcutaneous fat) is also widely assumed to act as a thermal insulation layer, but this theory is erroneous. Adipose tissue is not much better an insulator than muscle. Only for marine mammals, such as seals, in which the adipose tissue forms a thick layer of blubber, is its role in thermal insulation significant. For birds and mammals, insulation is provided by feathers and fur respectively, which trap a layer of air next to the skin. Static air is a very poor conductor of heat, so that air trapped in plumage or fur reduces heat flow between an animal's skin and the outside. Bird plumage is a remarkably effective insulator; it represents only 5–7% of a bird's mass and trapped air makes up 95% of its total volume. The texture and often the colour of birds' plumage and mammals' fur changes with the onset of winter, in comparison to the summer. This change is effected during **moult**, a seasonal process in which a bird changes all or many of its feathers and a mammal replaces its summer coat with a thicker winter coat, and the converse in spring.

In birds, the plumage has two major components: contour feathers, which form the exterior surface; and down, which lies beneath the contour feathers. Most feathers consist, in varying proportions, of pennaceous (fan-like) and downy components (see Figure 1.7). The large feathers in the wings and tail are wholly pennaceous; many other small feathers close to the skin are pure down. In winter, the number of down feathers is markedly increased. Only in a few species has the total number of a bird's feathers been counted; humming-birds have about 940, whereas a swan has 25 000. In the house sparrow (*Passer domesticus*) there are 11.5% more feathers in winter than in summer. Each feather has an individual muscle which enables it to be lifted away from the body. This capacity enables birds to regulate heat loss by altering the thickness of the air layer trapped among the feathers.

In mammals, fur contains fine hair close to the skin, underneath thicker and larger surface hairs. The insulative effect of hair is determined primarily by its length; the longer the hairs, the better is the coat as an insulator (Figure 1.8). Comparison of the insulative value of the pelts of arctic and tropical mammals with hair of similar length reveals that the pelts of arctic species are only slightly better insulators (Figure 1.8). The difference arises because arctic species have more hairs per unit area of skin. Figure 1.8 also shows how the insulative value of the coats of two species, the beaver and the polar bear, is completely eliminated when it becomes thoroughly wet.

In many species, the winter plumage or coat is very different in colour and pattern from the summer one. This seasonal change has nothing to do with temperature control, but is usually related to camouflage. The winter plumage of many birds, especially males, is much less brightly coloured than the summer plumage. In many polar mammals, such as the arctic fox (*Alopex lagopus*), the winter coat is white, making the animal well camouflaged in snow.

Figure 1.7 A body feather showing pennaceous (top) and downy (bottom) components.

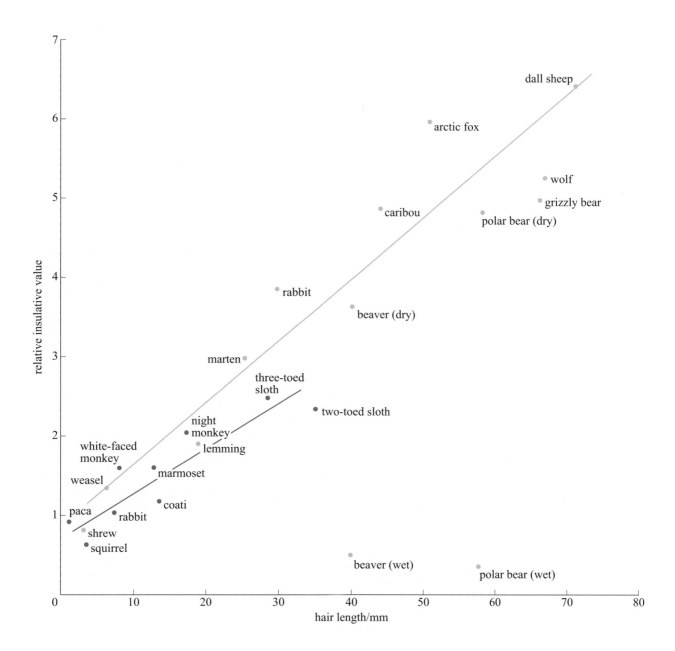

Figure 1.8   Relationship between the insulative value of the coats of arctic (blue) and tropical (red) mammals and the length of their hair. This figure also shows the effect of wetting on a coat's insulative value. Data from Pough *et al.* (1996).

The third response to cold, varying blood flow to different parts of the body, is well illustrated by the Eskimo dog (Figure 1.9). At a temperature of −30 °C the Eskimo dog maintains a core temperature of around +38 °C, but adjustments in blood flow mean that the temperature of some parts of the body, notably the extremities such as the feet and the nose, is allowed to fall.

In many endotherms, cooling of the extremities is achieved by a heat exchange mechanism called a **rete mirabile** (pronounced 'reeta mirah-bilay' and meaning

Figure 1.9 An Eskimo dog, at an environmental temperature of −30 °C, showing the temperature recorded at different parts of the body. Data from Irving (1966).

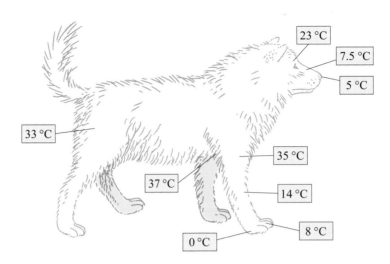

'wonderful net', Figure 1.10). Warm blood passing in arteries towards the skin runs close to colder blood passing back in veins towards the body core. Thus warm blood passing outwards gives up much of its heat before it reaches the skin. This effect is enhanced by constriction of blood capillaries near the skin when it is cold.

Very small mammals and birds that remain active in winter face a problem. Because their surface area is relatively large in relation to their mass, they lose heat in cold conditions faster per unit mass than larger animals and the amount of extra fur or feathers they would need to insulate themselves would make them immobile. The dwarf hamsters (*Phodopus* spp.) of Siberia and Mongolia have adapted to this problem in some interesting ways. They remain active in winter but run around, feeding on seeds and vegetation, under the deep snow, where they are not exposed to the wind and the extremes of cold. Whereas larger animals typically build up their adipose tissue and put on weight as winter approaches, dwarf hamsters get markedly lighter and leaner. Males lose about 50% and females 30% of their body mass and adipose tissue falls from 35 to 5% of the total body mass.

○ How might a lower body mass enable a dwarf hamster to better survive the winter?

● Having a smaller body reduces an animal's energy requirement for locomotion.

Finally, consider the unfortunate pig. Pigs are large mammals and, as the result of selective breeding during domestication, they have so little hair that it provides no insulation against the cold. Pigs have the usual depots of subcutaneous fat found in other comparable mammals, but pig fat is no thicker than that of other mammals of similar size; indeed, domestic pigs have been selectively bred to be lean. The subcutaneous fat of pigs contributes little to their ability to survive cold weather. In cold conditions, the skin temperature of a pig falls much more than that of a human, due to restriction of the blood supply to the subcutaneous fat, so the poor hairless animal may feel cold in winter.

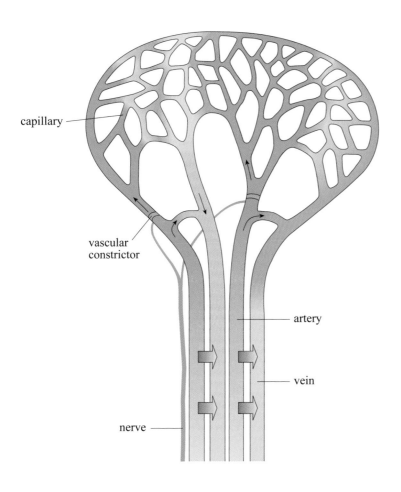

Figure 1.10 Schematic diagram of heat exchange in a single rete mirabile under the skin of an endotherm. The small black arrows show the direction of blood flow and the broad orange arrows show the direction of heat flow. Blood flow from the small arteries into the capillaries is controlled by vascular constrictors.

capillary

vascular constrictor

artery

vein

nerve

STORING FOOD IN WINTER

As described above, some animals solve the problem of remaining active in winter, when food is in short supply, by enlarging internal energy reserves in the adipose tissue. A problem with this strategy is that it increases body mass, which increases the energy cost of locomotion and, in extreme cases, may reduce mobility. An alternative strategy is to make external stores of food during the summer, when food is abundant, and to draw on them during the winter. Such behaviour, shown by a variety of birds and mammals, is called **hoarding** or **caching** (pronounced 'cashing').

There are two general kinds of hoarding behaviour. Larder-hoarding involves building up one or a small number of large food stores. Scatter-hoarding consists of hiding many individual food items in separate places over a wide area. An essential feature of a food cache, from the perspective of the animal that made it, is that it must not be exploited by other individuals of the same or different species. Typically, animals prevent theft by active defence in the case of larders, or by concealment if their caches are scattered. Scatter-hoarders include crows, nuthatches, tits, jays, squirrels and foxes; larder-hoarders include many small mammals, some birds, and honeybees.

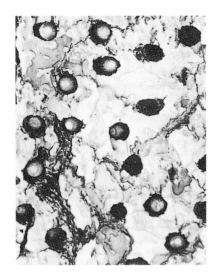

Figure 1.11 Part of an acorn woodpecker communal larder. Numerous holes have been drilled into a tree, and many of them contain acorns.

Pikas (genus *Ochotona*) are herbivorous, guinea pig-size animals, belonging to the same mammalian order (Lagomorpha) as rabbits and hares, which live in high altitude and desert habitats of Asia and North America. They do not hibernate in winter but rely on cached food to supplement what they can find to eat beneath the snow. In late summer they gather vegetation, storing it as a large haystack in a crevice beneath a rock, which they defend against their neighbours. Laboratory experiments on a variety of mammals reveal that hoarding behaviour is triggered by cooler temperatures and shorter days which are characteristic of autumn.

Among birds, an example of a larder-hoarder is the acorn woodpecker (*Melanerpes formicivorus*) of western North America. During the summer, acorn woodpeckers collect acorns and store them in the branches of dead trees, drilling a hole for each acorn (Figure 1.11). Where oak trees are abundant, acorn woodpeckers form very stable social groups, communally defending their larders, which provide group members with food during the winter.

The time for which food is stored varies from one species to another and depends, in part, on its perishability. Coal tits (*Parus ater*) store insects, having removed the head and the gut, in crevices in tree bark for a few hours. They also store pellets, each one consisting of 20–50 aphids compressed together. Owls store mice for a matter of days and jays and crows store seeds for a year. Ravens store meat for several weeks during the winter, burying it under snow, which keeps it frozen and so delays decay.

The energy that animals invest in food hoarding, and the importance of their cache for their winter survival is illustrated by the following observations:

- American biologist Bernd Heinrich observed an individual jay cache 127 food items in a single day.

- Individual Clark's nutcrackers (*Nucifraga columbina*), an American bird, collect up to 95 pine seeds at a time and hide them in locations as much as 22 km from their nest.

- Clark's nutcrackers breed in late winter, when there is no food available, and are totally reliant on cached food to rear their young.

Scatter-hoarding presents animals with a problem: if they hide their caches from competitors, how do they find them themselves? Leaving clues, such as scent marks, would lead rivals to the hidden food, and so they must rely on memory. Thick-billed nutcrackers (*Nucifraga caryocatactes*) store 15–20 hazelnuts in each cache and are able to find them even after thick snow has covered them. Detailed observations of birds in winter suggest that some species are able to memorize the exact location of several thousand stored food items over several months. David Macdonald of Oxford University studied caching in the red fox (*Vulpes vulpes*) by rearing a pet vixen which he took for walks in the countryside on a long lead. She frequently cached food items that he gave her, burying them in the ground. Over the course of several weeks, she subsequently found 96% of them and only rarely did she dig in places where she had not hidden food.

How do we know that animals rely on what appear to be extraordinary feats of memory to find their food caches? An alternative explanation is that they leave some kind of marker that neither their competitors nor humans can detect. Such an issue can only be resolved by carrying out experiments. Caching behaviour has been studied in American chickadees (*Parus* spp.) and European marsh tits (*P. palustris*). Captive-bred birds were trained to feed and hide food in an aviary containing artificial trees that had holes drilled in them, covered with Velcro lids. Opening these lids was very similar to the birds' natural behaviour of stripping bark off trees to find food. In the autumn, the birds spontaneously started to cache seeds in these holes. In a typical experiment, an individual bird was given 15 seeds to hide among a total of 72 open holes. When the bird had left the aviary, the seeds were removed and all the holes were covered up. Twenty four hours later, the bird was allowed back into the aviary. With very few errors, it visited the 15 holes where it had stored seeds the previous day, ignoring the others.

○ Why did the experimenters remove the seeds before the bird was allowed back into the aviary?

● To eliminate any possibility that the bird was using any cues coming directly from the seeds, such as odour.

Scatter-hoarding requires a remarkable memory for the location of a large number of items, a process called spatial memory. Anatomical studies of the brains of birds have revealed that the part of the brain that is involved in spatial memory, called the hippocampus, is relatively larger in species for which scatter-hoarding is particularly important. For example, the hippocampus of the marsh tit (*Parus palustris*) is significantly larger than that of its close relative, the blue tit (*P. caeruleus*), which is not a scatter-hoarder.

CHANGES IN SOCIAL BEHAVIOUR

For some animals living in temperate habitats, the onset of winter also brings about a marked change in their social behaviour. Most noticeably, many birds, having spent the spring and summer as breeding pairs, being highly aggressive towards all members of the same species, other than their mate, become gregarious and form large, cohesive flocks in which individuals behave cooperatively in a number of ways. As with other biological characters, sociality confers both benefits and costs on individuals.

A major benefit of flocking is that it reduces an individual's risk of being killed by a predator. There are three main reasons for this protection. Firstly, flocks detect predators more effectively than single birds. Secondly, predators become confused when attacking prey gathered closely together. Thirdly, members of flocks may defend themselves effectively against a predator even though, individually, they are not strong enough to do so.

Being in a social group increases feeding efficiency in other ways. Firstly, individuals gain information about the whereabouts of food by observing their fellow flock-members. Secondly, animals in groups can often disturb hidden animal prey more effectively than single individuals. Thirdly, predators in groups can hunt and kill prey that are too large for them to cope with on their own. Studies of captive great tits (*Parus major*), using an aviary similar to that described earlier, showed that individual tits looking for hidden food found it more quickly when released into the aviary in a small flock. Individuals observed one another and avoided places where other birds had not found food, concentrating their search instead on places similar to those where other birds had located food.

For some animals, joining a social group in winter can reduce heat loss, especially on cold nights. For example, pallid bats (*Antrozous pallidus*) expend less energy during roosting when they roost huddled together than they do if they roost alone.

There are two major costs to becoming gregarious in winter. First, close association between individuals increases infection rates by parasites and pathogens. For example, in colonies of American prairie dogs (genus *Cynomys*), there is a positive correlation between the number of animals in a colony and the abundance of external parasites. Secondly, living in a group brings animals closer together, increasing the likelihood that they come into competition over food and other resources. This cost is borne particularly by smaller and weaker individuals, which generally lose in competitive interactions with other group members.

SUMMARY OF SECTION 1.3

1 Coniferous trees are an example of plants that remain active during winter, with adaptations such as reduced water loss.

2 Endothermy allows some birds and mammals to remain active during cold winters, but places physiological and energetic demands on the organism, e.g. the need to maintain a high metabolic rate and/or reduce heat loss.

3 Bird plumage and mammal hair are highly effective insulators, reducing heat loss in winter. Heat loss is also controlled by heat exchange mechanisms and reduction in blood flow near the body surface.

4 The energy needed to sustain a high metabolic rate may be stored through either physiological and biochemical processes (adipose tissue) or changes in behaviour (hoarding or caching of food).

5 Some animals change their social behaviour during winter, becoming more gregarious.

1.4 STRATEGY 2: DORMANCY IN WINTER ('OPT OUT')

1.4.1 DECIDUOUS TREES

During the winter months, a combination of factors, including lower temperatures, reduced light intensity and shorter days, means that plants can only photosynthesize at a slow rate and for restricted periods. As a result, photosynthesis cannot produce energy as fast as respiration expends it. In addition, water is often in short supply because of freezing, and so plants that do not have adaptations to conserve water, as conifers do, would lose water. Deciduous trees avoid these problems in winter by dropping all their leaves and shutting off photosynthesis. Before they do so, they dismantle the photosynthetic apparatus in their leaves and withdraw many of the constituents to their branches, trunks and roots.

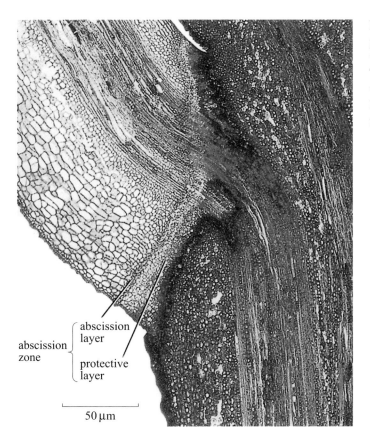

Figure 1.12 A section through the base of the petiole of a maple (*Acer* sp.) leaf before abscission, viewed under the light microscope after staining. The abscission zone comprises a layer of cells where the leaf becomes detached and a protective layer which seals the exposed surface of the stem following abscission.

Thus, in the autumn, sugars, amino acids and such minerals as nitrogen, phosphorus and potassium are transported from the leaves to woody tissues. Chlorophyll is broken down and the products are also withdrawn from the leaves. It is this process that causes leaves to change colour in the autumn. The breakdown of chlorophyll leaves behind other pigments, such as orange carotenes and yellow xanthophylls, which are normally hidden by the green chlorophyll. Once as many nutrients as possible have been withdrawn from a leaf, an **abscission** zone forms where the leaf stalk (petiole) meets the stem (Figure 1.12). Here the vessels that supply water and nutrients to the leaf are closed off and the leaf detaches, leaving a protective covering of cork over the scar. Leaf abscission is controlled by a complex system of hormones, responding to lower temperatures and light intensity and to shorter day length.

1.4.2 WINTER STORAGE IN PLANTS

Many plants that survive winter in a dormant state form storage organs below the ground which store nutrients during the winter, the rest of the plant withering away. Storage organs come in a variety of forms, including tap roots, bulbs, corms, rhizomes, root tubers and stem tubers (Figure 1.13). In the carrot, the root is greatly enlarged into a fleshy tap root; the bulbs of onions are modified leaves; crocus corms, iris rhizomes and dahlia tubers are modified stems, and the tubers of potatoes are modified tips of underground stems.

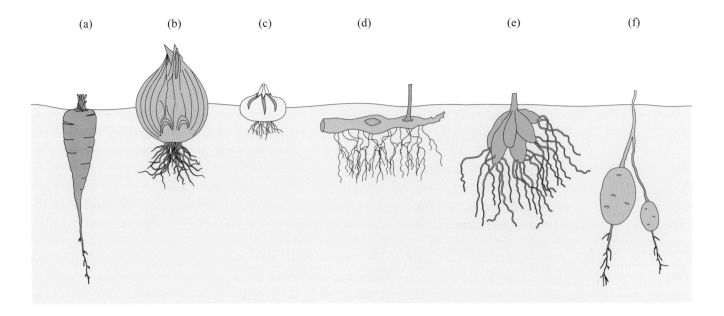

(a) (b) (c) (d) (e) (f)

Figure 1.13 Some examples of winter storage organs in plants: (a) tap root of carrot (*Daucus carota*, subsp. *sativus*); (b) bulb of onion (*Allium* sp.); (c) corm of crocus (*Crocus* sp.); (d) rhizome of iris (*Iris* sp.); (b) root tuber of dahlia (*Dahlia* sp.); (f) stem tuber of potato (*Solanum tuberosum*).

Unlike animals, few plants store energy reserves as fats (lipids). Those that do, generally store fats in seeds or fruits, a good example of the latter being the avocado (*Persea americana*). Storage in root organs is generally in the form of starch. Because they bind water, carbohydrates prevent desiccation of the storage organ and also reduce its freezing point, acting as 'antifreeze'. Plant storage organs provide ready-made larders for those herbivores that remain active in winter.

The root of a carrot serves as a storage organ, enabling the plant to complete its two-year life cycle. The storage organs of many plants are, however, also a means of asexual or vegetative reproduction. For example, the rhizomes of irises grow and branch and, as older parts of a rhizome die, two or more new plants are formed from the parts that are left. The tubers of a potato plant can each grow into a new plant and the bulbs of such plants as onions and daffodils (*Narcissus* sp.) divide to produce new bulbs and thus new plants.

1.4.3 FREEZE TOLERANCE IN ECTOTHERMIC VERTEBRATES

In Britain, the vertebrate class Amphibia is represented by frogs, toads and newts. Amphibians are ectotherms, meaning that they are unable to generate large quantities of heat within their bodies, so their body temperature is close to that of their surroundings. The majority of amphibian species avoid the lethal consequences of being frozen, by digging their way under a large object, such as a rock, or deep into the soil, below the level that is penetrated by frost. There are some species, however, that have evolved a physiological response to very cold weather that enables them to survive the winter on or close to the ground surface. Examples include the American wood frog (*Rana sylvatica*) and the Asian salamander (*Hynobius kyserlingi*), both of which have distributions that extend far north of the Arctic circle. What they do is to infuse their tissues with antifreeze.

In the wood frog, the onset of cold causes the animal to become immobile. As the temperature falls below 0 °C, water in its toes begins to freeze. Within 10–15 minutes of freezing, glycogen stored in the liver is converted into soluble glucose which is released into the bloodstream, whence it finds its way into the cells and the extracellular spaces (Figure 1.14). The dissolved glucose lowers the freezing point of water, as antifreeze does in a car's radiator, preventing the formation of ice crystals and any consequent movement of water out of living cells.

Whereas the wood frog uses glucose as an antifreeze, the Asian salamander and the grey treefrog (*Hyla versicolor*) use glycerol, suggesting that this adaptation may have evolved independently in a number of amphibian species. Freeze tolerance allows these amphibians to survive freezing conditions for one or two weeks. It is not their only adaptation for surviving the winter; in the wood frog, for example, breathing ceases and the heart stops beating at very low temperatures.

Some ectothermic vertebrates rely on supercooling to survive short periods of cold temperature (see Section 1.2.1). For example, the spring lizard (*Sceloporus jarrovi*), living in the Arizona desert, survives very cold nights by supercooling. This strategy is risky, however, and many lizards die as a result of becoming frozen. Allowing its tissues to supercool is not a viable option for a frog or salamander; living in damp places, they are virtually certain to be in contact with ice crystals which act as nucleation points.

As well as enabling them to survive frosty conditions, the capacity to tolerate extreme cold confers other advantages on some amphibians. Many breed in temporary ponds that dry up early in the spring or summer, making it

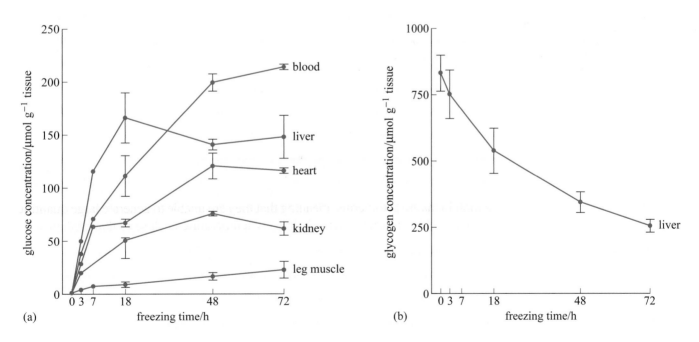

Figure 1.14 (a) Changes in the concentration of glucose in various organs of the wood frog (*Rana sylvatica*) over 72 hours of freezing at −2.5 °C in the laboratory. (b) The corresponding depletion of liver glycogen reserves. Note that the horizontal axes are non-linear. Data from Pinder *et al.* (1992).

advantageous for breeding adults to migrate to ponds as early as possible in the spring. Early breeding maximizes the time available for the aquatic egg and larval stages to be completed before a pond dries up. Some species, such as the American blue-spotted salamander (*Ambystoma laterale*) migrate to breeding ponds while snow is still on the ground, giving them an advantage over other salamander species that do not start to breed until the weather is warm.

1.4.4 HIBERNATION IN MAMMALS

Many animals become inactive for periods of varying duration during the winter and there is a diversity of terms used to describe this state, including: sleep, torpor, dormancy, lethargy and hibernation. The word **hibernation** is often used loosely to refer to general inactivity but, in biology, it refers to a specific phenomenon, sometimes called 'true hibernation'. Hibernation is defined as the condition of passing the winter in a resting state of deep sleep, during which metabolic rate and body temperature drop considerably. It occurs only in certain mammals and one bird species, the poorwill (*Phalaenoptilus nuttallii*), a North American relative of the nightjar.

The phenomenon of hibernation is one reason why the term homeothermy is going out of fashion, to be replaced by endothermy, because maintaining a stable body temperature is the very opposite of what hibernators do. Instead, body temperature falls, from around 38 °C, to about 1 °C above ambient temperature, which is often close to 0 °C. At the same time, a hibernator's metabolic rate falls to as little as 1% of its normal value. The heartbeat becomes slow and irregular and breathing rate also slows.

Hibernation is an active process, that is, it is a state which animals enter into, not in response to immediate external conditions, but to internal stimuli. Some species are remarkably precise and predictable. For example, the arctic ground squirrel (*Spermophilus undulatus*) enters hibernation between 5 and 12 October and emerges between 20 and 22 April, regardless of the weather on those dates. This behaviour is in contrast to other winter states such as torpor or lethargy which are immediate responses to current conditions. Brown and black bears, for example, are lethargic during very cold periods but are otherwise active in the winter. A feature of hibernation that distinguishes it from other kinds of winter inactivity is that hibernators can arouse themselves spontaneously and are not dependent on external conditions, such as warm temperatures, to do so. The arctic ground squirrel is described as an **obligate hibernator** because it hibernates every winter. There are some mammals that are categorized as **facultative hibernators**, entering hibernation in response to very cold weather and poor food supply. The North American pocket mouse (*Perognathus californicus*) is a facultative hibernator.

True hibernation only occurs in relatively small mammals, though not all small mammals living in temperate habitats hibernate in winter, as we have seen. The largest mammal to hibernate is the marmot, which weighs about 5 kg. There are several reasons why larger mammals do not hibernate. Firstly, they would warm up too slowly and therefore use too much energy. Secondly, they have a smaller surface area to volume ratio and so can conserve body heat better than smaller species. Finally, they are better able to carry a thick coat (Section 1.3.2) and sufficient adipose tissue to last through the winter. Hibernators are mainly found in the orders Rodentia, Chiroptera (bats) and Insectivora. The hedgehog (*Erinaceus europaeus*) is an example of a hibernating insectivore; in Britain, it hibernates from October/November to March/April. Note that although hedgehogs are in the order Insectivora they do not just eat insects!

The physiological features that are characteristic of hibernation are not maintained throughout the winter. Rather, the animal wakes up at intervals, its temperature and metabolic rate increasing to near-normal levels (Figure 1.15). The function of this periodic arousal is not wholly clear. Some species, such as the chipmunks (genus *Tamias*) eat from stored food reserves during arousal periods, but many others do not. Most species urinate and defaecate, move about and change their position, suggesting that arousal provides an opportunity for various essential physiological processes to be performed and to prevent the animal becoming moribund. From detailed measurements of Richardson's ground squirrel (*Spermophilus richardsonii*) in the laboratory, it has been calculated that, during the relatively brief periods of arousal (Figure 1.15), an individual expends 83% of all the energy that it uses up during the entire hibernation period.

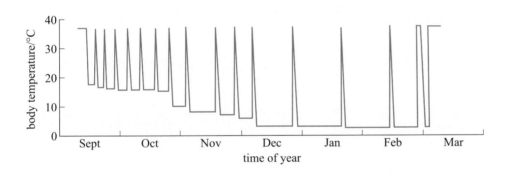

Figure 1.15 Record of body temperature from September to March for a Richardson's ground squirrel. Data from Pough *et al.* (1996).

Hibernation requires internal energy reserves in the form of adipose tissue and hibernators typically feed intensively prior to winter, building up their fat stores. Some species, such as the edible dormouse (*Glis glis*), switch to a carbohydrate- and lipid-rich diet, e.g. seeds, at this time. A characteristic of hibernating mammals is that they possess larger quantities of a particular kind of adipose tissue called **brown adipose tissue (BAT)**. This tissue gets its name from its dark colour, which is due to the larger numbers of blood capillaries that permeates it and the high concentration of mitochondria within the cells. BAT is rich in mitochondria with special properties that enable it to oxidize fatty acids and/or glucose to produce heat very rapidly. BAT deposits are found around some internal organs and between the shoulder-blades of hibernators and their function is to generate body heat very rapidly, especially during periods of arousal.

Hibernation might seem to be a safe, and rather agreeable way to spend the winter but, for some species, it is fraught with danger. For Belding's ground squirrels (*Spermophilus beldingi*) living at high altitude in Tioga Pass, California, hibernation lasts 7–8 months. Two-thirds of all juveniles, hibernating for the first time, and one-third of adult animals die during hibernation. Some die because their fat reserves run out before the end of hibernation; others are dug up and eaten by predators.

Some mammals spend the winter in groups, huddled together during periods of dormancy, and so conserve body heat. North American raccoons (*Procyon lotor*), for example, spend dormant periods in communal dens. Many species of bats hibernate communally. During hibernation, the body temperature of some bats can fall below 0 °C. In the autumn, they build up fat reserves that represent as much as a third of their total mass. During the winter, bats arouse themselves from hibernation to excrete and sometimes also to move to a new roost. A critical factor for hibernating bats is that roosting sites have high humidity and some populations have to migrate quite large distances to find suitable places, such as caves and hollow trees.

For some mammals, hibernation is closely associated with other important activities, notably reproduction and dispersal. Consequently, energy reserves may have to support more than one activity. For example, brown bears living at northern latitudes mate in the autumn and give birth to their cubs during winter lethargy. Edible dormice and some bats mate immediately after the end of hibernation. (In some species of bats, males wake up first and mate with the females before they have woken up!) The link between what animals do in winter and their reproductive cycles was discussed in Section 1.2.3.

Natal dispersal is the permanent departure of an individual from its place of birth, usually at the end of the breeding season. It is an important part of the life history of many animals, especially mammals, and tends to be sexually dimorphic, males dispersing further than females. Natal dispersal is potentially both hazardous and energetically expensive; dispersing animals tend to be vulnerable to predators and, being on the move, have little time to feed. Dispersal therefore requires internal energy reserves in the form of fat, the very same reserves that they later need to survive the winter. There may thus be a trade-off in the allocation of energy reserves to dispersal and to hibernation.

Scott Nunes of Michigan State University has studied dispersal and hibernation in Belding's ground squirrels in a locality where hibernation lasts for eight to nine months of the year. Young males typically disperse after the summer breeding season but show much variation in the extent to which they do so, with fatter males being more likely to move out of the natal area. In years when breeding is delayed, dispersal is inhibited; instead, young males remain near the natal area, building up their fat reserves prior to hibernation. The findings of this study are summarized in Figure 1.16.

If young males are ready to disperse early (date A in Figure 1.16), they leave with relatively small fat reserves. In this situation, they have time to travel further to a new area and then build up fat reserves before hibernation. If dispersal is delayed (dates B and C), males do not disperse unless they have built up a threshold level of fat reserves; the value of this threshold increases as winter approaches. In other words, the trade-off between dispersal and hibernation is resolved by hibernation suppressing dispersal, unless an animal exceeds a certain fat level. After date C, dispersal is inhibited regardless of the size of the fat reserves.

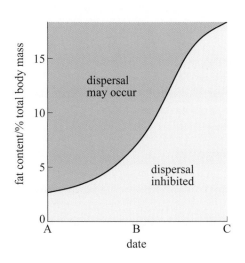

Figure 1.16 A graphical summary of the control of dispersal in male Belding's ground squirrels. See text for explanation.

SUMMARY OF SECTION 1.4

1   Deciduous trees avoid the problems of winter by shedding their leaves.

2   Plants can store nutrients over winter in a variety of structures.

3   Amphibians have evolved behavioural responses (e.g. burying themselves) and physiological responses (e.g. different types of antifreeze in the body fluids) to winter.

4   Hibernation occurs only in certain small mammal species and one species of bird and is accompanied by marked physiological and behavioural changes.

5   Prior to hibernation, animals build up their fat reserves and frequently possess larger amounts of brown adipose tissue than non-hibernators.

6   There may be a trade-off between hibernation and dispersal in some animals.

1.5   STRATEGIES 3 AND 4: JUVENILE SURVIVAL AND MIGRATION

1.5.1   JUVENILE SURVIVAL

For organisms that are able to complete their life cycles within a year there is the possibility of spending the winter in various juvenile stages. We have already considered annual plants, the adults of which may die before the onset of winter, with seed not germinating until the spring. Surviving the winter as seeds has the advantages that the seeds are robust, and because they have a low water content they are less affected by freezing temperatures. Disadvantages of this strategy include the possibility that the seeds may be consumed by ground-feeding herbivores and that newly germinating plants may lose out in competition with annuals that germinated in the previous autumn.

Butterflies are good examples of insects that survive the winter in a variety of immature stages. Indeed, in Britain, different butterfly species overwinter at each of the juvenile stages of the life cycle, i.e. as eggs, larvae and pupae, or as adults.

Table 1.2 lists the numbers of species, categorized by butterfly family, that overwinter in each of these four stages in Britain.

Table 1.2 The variety of overwintering strategies adopted by various juvenile stages (strategy 3) and adults (strategy 2) of butterflies in Britain. Data are numbers of species. Several species also migrate to Britain (strategy 4) and lay eggs. However, few individuals complete their development and return south; hence migration is not an important strategy for butterflies breeding in Britain.

Butterfly family	Juvenile stage			Adult
	Egg	Larva	Pupa	
Satyridae	0	11	0	0
Nymphalidae	1	9	0	4
Lycaenidae	6	7	2	0
Pieridae	0	0	5	1
Hesperiidae	2	5	1	0
other	0	0	2	0
total	9	32	10	5

○ Based on Table 1.2, what is the predominant overwintering stage of butterflies?

● Larvae (caterpillars), occurring in 32 out of 56 species (57%).

There appear to be some phylogenetic patterns in overwintering strategy amongst the butterflies, i.e. some butterfly families in Britain are restricted to certain strategies.

○ Which butterfly families are restricted to overwintering at one immature stage in Britain?

● The Satyridae (browns) only overwinter as larvae and the Pieridae (whites) overwinter as pupae.

In other families, such as the Lycaenidae (blues) and Hesperiidae (skippers), there is a mixture of overwintering strategies. However, these butterfly families are large and heterogeneous, and more careful inspection of subfamilies indicates phylogenetic patterns. For example, most hairstreaks (family Lycaenidae) overwinter as eggs. Across families, it seems there are common factors in the types of species that overwinter as a particular stage. For example, all of the species that overwinter as eggs have only one generation a year and are on the wing (and therefore breeding) later in the year, mainly July and August.

1.5.2 STRATEGY 4: MIGRATION ('GO AWAY')

About 40% of the bird species that breed in Britain do not spend the winter there but migrate south, some to southern Europe, others much further afield. The swallow (*Hirundo rustica*), for example, may migrate as far as the Cape of southern Africa. From one perspective, migrants are European species that avoid the northern winter by migrating to a less severe environment. On the other hand, the swallow can also be regarded as an African bird that migrates to northern latitudes to breed. Why should an African bird migrate thousands of miles to breed, exposing itself to obvious risks? Swallows suffer 67% annual mortality, much of it occurring during migration. Long-distance migration also involves a huge energetic cost. The answer is that northern latitudes provide very good breeding habitats for birds. In late spring and summer these habitats support a rich food supply, in the form of seeds, fruits and insects, and there are relatively fewer herbivorous and insectivorous species living at northern latitudes, so that competition for food with which to rear their young is relatively low. Evidence for this conclusion comes from data on the clutch size of birds of the same or related species breeding at different latitudes. Temperate-breeding birds lay much larger clutches than similar species breeding at more southerly latitudes. This effect is also seen within species; for example, in the European robin (*Erithacus rubecula*), mean clutch size is 6.3 eggs in Scandinavia, 5.9 in central France, 4.9 in Spain, 4.2 in north Africa and 3.5 in the Canary Islands.

Birds are not the only animals that migrate. Among mammals, some populations of caribou or reindeer (*Rangifer tarandus*) make mass migrations of more than 1000 km, covering up to 150 km per day, in search of good grazing. Some insects also migrate over long distances. For example the monarch butterfly (*Danaus plexippus*) migrates from Canada and northern USA to Mexico, flying 120 km per day. Some 30% of the monarch population, however, does not migrate but hibernates during the winter.

Migration in birds requires considerable physiological preparation. Some time before they leave, migrants increase their feeding rate and lay down fat reserves, amounting to between 20 and 50% of total body mass, depending on the species. At the top of this range are the ruby-throated humming-bird (*Archilochus colubris*), which flies across the Gulf of Mexico, and the sedge warbler (*Acrocephalus schoenobaenus*), which migrates from Britain to west Africa. Both these species complete their migration in a single sustained flight. Species that carry smaller loads of fat typically fly in a series of stages, stopping to feed and put on weight along the route. The rate at which migratory birds put on weight prior to migration is remarkable. Whitethroats (*Sylvia communis*) preparing to migrate from Sweden increase their food intake by about 70%, their body mass increases by 7% per day, and they depart 50% heavier than normal.

Prior to migration, smaller birds build up larger fat reserves, relative to their body size, than do larger birds. This size effect is related to a measure of the amount of power that a bird can generate, called the **power margin**, which is defined as the difference between the maximum power than can be developed by the flight muscles and the power required for unladen (with no extra fat) level flight at a standard speed in still air. A large bird such as a swan has a small power margin, so swans need to build up speed before they can take off, and, once airborne, they climb rather slowly. Small birds, with a large power margin, can take off vertically and climb very rapidly (Hedenstrom and Alerstam, 1992). The small power margin of large migrants, such as white storks (*Ciconia ciconia*) which migrate from Europe to Africa and back, means that they cannot carry large amounts of fat to support long flights. They economize on fuel, to some extent, by soaring on thermals, rather than using flapping flight, but these habits constrain them to routes that do not cross the sea. Storks migrate either over Gibraltar in the west, or over Israel in the east, depending on where they breed. They also make frequent stops to feed.

As birds put on weight prior to migration, they start to show **migratory restlessness**. Birds held in captivity just before the migration season do a lot of hopping about and experiments have shown that this hopping is not random, but is oriented in different directions in spring and autumn (Figure 1.17).

Experimental studies of captive birds have revealed that the proximate factors that stimulate increased feeding prior to migration and migratory restlessness are decreases in the L : D ratio (i.e. longer nights) and, in some species, a circannual clock.

To complete their life cycle, migratory birds make at least two journeys: outwards to the wintering site and a return journey next spring back to the breeding site. A major determinant of reproductive success for many temperate bird species is the

Figure 1.17 Orientation of migratory restlessness in a caged bird. (a) The cage has an inkpad at the centre and a wire mesh lid. (b) View downwards into the cage. Every time the bird jumps from the inkpad towards the edge, its feet leave a mark. These marks are oriented in a northerly direction in spring (c) and towards the south in autumn (d). Data from Pough *et al.* (1996).

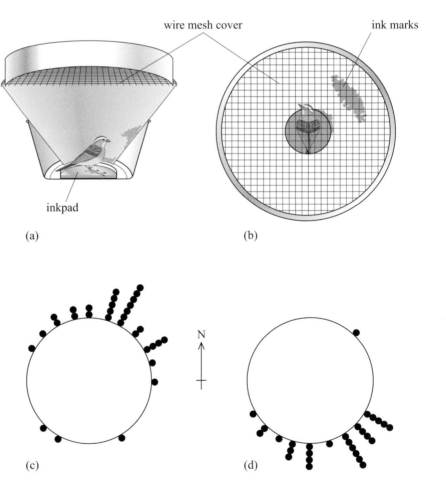

date on which they start to breed. In the majority of species, pairs that start to breed early in the spring fledge more young. There are several reasons for this correlation, the relative importance of which varies from species to species. Firstly, early breeders generally secure better territories, in terms of the abundance of food that they contain. Secondly, an early start often means that a pair has time to produce and rear a second clutch in the same season. Thirdly, in some species the earlier breeders are better synchronized with their environment, such that the time of peak food requirement (i.e. during feeding of the young) is synchronized with the time of maximum food availability.

A recent study of the American redstart (*Setophaga ruticilla*), suggests that a further factor could be important. It was found that the earliest birds to arrive at breeding sites were in better condition than later birds, some of which arrived up to a month later. This study investigated the tropical wintering habitat of this species and found that the early-arriving, good-condition birds had wintered in better habitats than later arrivers. This study therefore suggests that the quality of winter habitats may be an important determinant of fitness for migratory birds. It also reinforces the point that, in considering the success of organisms, it is important to consider all parts of their life cycle.

SUMMARY OF SECTION 1.5

1   Some annual plants and insects can spend the winter at juvenile stages, such as seed, egg, larva or pupa. Butterflies in Britain display a variety of juvenile overwintering strategies.

2   Migration often results in high mortality, but completion of the journey results in higher breeding success, due to increased availability of food and fewer competitors.

3   Birds increase their body mass, sometimes by up to 50%, prior to migration. The body mass increase is related to the power margin of the birds.

4   Early arrival of migratory birds at the breeding site confers important advantages on those individuals.

1.6   CONCLUSION AND OVERVIEW OF BOOK THEMES

This chapter has presented an overview of the ways in which organisms living in temperate habitats are adapted to survive the winter. The chapter has shown how a limited set of environmental changes associated with the onset of winter can lead to a diversity of adaptations and therefore a large diversity of species.

On the basis of the examples discussed in this chapter, we can identify four factors that contribute to the diversity of adaptive strategies for coping with winter.

1   *Alternative strategies and trade-offs*   For any one environmental 'problem', there may be two or more solutions that may be appropriate in certain species under certain conditions. Thus, remaining active, becoming dormant and migrating are all viable options for long-lived organisms to cope with winter. Among animals that become dormant, building up reserves in the form of a larder is an alternative to depositing lipids in adipose tissue. These adaptive

solutions may be thought of as being traded off, i.e. natural selection may lead to an organism adopting one particular adaptive solution. This effect is reinforced by an organism's evolutionary history (see below).

2   *Phylogeny*   The evolutionary history of different groups of organisms has equipped them with a range of adaptations that predispose them towards one strategy rather than another. For example, endothermy and thick fur make hibernation a viable strategy for mammals, wings make long-distance migration a viable strategy for birds.

3   *Size*   Body size can have a marked effect on what organisms do in winter. Dying back and overwintering as an underground storage organ is a viable option for small plants, but not for large woody ones; hibernation is possible for small to medium-sized mammals but not for large ones.

4   *Life history*   The particular life history of organisms allows them to survive the winter in different ways. Thus annual plants have the option of overwintering as small plants or seed whilst herbaceous perennial plants have the extra option of surviving the winter underground. As life history is itself subject to natural selection, it is another example of evolutionary history restricting the options of adaptive solutions.

A fifth factor, which we have not had the space to explore in this chapter, is coevolution. This concept will be developed in Chapters 4 and 5. Through coevolution, adaptations by one group of organisms create opportunities for other groups. Thus, in the context of the present chapter, if it were not for the fact that many plants store food over the winter, there would be little opportunity for many herbivores to remain active in winter. Coevolution implies that, if selection favours herbivores that can exploit underground storage organs, then, equally, selection also favours plants that are able to defend these resources.

These five factors serve as major themes for this book in which we attempt to understand the *processes that generate diversity*. Chapter 2 concerns ways that heterotrophic organisms acquire and process food. Food is important, as the supply of energy and nutrition is the basis upon which activities such as growth and reproduction can be traded off with other biological processes, such as defence. In Chapter 3 we review the genetic basis of the diversity of organisms. This chapter is a key one, as all adaptation and variation, and therefore all biological diversity, has a genetic basis. Chapters 4, 5 and 6 cover three major processes in the life history of organisms: reproduction, defence and longevity. All three processes are traded off within an organism's life history. Thus for a given energy input, a high-energy burst of reproduction may be associated with subsequent low levels of survival, as discussed in Chapter 6. These trade-offs within an organism's life history are reflected in the range of strategies evolved by individuals of different species. Chapter 4 shows how the bewildering array of reproductive strategies has been generated and, in turn affects the generation of genetic diversity described in Chapter 3. In Chapter 5 we see strong evidence for coevolution generating diversity in hosts and their pathogens.

REFERENCES

Baker, J. M. R. (1992) Body condition and tail height in great crested newts, *Triturus cristatus*, *Animal Behaviour*, **43**, pp. 157–159.

Bronson, F. H. (1987) Environmental regulation of reproduction in rodents. In: *Psychobiology of Reproductive Behavior,* D. Crews (ed.), Prentice Hall, New Jersey. p. 209.

Hedenstrom, A. and Alerstam, T. (1992) Climbing performance of migratory birds as a basis for estimating limits for fuel-carrying capacity and muscle work, *Journal of Experimental Biology*, **164**, pp. 19–38.

Irving, L. (1966) Adaptations to cold, *Scientific American*, **214**, pp. 94–101.

Kenagy, G. J. (1981) Effects of day length, temperature, and endogenous control on annual rhythms of reproduction and hibernation in chipmunks (*Eutamias* spp.), *Journal of Comparative Physiology A*, **141**, pp. 369–378.

Macdonald, D. W. (1976) Food caching by red foxes and some other carnivores, *Zeitschrift fur Tierpsychologie*, **42**, pp. 170–185.

Pinder, A. W., Storey, K. B. and Ultsch, G. R. (1992) Estivation and hibernation, in: *Environmental Physiology of Amphibians*, Feder, M. E. and Burggren, W. W. (eds), Chicago University Press, pp. 250–276.

Pough, F. H., Heiser, J. B. and McFarland, W. N. (1996) *Vertebrate Life* (4th. edn), Prentice Hall, New Jersey, pp. 589, 688, 695.

Nunes, S., Ha, C.-D. T., Garrett, P. J., Mueke, E. M., Smale, L. and Holekamp. K.E. (1998) Body fat and time of year interact to mediate dispersal behaviour in ground squirrels, *Animal Behaviour*, **55**, pp. 605–614.

Valerio, P. F., Kao, M. H. and Fletcher, G. L. (1992) Fish skin: an effective barrier to ice crystal propagation, *Journal of Experimental Biology*, **164**, pp. 135–151.

FURTHER READING

Barnes, R. S. K., Calow, P. and Olive, P. J. W. (1988) *The Invertebrates: a New Synthesis*, Blackwell Scientific Publications, Oxford. [A comprehensive review of diversity, evolution and ecology of invertebrates.]

Irving, L. (1966) Adaptations to cold, *Scientific American*, **214**, pp. 94–101. [An important and accessible summary of physiological adaptations of vertebrates to cold.]

Krebs, J. R. and Davies, N. B. (1987) *An Introduction to Behavioural Ecology* (2nd edn), Blackwell Scientific Publications, Oxford. [A collection of essays by leading researchers on key themes in behavioural ecology.]

Pond, C. M. (2000) *The Fats of Life*, (2nd edn) Cambridge University Press. [This book explains in simple language the biology of feasting and fasting, fattening and slimming in wild animals as well as people.]

Pough, F. H., Janis, C. M. and Heiser J. B. (1999) *Vertebrate Life* (5th. edn), Prentice Hall, New Jersey. (6th edn expected 2001) [A wide-ranging review of the diversity, function and evolution of vertebrates.]

Raven, P. H., Evert, R. F. and Eichhorn, S. E. (1999) *Biology of Plants* (6th edn.), Freeman, New York. [A richly-illustrated book that deals with all aspects of plant biology, from cellular mechanisms to ecology, and covering physiology, evolution and diversity.]

DEALING WITH FOOD

2.1 INTRODUCTION

Organisms need materials with which to build the fabric of their bodies and fuel to power movement and the synthesis of secretions, growth and repair of tissues, and the production of gametes for the next generation. These interconnected processes are collectively known as metabolism, and they depend upon adequate supplies of carbohydrates, lipids and proteins of appropriate composition, and smaller quantities of certain metallic ions, notably sodium, potassium, magnesium and calcium, and organic molecules which, when derived from the diet, are known as **vitamins**. The principles of metabolism are broadly similar in all animals, but how much material can pass through any particular pathway, and the rates of the processes, differ enormously between species.

Heterotrophs obtain all their energy supplies and most of their other nutrients from the tissues of other organisms. Animals and fungi are the main multicellular heterotrophs, though there are a few lineages of carnivorous plants. Fungi more often feed off dead or dying organisms, and animals actively kill living plants and animals, but there are many exceptions. Carnivorous plants fall outside the definition of typical heterotrophs because they make organic molecules from inorganic carbon dioxide by photosynthesis, like typical green plants. But they resemble animals in obtaining nitrogenous materials by catching and digesting insects and other small invertebrates. They therefore share many of the problems faced by carnivorous animals: how to obtain nutrients from organisms that actively avoid their predators.

The key features of heterotrophy are the production of digestive enzymes which break down complex organic materials, absorption of the breakdown products, and getting near enough to the food source for these processes to be efficient. Heterotrophy is not an 'easy option' compared to autotrophy: obtaining and processing other organisms as food are energetically expensive activities requiring elaborate anatomical and biochemical adaptations. For most animals, many of their tissues, and a large fraction of the total energy they expend, are devoted to foraging and to the digestion and absorption of nutrients. With a few exceptions (fruit, nectar, etc.), organisms actively avoid making their tissues or secretions available as food for other organisms, at least while they are alive. They disperse, hide, run away, protect themselves with shells, spines or tough skeletons, or make themselves poisonous or distasteful. Some of these topics are discussed in Chapter 5.

The basic mechanisms of digestion and absorption are similar in all animals, though details such as the relative abundance of enzymes and the conditions under which they function most efficiently differ between species. In contrast, there are many different sources of food, and many ways of obtaining and processing it. The huge variety of animals, at least one million described species, is due mainly to the diversity of strategies for counteracting the food organism's defences against its eater, i.e. differences in diet, and in ways of finding, catching, fragmenting and digesting food, and of avoiding being eaten themselves. This chapter outlines these fundamental and contrasting aspects of obtaining and dealing with food. The range of examples shows how the variety of solutions to the problems of nutrition and digestion contribute greatly to the diversity of organisms.

2.1.1 STRUCTURE OF THE MOUTH AND GUT

The gut is one of the defining characters of animals: it is a hollow sac or tube lined, except near its openings, with a layer of tightly linked cells called intestinal **epithelium** which both produces digestive enzymes and regulates nutrient uptake (Figure 2.1). The interior of the gut is thus morphologically part of the outside world, and its lining may be compared to a skin, controlling interactions between the contents and the body. The structure and anatomical relations of the gut are, together with limbs and other locomotory apparatus, among the most important features that distinguish animal phyla from one another. The relative masses of the guts and their component parts differ enormously between species, depending upon diet and digestive mechanisms.

In simpler invertebrates, ciliated cells, aided by wriggling movements of the whole body, stir the gut contents, bringing them into close contact with the lining and propelling them towards the anus, where undigested material is expelled. In vertebrates and some more complex invertebrates, including arthropods, layers of muscle (Figurer 2.1a) surrounding the epithelium perform these functions with waves of squeezing movements called **peristalsis**. These muscles may be very powerful, especially in animals that suck, or whose food consists of large, tough particles. For example, those of the South American bedbug *Rhodnius* generate forces of 3–6 times atmospheric pressure, sucking in mammalian blood (they prefer that of humans) at $4\,\mathrm{m\,s^{-1}}$ through their syringe-like mouthparts, whose internal diameter is only $10\,\mu\mathrm{m}$. Such power enables the insects to take in several times their own mass of blood in just a few minutes, thus minimizing the time for which they have to linger where their victim might swat them.

All vertebrates except the class Agnatha have jaws and most have teeth, enabling them to bite, tear, grind or chew large food items into small fragments. (In birds, tortoises and a few other groups, the teeth are replaced by a horny beak.) The structure of the teeth, beaks, mouthparts, tentacles, etc. and the muscles that operate them are intricately adapted to the diet, especially in animals that feed only on one or a few kinds of prey or food plant. The structure and operation of the mouthparts, beaks or teeth often provide the best clues about an animal's diet and food-gathering strategy. In many vertebrates, the jaw muscles are among the most powerful and accurately controlled muscles in the body, and many birds, including parrots, woodpeckers and weaver-birds, as well as certain mammals, use the mouth for tasks such as nest-building, which involve strength, speed and skill, in addition to food manipulation.

Arthropods do not have true jaws like vertebrates, but they have one or more pairs of limbs called **mouthparts** in front of, behind or beside the mouth, which are specialized for food manipulation. They are enormously diverse in structure, adapted to grasp, tear, filter, wipe, bite, chew, rasp, suck and inject poison.

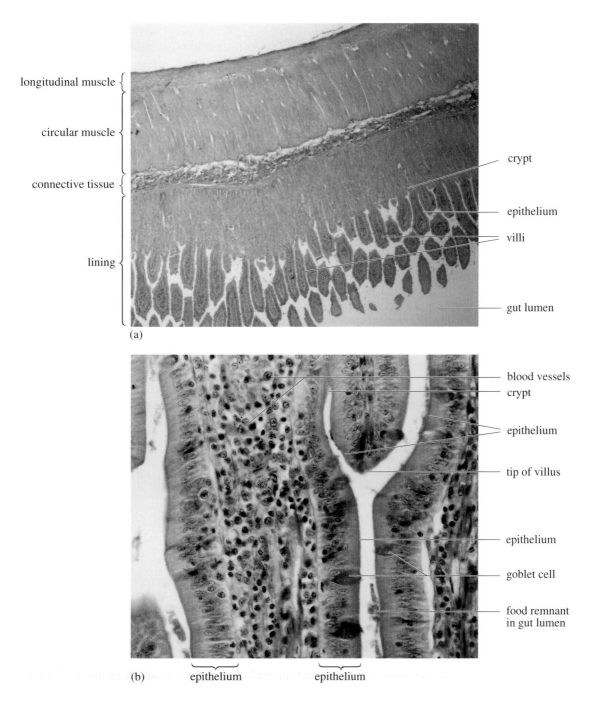

longitudinal muscle

circular muscle

connective tissue

lining

crypt

epithelium

villi

gut lumen

(a)

blood vessels
crypt

epithelium

tip of villus

epithelium

goblet cell

food remnant
in gut lumen

(b)   epithelium   epithelium

Figure 2.1   Cross-section of the small intestine of a rat. (a) Magnified 25 times. The two layers of powerful muscles are clearly visible, and many of the finger-like projections (villi) in the lining have been sectioned at a variety of angles. (b) When magnified 400 times, the continuous layer of epithelium is clearly seen, containing dark-stained goblet cells, which secrete mucus, and other cells that secrete digestive enzymes. The core of each villus contains numerous blood vessels. The green-staining fragments between the villi are the remains of the rat's final meal.

Mechanical fragmentation of food increases the surface area on which chemical breakdown of large molecules can take place, enabling digestion to be faster and more complete. It begins in front of or inside the mouth, where **saliva**, a watery fluid containing mucus to make particles slippery, and sometimes enzymes, is secreted as soon as eating begins (or even in anticipation of it!). The food passes through the **oesophagus** to the **stomach**, where muscular churning movements continue its fragmentation, and digestive enzymes and, in vertebrates, acid are secreted onto it. The lining of the stomach is often pleated (Figure 2.2), which maximizes the area of secretory epithelia, with regions of contrasting appearance producing different secretions.

Figure 2.2   The inside of the stomach of (a) a dogfish (*Squalus* sp.) and (b) a polar bear (*Ursus maritimus*). In (a) note the distinct appearance of different regions of the stomach and its pleated surface, which increases the area of contact with the food and allows for expansion. (b) This animal's stomach has shrunk (to about 50 cm across) because it has been fasting for several weeks, but the flexible walls enable it to expand enormously.

(a)

(b)

○ In which terrestrial vertebrates would breaking up food in the stomach be important?

● Birds. They do not have teeth, although many are predators and/or eat hard seeds.

Part of the avian stomach forms a massively muscular **gizzard** which grinds tough food items, sometimes with the help of hard grit or pebbles which the bird swallows deliberately. The stomach has a similar role in many large invertebrates. Crabs and crayfish shred their food with their large claws and several pairs of stout mouthparts, ingesting the fragments one at a time through their relatively small mouth (Figure 2.3a). Mechanical breakdown continues in the stomach (called the proventriculus) which is equipped with hard 'teeth' and powerful muscles, shown in Figure 2.3b.

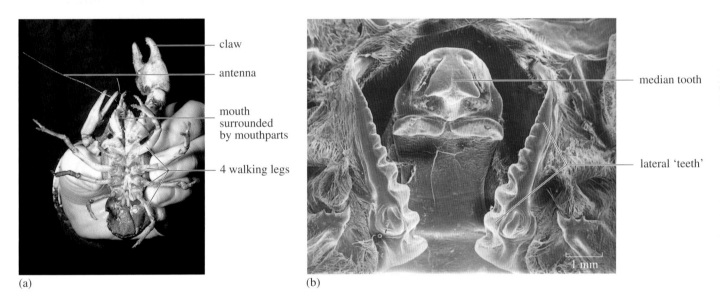

(a)

(b)

Beyond the stomach is the **intestine**, which is devoted to chemical digestion of food and the absorption of the small molecules so released. The digestive enzymes and other substances secreted by the gut epithelium are supplemented in many larger, more complex animals by those produced in associated glands, including the liver and pancreas in vertebrates. In simple animals, the whole gut has a similar structure but the presence of these additional glands, and specialization of the intestine itself, define distinct regions in vertebrates and large arthropods. The 'small' intestine is narrow but long and often coiled or folded. The 'large' intestine, also called the hindgut or the **colon**, is usually much shorter but wider and is specialized for absorbing salts, and with them water, from the gut contents. Maximizing the area of epithelium in contact with the food makes digestion and absorption faster and more efficient, so the lining of vertebrate guts has finger-like processes called **villi** (singular villus) which project into the gut contents (Figure 2.1), especially in absorptive regions. Any material remaining after digestion and absorption are complete is expelled through the anus as **faeces**.

Figure 2.3 (a) Ventral view of an adult crayfish, *Austropotamobius pallipes*. This native species used to be common in streams and shallow rivers in southern England, where it eats soft vegetation and picks flesh from dead animals. (b) Scanning electron micrograph of proventricular teeth in the lining of the stomach of a crayfish. The teeth are moved by the indirect action of strong muscles attached to the wall of the stomach, resulting in grinding of food between the lateral teeth and the median tooth.

Although the overall movement of the gut contents is from mouth to anus, the rate of passage is highly variable, and reflux motion is common, especially in birds and herbivorous mammals. In vertebrates, the muscles associated with the gut differ from those of the limbs and trunk in their internal structure and in the physiological mechanisms that control them. The movements and secretions of the gut and its associated glands are controlled by neurons located in small groups (known as ganglia) that are in or near these organs. Those that lie within the gut wall are known as *enteric* neurons and form part of the *autonomic* nervous system, so their activities are outside voluntary control.

○ How does this difference in innervation reveal itself in our ability to control and perceive these regions of the gut?

● We can control the mouth and anus because their nerves and muscles are similar to those of limbs, but we are largely unaware of and unable to control most of the gut.

Microbes are present in the guts of all free-living animals. Most are harmless, indispensable symbionts that aid digestion, especially by breaking down cellulose and toxic substances from plants. A few pathogens inevitably slip in with food, and the gut lining of most higher animals contains components of the immune system (see Chapter 5) which protect the delicate, permeable surface from disease.

SUMMARY OF SECTION 2.1

1   Intestinal epithelium lines the gut except around the mouth and anus, and in vertebrates and advanced invertebrates is surrounded by muscles that propel and/or grind the food. The muscles are controlled by the autonomic nervous system.

2   Most vertebrates have jaws, and arthropods mouth parts, often armed with hard and/or sharp teeth, which fragment food before it is taken in. Gizzards and stomachs also grind large particles.

3   The stomach and intestine differ in muscularity, and secretory or absorptive capacity. In more complex animals, the secretory functions of the gut itself are supplemented by associated glands. The effective surface area of absorptive regions is greatly increased by numerous villi.

2.2   CARNIVORY

The majority of animal species are partly or entirely carnivorous (flesh-eating) but predators kill as well as eat other animals. Most animal tissues are nutritious and digestible to other animals, so the main problems for predators are catching and subduing their prey, rather than with digestion itself. As well as running away or hiding, potential prey protect themselves with shells and spines, and/or produce poisonous secretions which could injure the predators, and in some, the flesh itself is toxic. There is an almost infinite variety of styles of predation; as well as chasing or ambushing the prey, predators use traps, nets or lures, often combined with elaborate camouflage. Diversity of predation strategies is a positive advantage to the predators, as prey cannot hide from all possible predators all of the time.

Most fish and amphibians generally gulp small prey with little or no fragmentation, or tear it into chunks small enough to be swallowed. Large items may be tossed around until they are in a favourable orientation for swallowing. This style of feeding is retained in many carnivorous reptiles and birds: the main function of their teeth or beak is to pierce and hold the prey, rather than to chew or slice it.

Crocodiles and alligators belong to an ancient lineage of reptiles whose style of killing and dismembering large prey typifies that of predatory vertebrates. Mature crocodiles conceal themselves under water as they approach a mammal or large bird while it is drinking or swimming across a river, then lunge at it, usually from one side. The jaws and teeth are rarely strong enough to kill the prey by destroying a vital organ such as the brain or heart. Instead, the reptiles exploit the fact that they need to breathe air much less frequently than warm-blooded terrestrial animals: they drag the prey under water and hold it there until it drowns. The rigid skull and jaws (Figure 2.4) support stout, cone-shaped teeth and powerful jaw-closing muscles, enabling the predator to maintain a firm grip for several minutes. Struggling prey may cause injuries, but fish, amphibians and reptiles can replace broken teeth and add new ones throughout life.

eye socket
nostril

lower jaw

jaw joint

Figure 2.4 The anterior half of a crocodile skeleton. Note the long stout jaws and numerous simple, pointed teeth.

Once the prey is dead, the crocodile clamps its teeth around the edge of a limb or the neck, and flails its tail and legs, often turning itself right over in the process, until it rips off a morsel small enough to be swallowed. Several large crocodiles tearing a zebra or wildebeest to bits in this way make an impressive sight: almost every muscle in the crocodiles' bodies contributes to food collection. Fragmenting the prey is wasteful, of course, as blood and gut contents usually flow away, and only the smaller bones can be swallowed whole. Even with such vigorous pre-shredding of the food, digesting a large catch can take weeks. Juvenile crocodiles and alligators, which eat insects and small fish, feed frequently throughout the year, but large adults, which live mainly on mammals, may kill as rarely as once or twice a year.

The additional weight of undigested materials does not matter much to aquatic predators, such as fish and crocodiles, but it can be significant for birds like eagles, hawks and owls, which carry prey or catch it in flight. Within hours (minutes in small species) of feeding, owls regurgitate pellets consisting of bones, feathers, hair and other indigestible parts, thus removing unnecessary weight before hunting again.

Almost all animal phyla include some carnivorous species and the range of predation strategies is enormous. Snakes and spiders are among the most specialized and successful predators and have evolved sophisticated ways of subduing prey that are large relative to themselves and of combining predation with digestion.

2.2.1 SNAKES

All snakes are strictly carnivorous, feeding mostly on other vertebrates, though many species eat snails, large insects and other invertebrates when immature. Although they have similar diets, and both are reptiles, crocodiles and snakes have very different styles of predation.

○   What are the major contrasts in the general structure of snake skulls (Figure 2.5) and a crocodile skull (Figure 2.4)?

●   The snake skulls appears fragile, obviously unsuited to grasping and holding active prey, or for tearing food. The snake's teeth point backwards and are long and slender. Crocodile teeth are stout and upright.

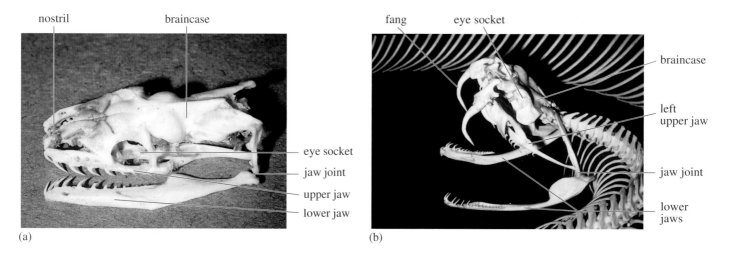

(a)   (b)

Figure 2.5   The skull of (a) a python, a large constricting snake and (b) a Gaboon viper (*Bitis gabonica*), a venomous snake. Notice that the jaws are only loosely attached to the skull and can separate from each other, and the teeth point backwards. The fangs are modified teeth on the front part of the upper jaw.

In snakes, the upper and lower, left and right jaws can move relative to each other and the rest of the skull, while in crocodiles, the upper jaws are firmly attached to the nose and braincase, and the lower jaw forms a single rigid structure. Non-venomous boas, pythons and anacondas kill by constriction using the body muscles. The teeth (Figure 2.5a) serve only to grasp the prey and swallow it after it is dead. Venomous snakes such as cobras and vipers have fangs, which are enlarged teeth (Figure 2.5b) attached to bones of the jaw, and can be swung forward to stab prey. They enclose a duct formed from a modified salivary gland which synthesizes and secretes venom, some ingredients of which are listed in Table 2.1.

Table 2.1   Some major ingredients of snake venoms. The proportions differ greatly between species, depending upon type of prey and predation strategy.

Toxins	Mode of action	Effect on tissues
phospholipases	break ester bonds in phospholipids	destroy cell membranes, so cell contents spill out
proteases	break up proteins at links between amino acids	destroy enzymes and blood haemoglobin
phosphatases	fragment ATP	disable cellular energy supply
hyaluronidases	break up extracellular materials	destroy mechanical links between cells in tissues, enabling poison to spread
neurotoxic peptides*	bind strongly to molecules that receive chemical messages from neurons	block the transmission of signals from nerves to muscles, causing paralysis

* Certain families only, including sea snakes.

Venomous snakes wait near nests or feeding areas of small mammals or birds and strike when the prey comes within range, making a small but sometimes quite deep wound into which **venom** from the gland is squirted. The strike may be complete in as little as a few milliseconds, and the snake retreats at once, thereby minimizing scope for the prey to retaliate and injure its predator, and follows the poisoned animal at a discreet distance until it collapses. Field experiments show that snakes can distinguish a stricken individual from others of the same species, probably by smell.

As soon as the prey is no longer able to struggle, the snake swallows it whole. This process often takes many minutes, even hours, as the snake disconnects each half of its flimsy jaws from the rest of the skull, slowly engulfing an object much wider than its own head and forcing it down the throat with its backward-pointing teeth (Figure 2.5). When combined with a sit-and-wait strategy, injecting venom greatly reduces the muscle mass and power required to subdue prey. Many highly poisonous snakes such as mambas and sea snakes are slender and positively delicate compared to the muscular, non-venomous pythons and anacondas.

The neurotoxins (Table 2.1) prevent the prey from struggling, thus making it easier to swallow. Most sea snakes, including the widespread and, in tropical seas, abundant genus *Pelamis*, are slender with small, narrow heads, but their venom is one of the fastest-acting and most lethal of all known natural toxins, paralysing vertebrate muscles in seconds. Sea snakes do not let go of their prey, or do so only very briefly. If they did, the dying prey might sink beyond their reach. But a struggling fish could seriously injure a snake's mechanically weak jaws.

If the dose of neurotoxins was large enough to paralyse their respiratory muscles, terrestrial mammals and birds, and fast-swimming fish, which need lots of oxygen and actively ventilate their lungs or gills, would quickly die from suffocation. But amphibians, which take up oxygen through the skin, and reptiles, especially semi-aquatic species, which breathe infrequently, would take much longer to die from the enzymatic breakdown of tissues. The immediate cause is usually the destruction of blood cells and the lining of blood vessels. Many invertebrates are even less disabled by snake venom.

○ Would snakes' style of feeding be effective in avoiding infection by parasites in its prey?

● No. Very little venom reaches most internal parasites and absence of the capacity for mechanical breakdown of the prey means that they enter the snake's gut unharmed. The very slow digestion gives the parasites plenty of time to establish themselves in the snake's body.

Snakes harbour a wide variety of animal parasites, almost all derived from their prey. Compared to other extant groups of reptiles (lizards, the tortoises, turtles and terrapins and the crocodiles and alligators), snakes have quite short lives, rarely more than 30 years. Some connections between longevity and susceptibility to disease are discussed in Chapter 6.

2.2.2 SPIDERS

Spiders are among the most ancient and successful terrestrial predators. All of the many thousands of species of spiders are predators, as are many other groups of the class Arachnida (e.g. scorpions, opiliones ('harvestmen'), some mites and ticks). Spiders' main prey is (and so far as we know always has been) other arthropods, especially flying and walking insects, although a few famous spider species are large enough to handle small vertebrates such as birds, hatchling lizards or small fish.

Spiders owe their success in subduing prey that are often much larger and stronger than themselves to the capacity to make **silk**, an unusual protein that forms traps, webs and draglines, and to various poisons which immobilize (but may not always kill) their victims. Both these aids to predation are based on some remarkable protein chemistry and, since the materials are secreted out of the spider's body, they are readily accessible for detailed study. Understanding how they work, and how they can be adapted to thousands of different styles of capturing prey, has involved engineers and crystallographers as well as biochemists and animal behaviourists.

Many insects also produce silk but usually do so only at certain stages of the life cycle, such as to make a cocoon for the pupa, or to attach egg cases to fixed objects. Spiders can produce silk throughout their lives, though its functions may change as the animal matures. Arachnid and insect silks are basically similar, although that of the silk-worm has been much more intensively studied because of its industrial importance.

Silk consists mainly of the small amino acids glycine and alanine, and forms a tightly packed protein consisting of short lengths of stiff 'crystallites', which make the material strong, embedded in a more disordered rubber-like matrix, which confers flexibility, elasticity and resistance to tearing. Stiffer, harder silks contain more, larger crystallites while the matrix predominates in tough, flexible or very stretchy materials, which can be stretched to form continuous very fine strands. Weight for weight, silk is stronger than cellulose or bone, and can be as strong as nylon.

In its chemical structure and mechanical properties, and in the fact that its uses are always external, silk resembles keratin, the protein that forms hair, feathers, horns and claws in terrestrial vertebrates, but differs from it in the way it is produced. Keratin accumulates in the cells that synthesize it until they die, stuck together to form a strand or sheet. Silk is a secretion that, in various different kinds of arthropods, may be produced from modified salivary glands or other parts of the gut, or from reproductive glands. Like all secretions, silk is initially in solution, but the final region of the special ducts through which it is extruded secretes a strong acid, which polymerizes the protein to form an insoluble, biochemically inert material. Web-building spiders build by running round the web as shown in Figure 2.6a, at a pace that matches the rate of extrusion of the silk, thus stretching it to form a very thin thread as it toughens. *

The first web-building spiders appeared in the early Devonian 400 Ma ago; some probably caught walking prey by means of trip-lines set from small holes in the ground, while others spun three-dimensional cotton-wool-like masses which entrapped animals that fell onto them. Both these methods of catching prey are still found among living species, but the most sophisticated, and most recently evolved, kind of web is the flat, two-dimensional 'orb web' which catches flying insects. One of the most familiar orb weavers in Britain is the garden cross spider (*Araneus diadematus*), which is common in woodland, pasture and gardens, where its varied diet includes flies, bees, wasps, aphids and beetles, depending on location and season. In captivity, it thrives on meals of *Drosophila* and young locusts or crickets, and has thus been the subject of detailed laboratory investigation.

Catching a fast-flying insect on a flat web is comparable with trying to stop, and hold, a ballistic missile with a wire fence, and requires some subtle engineering. *Araneus* can produce at least seven kinds of silk, each of slightly different chemical composition, which are synthesized and secreted from structurally distinct glands, together occupying a large fraction of the bulbous abdomen. The spider uses different silks for the radial and spiral threads of the web (Figure 2.6a), a third kind for binding these two strands together and for the attachments to twigs or other suitable moorings, and yet more kinds for roles such as wrapping prey and as climbing lines.

As it is extruded, the silk used to form the spiral strands is coated with a viscous mixture of glycoproteins (proteins with sugar side-chains) and certain free amino acids secreted from yet another gland. The glycoproteins readily form weak chemical bonds with other substances, including water, so the mixture is hygroscopic (water attracting) and sticky. It takes up water vapour from the air, forming sticky globules that are large enough to be visible in bright sunlight as tiny 'beads'. Like many fibres (e.g. wool), this type of silk is much more elastic when damp, enabling it to absorb the energy of an insect hurtling into the web.

* Spiders are often said to 'spin' silk thread. This term is avoided here because the mechanics of silk extrusion have little in common with 'spinning' yarn from wool or cotton and more closely resemble making wires or cables.

The impact stretches the threads to up to three times their normal length, but the energy is stored elastically, so the web recoils quickly to its original shape. The capacity to absorb impact in this way makes the web durable when built in places where it is most likely to intercept plenty of prey. Fast-flying insects such as bees, and wind-borne debris, may punch holes in the web or rip it from its moorings, thereby disabling it and dispersing its materials.

The stickiness conferred by the glycoproteins helps to hold the prey to the web, otherwise the insect would bounce off, like a person landing on a trampoline, and be lost to the spider (sometimes prey do escape in this way). Although densely woven, sticky webs catch prey more efficiently, they are also more resistant to air currents so are more likely to be torn by strong winds. Many spiders that thrive in a variety of habitats adjust their style of web-building to the weather. Experiments on captive *Araneus* show that under moderately windy conditions, spiders build smaller, rounder webs than they do in still air, and they preferentially place them parallel to, rather than perpendicular to, the direction of the prevailing wind. Orb webs cannot be used at all in exposed positions in very windy climates. *Araneus* webs are largest and most abundant, and hence most easily noticed, in sheltered woodland and gardens, and inside buildings.

A substantial amount of the spiders' body mass is cuticle and other non-reclaimable tissues, so making a web represents a significant outlay of protein. *Araneus* replaces its web about once a day during the summer hunting season, but other species build massive, elaborate webs that last for weeks. If spiders are induced to build new webs more frequently than normal, they use less and less silk each time, suggesting that the rate of silk synthesis limits web-building capacity.

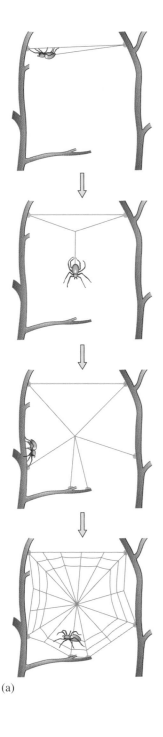

(a)

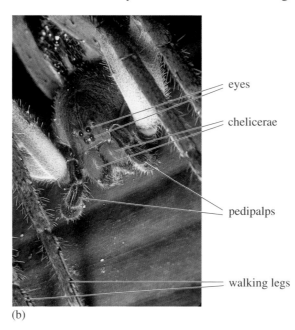

(b)

eyes

chelicerae

pedipalps

walking legs

Figure 2.6 (a) Stages in the construction of a typical orb web. The spider uses different silk for anchoring the web (top), the radial threads (middle) and the spiral threads (bottom). (b) Photograph of a large tropical spider showing the pedipalps and chelicerae, which are paired feeding appendages in front of the very small ventral mouth (not visible). See text for details.

○ From the information in Table 2.2, how long does it take to make a new web?

● The total length of the thread is 14 + 4 = 18 m, which is produced at an average rate of $1\,cm\,s^{-1}$, or $(60 \times 60)/100\,m\,h^{-1} = 36\,m\,h^{-1}$. To produce 18 m at $36\,m\,h^{-1}$ takes 0.5 h, so a new web is made in about 30 min.

Table 2.2   Some average properties of orb-weaving spiders and their webs. Data from Vollrath *et al.* (1997).

Body mass	up to 50 mg
Number of radial threads	33
Diameter of silk thread	1–2 µm
Total length of radial threads	4 m
Total length of spiral strands	14 m
Web area	400 cm^2
Mass of web	0.1–0.5 mg
Rate of extrusion of silk	1 cm s^{-1}

Web building is quite strenuous, because the spider runs around the web to lay its thread. Only a small fraction of the day is spent in this activity. For the rest of the time, spiders maintain mechanical contact with their web, usually waiting near the centre or at an attachment point. Their legs (see Figure 2.6b), like those of almost all arthropods, are very sensitive to vibration. As soon as the spider feels the impact of an insect on its web, it scrambles towards the disturbance and immobilizes the prey before its struggles do too much damage to the delicate fabric.

○ From the information in Table 2.2, what percentage of the total body mass is used to make a new web?

● Spiders weighing 50 mg secrete up to (0.5/50) × 100 = 1% of the total body mass as silk to make each web.

Under ideal conditions, spiders catch prey amounting to about 3–12% of their body mass each day. Many spiders, including *Araneus,* eat their own web when it becomes too tattered to be effective, thereby reclaiming much of the protein they put into it. The water absorbed from the air by the glycoprotein glue, or collected as dewdrops, is a bonus, as spiders do not normally drink. The soft tissues of their prey are the only other source of water, and their respiratory and excretory mechanisms are well adapted to conserving water.

○ Why can such recycling of the silk not sustain web-building indefinitely?

● Metabolic energy is used in producing enzymes that digest the silk to its component amino acids in the gut, in transporting them from the gut into the bloodstream, and in re-using them for synthesizing more silk, or another kind of protein.

If their webs fail to net any edible prey, the spiders' body reserves are gradually depleted until they are unable to support further web building. Without its means of capturing prey, a webless spider starves to death, often leaving its final web unreclaimed. Like other opportunist predators, most spiders can fast for a remarkably long time, over 200 days in the case of adult black widow spiders. Their rate of using energy falls by as much as 80% and the spiders' tissues are slowly depleted of glycogen, fats and finally proteins.

Larger, more conspicuously placed webs have a better chance of catching prey, but they also use more silk, and are more susceptible to damage. Establishing a satisfactory ratio of the energy outlayed to collect food and the nourishment so obtained is called **optimal foraging**. In the case of orb weavers, predation is most efficient when the silk remains strong when stretched into a fine thread, thus minimizing the quantity of material used, and there is a good match between the chemical and mechanical properties of the web and how and where the spider deploys it.

As you would expect, several lineages of insects have evolved countermeasures that help them avoid entrapment in spiders' webs. Among the most familiar are the fine, loose, often highly coloured scales on butterflies' wings. If a wing touches a newly formed web, the butterfly is often only briefly disorientated, because its scales stick to, and thereby inactivate, the web, enabling the insect to escape with only minor damage. Sticky webs also accumulate fine particles of dust. Except when coated with dew on a sunny morning, we do not usually notice orb webs until they become so covered in dirt as to be useless to the spider. Such tough, dry protein is only slowly degraded by bacteria and fungi, so unless fragmented by wind or rain, old spiders' webs accumulate, especially in sheltered corners of unused buildings.

The use of webs has made spiders by far the most important predators of insects on the wing, competing only with a few species of birds, such as swifts, swallows and flycatchers, insects such as dragonflies, damselflies and certain wasps, and insectivorous bats. With such subtle relationships between web structure, durability and function, it is not difficult to see how spiders have diversified in structure and habits, each species producing webs and draglines suited to different conditions of weather and terrain, and catching different kinds of prey.

Most spiders wrap captured prey in silk, then inject venom through the powerful, stabbing appendages called chelicerae (see Figure 2.6b). The poison glands are squeezed by muscles, enabling the spider to control how much is administered. 13 ng (1 ng = 10^{-9} g) of the poison of black widow spiders is sufficient to kill a housefly, and about 15 µg (1 µg = 10^{-6} g) disables a large cockroach within 10 minutes. Most spider venoms contain toxins that interfere with aspects of nerve transmission that are specific to arthropods and do not affect vertebrate neurons, so only a few species are dangerous to humans. The spider may eat its prey at once, or enfold it in a mesh of silk and store it alive but paralysed on or near its web for later consumption.

○ What is the advantage to the predator of keeping the prey alive?

● Although it cannot move, the prey's cellular mechanisms that protect its body from invasion by bacteria and fungi continue to operate, thereby preventing the normal processes of decay.

The capacity to store prey in this way enables spiders to take maximum advantage of transient gluts of food without greatly increasing their rate of feeding or size of internal storage tissues.

Some predatory insects, notably digger wasps, also use venoms that paralyse but do not kill their prey. This strategy works much better with terrestrial arthropods whose respiratory organs can operate without muscular activity, than with vertebrates whose lungs or gills must be actively ventilated and the blood pumped around the body. Enough oxygen diffuses through arthropods' respiratory surfaces to vital tissues to keep them alive as long as they remain sedentary, but when a vertebrate's muscles are paralysed, it dies from suffocation, usually within a few minutes.

Spiders feed by squirting digestive enzymes through the mouth onto the immobilized prey, then using the muscular gut to suck up the liquidized tissues through fine filters around the mouth and in the anterior part of the gut. All particles larger than about 1 μm are excluded, and the filter is cleaned from time to time by spitting out digestive juices. Tough cuticle and other parts of the prey that cannot be digested often remain on or near webs and may be sufficiently intact to be recognizable.

Because so much digestion occurs outside the body, the spider gut is quite short, though the glands that produce the digestive enzymes can be extensive. These enzymes accumulate in granules inside secretory cells in the gut lining, and can be expelled into the gut within a few minutes when required. Other absorptive cells take up the digested material into vacuoles.

○ Would spiders produce much faeces?

● No. Sucking in partially digested prey avoids taking in indigestible material such as cuticle.

The small quantity of faeces is mainly material from the gut itself.

○ Compared to vertebrates, how would this style of feeding affect susceptibility to pathogens in the prey?

● Sucking in the liquefied remains of externally digested prey avoids contact between the gut lining and many pathogens, reducing the risk of infection compared to vertebrate predators that ingest the prey whole or in large chunks.

External digestion of prey similar to that of spiders is common among carnivorous insects and other invertebrates.

2.3 HERBIVORY

Consumers of terrestrial plants face very different problems from those of predators. Plants are often widespread and abundant but much of the tissue is indigestible, each cell being surrounded by a tough cell wall. The nutritious components can be reached only by piercing through the cell walls or by mechanically crushing the cells to release their contents, strategies that require hard tissues such as toughened cuticle or teeth, operated by powerful, well controlled muscles, or by chemically digesting away the tough protective materials. As well as this mechanical protection, the leaves and roots of many plants, especially large, long-lived species, also synthesize various toxins that deter herbivory by destroying or impeding animals' secretions or intracellular processes.

○ How could herbivorous animals deal with toxins distributed throughout the plant?

● They would be unable to avoid ingesting toxins along with the nutritious tissues, so their digestive system has to prevent them being absorbed, or detoxify them and excrete the waste.

In view of these fundamental problems of eating living plants, it is not surprising that, although almost all phyla and major classes of animals include predatory species, only a few lineages have become as diverse and widespread as terrestrial herbivores. Most terrestrial slugs and snails (phylum Mollusca, class Gastropoda, order Pulmonata) rasp leaves and stems, though many species are limited to foraging in damp habitats or at night. Many roundworms (phylum Nematoda) burrow into plant roots and other underground structures such as bulbs and tubers, sucking out their nutrients.

By far the most ancient and numerous consumers of living plants are the arthropods, including millipedes and above all insects, which comprise the great majority of terrestrial herbivores. Major orders that consist almost entirely of herbivores include Isoptera (termites), Orthoptera (locusts, grasshoppers and crickets) which bite and chew leaves and stems, Hemiptera (cicadas, shield bugs, leaf hoppers, spittlebugs, aphids, whiteflies) which feed by piercing and sucking plant sap, and Lepidoptera (butterflies and moths) of which most larvae (caterpillars) nibble leaves, and many adults take nectar. Most earwigs (Dermaptera) and many families of Coleoptera (beetles), including chafers, weevils, leaf beetles and woodworm, are also obligate herbivores, and many Diptera (flies) and Hymenoptera (ants, bees and wasps) depend on plants during part of their life cycle.

Jawed vertebrates are now, and have been throughout their evolutionary history, primarily predators, though a few species of most classes have become herbivores. Among living vertebrates, a few fish (including goldfish) eat free-floating or encrusting algae and/or aquatic plants such as pondweed. Most tortoises and a very few lizards (iguanas and their relations) eat leaves and flowers, at least when fully grown, though almost all species supplement their diet with snails, worms, insect larvae or carrion if they find them. Many kinds of birds (e.g. parrots, pigeons, finches, grouse, pheasants) feed on concentrated plant tissues such as seeds, buds or fruits, but only a few, notably ostriches and their relatives, and geese, plus some ducks and moorhens, eat mature leaves in large quantities. Throughout the Tertiary, the most important vertebrate consumers of foliage have been the mammals, mainly because they can chew very efficiently.

○ From your own experience, what features of the mouth and teeth are necessary for chewing?

● Chewing requires broad, fairly flat teeth mounted on exactly opposable jaws so the teeth 'fit' together to form a grinding surface. The process also entails being able to breathe while the mouth is full, and manipulating food around the mouth with the tongue and cheeks.

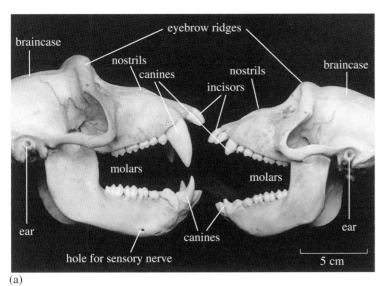

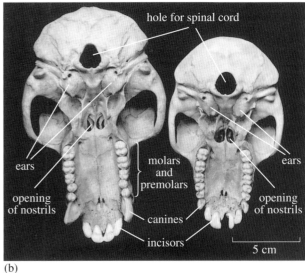

(a)

(b)

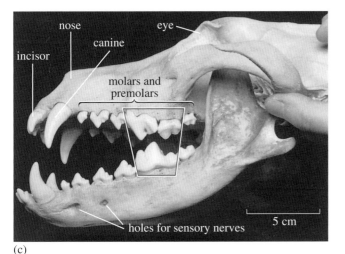

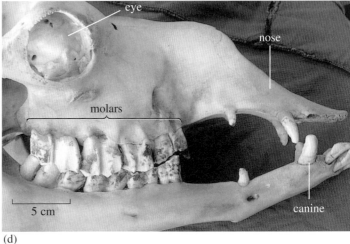

(c)

(d)

Figure 2.7 Some mammalian skulls. (a) and (b) The skulls of an adult male (left) and female (right) macaque monkey, showing the main features of mammalian dentition. The opening of the nostrils into the throat at back of the mouth can be seen in (b). (c) The skull of a timber wolf, a specialized carnivore, with cutting molars outlined. (d) The teeth and jaws of a camel, showing the grinding molars and the exact fit between the upper and lower teeth.

○ Comparing Figure 2.7 with Figures 2.4 and 2.5, how do mammalian teeth differ from those of reptiles?

● The mammals have fewer teeth than reptiles, but they are complex in structure, highly differentiated and those of the upper and lower jaws are exactly opposed.

With a few exceptions (notably the marine mammals), the dentition consists of front, gripping incisors, piercing canines and grinding molars and premolars, as shown in Figures 2.7a and b. In carnivores, the dagger-like canines are massive and the stout, pointed molars are adapted for shearing (Figure 2.7c). The canines are reduced in most herbivores, * which nibble, tear or gnaw plants between their incisor teeth and/or lips, then grind each mouthful between their broad, hard, elaborately sculptured molar teeth (Figure 2.7d). Chewing breaks insoluble plant tissues into tiny fragments which form a suspension in the copious saliva, maximizing the surface area on which enzymes can work.

Digestion of plants is slower and usually less efficient than that of animal tissues, so nearly all herbivorous animals have more extensive guts than their carnivorous relatives. Most herbivorous vertebrates rely upon some form of microbial-assisted digestion. The guts of foliage-eating mammals (and those of a few herbivorous birds) have special anatomical structures that enable them to harbour huge numbers of symbiotic microbes. In 'hindgut fermenters', the colon, and/or the **caecum**, a blind-ended sac extending from the junction of the small and large intestine, are greatly enlarged and harbour symbiotic microbes. The gut contents thus reach the microbes after the animals' own enzymes have digested them as much as they can. In other groups of herbivores, the microbes are concentrated in forestomachs, which form as a pouch in the oesophagus, anterior to the true stomach. The lining of forestomachs does not produce secretions and does not actively take up nutrients. The microbes thus have access to the food before the animals' own enzymes reach it, which has profound implications for the mammals' diet, nutritional requirements and metabolism.

SUMMARY OF SECTIONS 2.2 AND 2.3

1   Animals can prey upon each other in a huge range of ways, and predators have a variety of habits and body form.

2   Primitive vertebrates, such as crocodiles, stalk prey and then seize it with stout teeth, tearing and shaking it with their powerful jaws and body. Large chunks are swallowed whole.

3   Poisonous snakes inject venom into prey. It contains enzymes that break down tissues and red blood cells, and, in more advanced families, neurotoxins. The fangs are modified teeth. The jaws are mechanically weak but can be disarticulated to swallow immobilized prey whole. Digestion of large prey may take weeks.

4   Spiders build webs which trap flying or walking arthropods by secreting several different kinds of silk and associated materials. Web building requires a significant outlay of body reserves, which cannot be sustained unless enough prey are caught and eaten.

5   The main consumers of terrestrial plants are insects, gastropod molluscs, nematodes, a few birds and many kinds of mammals, whose guts are modified to harbour microbial symbionts.

* Canine teeth are enlarged in adult males of certain primitive deer that lack antlers, including the Chinese water deer (*Hydropotes inermis*) now living wild in parts of southern Britain. They function in social and sexual behaviour.

2.4 DIGESTION

Digestion is the chemical breakdown of ingested food. Organic material is attacked by **digestive enzymes**, while inorganic matter (the mineral components of shells, bone, etc.) is dissolved by acids. The main sites of digestion are the stomach and anterior part of the intestine, though in many animals, the saliva also contains some enzymes, enabling digestion to begin in the mouth. The main classes of digestive enzymes are **proteases** * which fragment proteins by hydrolysing peptide bonds between amino acids, **lipases** which hydrolyse the ester bonds that link fatty acids to glycerol in membrane phospholipids and storage triacylglycerols, and various enzymes that break down complex carbohydrates into monosaccharides.

Digestive enzymes are basically similar in all heterotrophic organisms, bacteria and fungi as well as the huge range of animals, though species differ in the amounts of the different kinds of enzymes they produce, and in the chemical conditions (e.g. pH, temperature) under which they operate, depending upon their diet and habitat. Those produced by carnivorous plants such as sundews (*Drosera*), which digest insect prey, are remarkably similar in molecular structure and mode of action to the corresponding secretions found in animals, even though other green plants do not break down complex organic molecules to obtain nutrients.

Digestive enzymes are usually less specific than intracellular enzymes, acting, with various degrees of efficiency, on a wide range of similar molecules, especially in omnivorous organisms which eat many different foods. Those of vertebrates tend to be more specific than those of fungi and invertebrates, both for the kinds of bonds they attack, and the chemical conditions under which they work most efficiently, and so they often occur in greater variety. For example, of the proteases, **pepsin** is secreted by the stomach epithelium; it works best in strongly acidic solution and cleaves peptide bonds formed by amino acids in which the R group is negatively charged, i.e. acidic (e.g. aspartate), or has a ring structure (e.g. phenylalanine). **Trypsin** is secreted into the small intestine by the **pancreas** gland. This enzyme functions at or near neutral pH and preferentially attacks bonds involving the amino acids arginine or lysine, both of which have positively charged (basic) R groups. The variety is further increased by the fact that some proteases, including pepsin and trypsin, can cleave peptide bonds in the middle of a polypeptide chain, but others work preferentially on the N- or C-terminal amino acids. The combined action of these enzymes can reduce a wide variety of proteins to single amino acids or small peptides, molecules that are small enough to be conveyed through the absorptive epithelium of the intestine.

○ How could bonds that are usually broken by digestive enzymes escape hydrolysis?

● Breakdown could be very slow if the higher-order structure (i.e. folding) of the molecule were such that the enzymes could not get close enough to the relevant chemical bonds.

---

* Some, but not, all enzymes are named after their substrate, e.g. protease (proteins), lipase (lipids), cellulase (cellulose), lactase (lactose).

The acidity of the stomach helps to open up tightly folded proteins, thus facilitating their digestion, but most vertebrates cannot break down tough materials such as keratin (see Section 2.2.2), silk or tooth enamel fast enough to yield useful amounts of amino acids. These molecules may pass right through the gut with little or no digestion.

As well as immobilizing the prey, snake venom also contributes to digestion.

○ Which components of venom listed in Table 2.1 aid the digestion of the prey?

● The phospholipase, protease and hyaluronidase enzymes.

The combined action of these injected enzymes which break down the tissue from the inside and secreted enzymes attacking it from the outside speeds up the snake's digestion. But the process is still slow compared to that of animals that shred or chew their food before swallowing it. Even under ideal, warm conditions, snakes can take weeks to complete the digestion of a large meal.

○ Would the neurotoxin component of the venom help to digest the prey?

● No. Neurotoxins bind to proteins, rather than enzymatically break them down, so they contribute nothing to digestion.

Detailed studies of the amino acid sequences of enzymes reveal that many of those secreted for digestion are similar to the enzymes that perform analogous transformations in other tissues. For example, pancreatic lipase which, in the vertebrate intestine, breaks down triacylglycerols and phospholipids in seeds and in the adipose tissue of prey (see Section 2.4.2), proves to be only slightly different from the lipoprotein lipase found in muscle, adipose tissue and many other tissues which hydrolyses blood-borne triacylglycerols, releasing fatty acids that these tissues take up and use themselves (see Section 2.6.2).

○ What changes in gene activation could have led to the evolution of venom production (Section 2.2.1)?

● As shown in Table 2.1, snake venom consists mainly of enzymes that in other vertebrates are involved only in digestion. The genes for these proteins are present in all cells, so the major evolutionary change was their activation in the salivary glands as well as in the lining of the gut and/or in the pancreas.

The evolution of venom production is thus probably quite simple, and indeed comparative studies suggest that it has happened many times in different lineages of animals. The adaptations of the teeth and jaws (Figure 2.5b), not to mention those for detecting and striking at prey, are more complicated, and are unique to snakes. The salivary glands of the Gila monster (a predatory lizard found in the deserts of southwest USA) also produce venom, but poisonous secretions are rare among birds and mammals, being known from only a few species, notably shrews. Other large lizards, the Varanidae, harbour many potentially dangerous bacteria in the mouth, so a shallow bite on a limb is very likely to turn septic. The swelling and delayed healing lames the potential prey, which is much easier to catch while it is partially disabled.

2.4.1 ADJUSTING THE ENZYMES' WORKING ENVIRONMENTS

All enzymes have a narrow range of concentrations at which they work most efficiently. To maximize the speed and thoroughness of digestion, the dilution of the gut contents is adjusted by removing or adding water. Sea-anemones and their relatives *Hydra* have one of the simplest means of doing so: the body retracts after prey is caught, expelling much of the water in the enteron (gut), and remains closed for hours or days, thus trapping the food and digestive enzymes together (Figure 2.8).

Another means of preventing loss and excess dilution of digestive enzymes is phagocytosis, which is followed by intracellular digestion. In heterotrophic protoctists, including the unicellular *Amoeba*, the products of digestion diffuse into the rest of the cell, and any insoluble waste is expelled as the vacuole reaches the surface. Similar processes occur in the cells lining the guts of many kinds of invertebrate animal, especially particle-feeders.

Terrestrial animals usually need to add water to the food before digestion begins, turning the mixture into a slurry. The gut epithelium or associated glands (e.g. the salivary glands of insects and vertebrates) may secrete large quantities of water, which persists in the stomach and intestines and is reabsorbed, together with salts and other small molecules, in the hindgut after digestion and absorption are complete. The faeces of terrestrial reptiles, birds and mammals are thus comparatively dry. Terrestrial insects also reabsorb most of the water in the gut contents.

(a)

The mechanisms and cellular conditions by which water passes into and out of the gut are explained later. The important point is that they require energy and may entail excessive loss of ions in body fluids. Extracting water from the faeces contributes substantially to the metabolic cost of digestion, so the process is less thorough (i.e. the faeces remain wetter) in animals with easy access to drinking water than in desert-adapted animals.

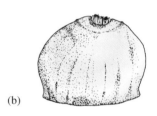

(b)

Figure 2.8 A sea-anemone (*Metridium senile,* phylum Cnidaria) (a) expanded with tentacles protruded to collect food and (b) closed up while digesting food.

○ Would aquatic animals have a well-developed hindgut?

● No. There is little active reabsorption of water where plenty is available to the animal.

Among vertebrates, fish have no distinct hindgut. In terrestrial reptiles, birds and mammals, the water-absorbing colon is clearly differentiated from the nutrient-absorbing small intestine.

Some animals, including a few land-dwelling forms, have the opposite problem: to remove excess water from dilute foods. As well as diluting enzymes, water also adds to the body mass, which does not matter for aquatic (i.e. neutrally buoyant) or sessile species, but can be a significant problem for flying animals, such as insects. Special physiological adaptations are needed to enable bees to utilize nectar, which is nutritious and contains no toxins, but is too dilute to be digested efficiently.

BUMBLEBEES

Although sedentary as larvae, adult bumblebees (*Bombus lucorum*) fly to find mates and suitable places in which to lay eggs. Flight requires large quantities of metabolic fuel which, in the case of bumblebees, comes almost entirely from nectar, a concentrated solution of fructose, sucrose and other simple sugars in water. *Bombus* flies from flower to flower, sucking in 0.01–0.1 µl of nectar at each visit (depending on the species).

In a detailed study of captive bumblebees fed from artificial 'flowers' that provided about 1 µl of 'nectar', males that weighed about 220 mg foraged for about 4 h a day, flying an average of 17 km to collect about 220 mg of 50% sugar solution (i.e. 110 mg of sugar in 110 mg of water). Complete oxidation of 110 mg glucose yields about 66 mg of water, which together with the 110 mg of water in the nectar, makes a total of 176 mg. Only 40 mg of water is lost by evaporation, mostly through the respiratory organs (spiracles). So to maintain constant body mass, about 136 mg of water must be expelled as urine each day. That might not sound a lot, but it represents 62% of a bumblebee's total body mass, and so adds significantly to the energy needed to power flight. The bees cannot avoid taking in this water, but some physiological and behavioural modifications, summarized in Figure 2.9, reduce its impact on their foraging efficiency.

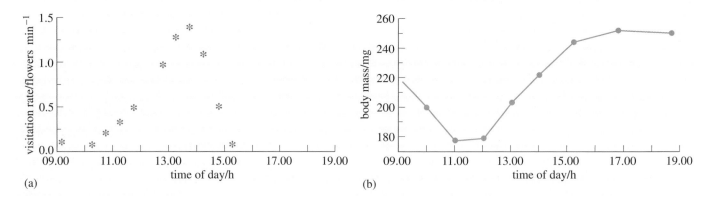

Figure 2.9 Graphical summary of (a) average frequency of visiting flowers and (b) changes in body mass of male bumblebees between 9 a.m. and 7 p.m. Data from Bertsch (1984).

○ What is the relationship between time spent flying and body mass?

● The bees fly most during the time when the body mass is well below maximum.

The body mass falls to a minimum of 28% (= (250 − 180)/250) below its value during the previous night, due to oxidation of sugars stored from the previous day's foraging, and to the excretion of excess water. Nearly all the synthetic 'nectar' was taken in over 3 hours during the warmest part of the day, and when the body mass had increased by about 20% of the minimum value measured at 9 a.m., the bees landed at a suitable roost and rested.

Nectar-feeding bats and humming-birds face similar problems, but the energetic cost of flying is lower, and the rate of water loss through the lungs is higher, for vertebrates than the corresponding values for insects, and their kidneys can excrete excess water more efficiently. So these larger animals can live on nectar that contains as little as 25% sugar, too dilute to serve as a food source for bumblebees, which are limited to plants that produce nectar with 35–50% sugar. Blood is another dilute solution of useful nutrients; the excretory mechanism of blood-sucking insects such as mosquitoes is so efficient that the excess water is expelled within a few minutes, often while sucking is still in progress, thus allowing for a quick getaway should their host try to swat them.

Whether a food forms an adequate diet for a particular species depends not only upon the nutrients it contains, but also upon how they are presented and the physiological capacities of the eater. This example was chosen because it is particularly clear-cut and easy to quantify, but the principle it demonstrates applies to many other plant–herbivore and predator–prey relationships. Apparently irrelevant abilities, in this case the rate of water loss and flight energetics, determine food choices and diet composition, and hence where and when species can live.

2.4.2 DIGESTING WAXES

Digestion of proteins and carbohydrates takes places in aqueous solution but for lipases (lipid-digesting enzymes) to work fast and efficiently, lipids must first be freed from the cells that contain them, and emulsified (i.e. mixed with water). In most vertebrates, lipid digestion does not begin until food reaches the small intestine, after the cells have been ruptured by biting or chewing, churning of the stomach and the action of proteases. After they leave the stomach, the gut contents are mixed with **bile**, a secretion of the liver which (at least in most vertebrates) accumulates in a pouch called the gall bladder before being released into the small intestine as required. Bile emulsifies lipids, including triacylglycerols, phospholipids and waxes, thus enabling the lipases secreted by the pancreas to bind them and hydrolyse their ester bonds.

Samples of bile and pancreatic secretions can be easily obtained from freshly killed animals, and their chemical composition and capacity to digest lipids measured *in vitro*. The volume of bile secreted and the concentration of salts in it depend greatly on the diet, being more than 20 times higher in birds such as storm petrels, *Oceanodroma leucorhoa* (Figure 2.10a) and Gentoo penguins, *Pygoscelis papua* (Figure 2.10b) than in chickens or pigeons. These marine scavengers and predators eat krill (large shrimp-like crustaceans) and other planktonic invertebrates in the cold Southern Ocean.

Many surface-living animals contain lipids which make them more buoyant and/or act as an energy reserve, but those that live in cold waters usually have a greater proportion of waxes and a smaller proportion of triacylglycerols, because the latter tend to solidify at low temperatures (like cooking oil kept in the fridge). Waxes mix with water even less readily than triacylglycerols, so they can only be emulsified in more concentrated bile. Conversely, the more dilute bile and pancreatic lipases of seed-eating chickens and pigeons digest triacylglycerols much faster and more efficiently than waxes.

As well as these biochemical studies, the development of new computer-based techniques for scanning *in vivo* has confirmed what has long been suspected: reverse peristalsis, propelling the gut contents back and forth, is frequent in bird intestines, especially those equipped to digest waxes and other difficult foods.

(a)

(b)

Figure 2.10 (a) Storm petrels cruise just above the waves on long, narrow wings and skim off small floating invertebrates with their long beaks. (b) Gentoo penguins breed near the coasts of islands in the Southern Ocean and Antarctica, where they swim through surface waters catching krill (large swimming crustaceans) and small fish.

The capacity for digesting waxes greatly increases in animals whose dietary habits require it. The genes for the relevant enzymes and modulation of bile secretion mechanisms are probably present in most or all birds, but have become strongly active only in those species whose diet is rich in waxes. Comparative studies of digestion indicate that this principle is generally true: adjustments to digestion parallel changes in diets. Concentrations of secretions and activities of enzymes can differ enormously in animals adapted to different diets.

Among terrestrial organisms, thick masses of wax occur only in certain special structures such as honeycombs, but most green plants and terrestrial arthropods have a thin waxy layer on their outer surfaces which aids waterproofing. Most leaf-chewing insects (e.g. caterpillars) and herbivorous or insectivorous vertebrates can digest small quantities of waxes in this form. This capacity is greatly enhanced in the caterpillar of the wax moth, *Galleria mellonella*, which lives in honeycombs and is a common and sometimes serious pest in commercial honeybee hives. *Galleria* digests waxes and utilizes the resulting fatty acids and alcohols so efficiently that, although almost all other caterpillars obtain most of their energy from the sugars and starches in the plants they eat, this species can be bred successfully on a carbohydrate-free diet.

2.4.3 RUMINANTS

Ruminants are the most abundant and diverse mammalian consumers of grasses and leafy shrubs. Their first and largest forestomach (anterior to the true stomach, Section 2.3) is the **rumen**, a huge warm vat of microbes whose activities are greatly facilitated by the habit of **chewing the cud**. The 'true ruminants' are advanced families of artiodactyls, including giraffes, pronghorns, antelopes, gazelles, goats, buffalo, bison, cattle, sheep, and most kinds of deer, which have four stomachs, and camels, llamas and a few primitive deer, which have three.

Ruminants take numerous small bites in quick succession, with only a minimum of grinding between the molar teeth. The coarsely fragmented plant material is combined with large quantities of saliva (several hundred litres per day in the case of cattle) and swallowed into the rumen (Figure 2.11a and b), where powerful muscular churning mixes it with symbiotic bacteria, fungi and protoctists (mostly ciliates) in combinations that depend greatly upon the species of plants the animal habitually eats. Larger particles of plant material float to the top of the rumen and pass into the reticulum (Figure 2.11b), a much smaller chamber whose function is primarily mechanical, forming boluses of cud which are regurgitated for further chewing. At intervals from minutes to hours (usually longer in larger species), ruminants pause to chew the cud, often lying down in groups to do so. Morsels of cud pass back to the mouth where they are ground between the large molar teeth by slow, powerful side-to-side movements of the jaws. The cud is re-swallowed and, if its particles are fine enough, sinks into the rumen where it is fermented by microbes over a period of from a few hours to several days, depending on the quality of the forage.

Efficient fermentation requires the microbes to adhere well to the plant fragments so that the enzyme concentration at the exposed surface is as high as possible. Adhesion is assisted by thorough chewing, which greatly increases the surface area to which the symbionts can attach, but also depends upon the chemical

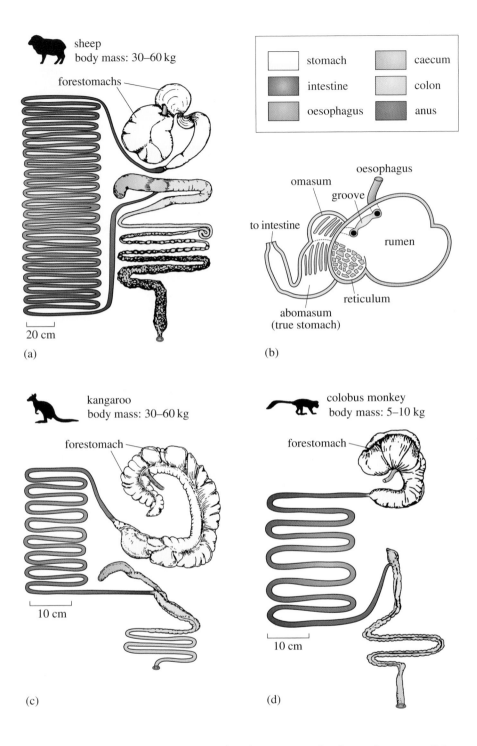

Figure 2.11 Plans of the guts of some herbivorous mammals that have foregut fermentation: (a) and (b) sheep (a true ruminant); the rumen is huge — in many wild ruminants, larger than all the rest of the gut; (c) kangaroo (*Macropus giganteus*); (d) colobus monkey (*Colobus abyssinicus*).

composition of the fragment. Many microbes can synthesize only some of the enzymes required to complete digestion: those that can digest cell walls forge access for those that preferentially attack starch or proteins. Digestion seems to proceed fastest when several species of bacteria and eukaryotic organisms assemble into structured 'consortia', producing complementary enzymes and often utilizing the products of each other's metabolism.

The microbes produce enzymes that liberate glucose from the cellulose of the plant cell walls, and use it and other nutrients from the plant cells to build their bodies and proliferate. Glucose cannot be oxidized completely because any molecular oxygen associated with the food is quickly used up by the microbes, making the rumen anaerobic. Instead, glucose is fermented to form **short-chain fatty acids**, particularly butyric ($CH_3(CH_2)_2COOH$), propionic (CH_3CH_2COOH) and acetic (CH_3COOH) acids, sometimes called 'volatile' fatty acids because, being of low molecular mass, they evaporate readily.

These fatty acids are soluble and readily diffuse through the wall of the rumen and into tissues which use them, as well as or instead of glucose or long-chain fatty acids, to produce metabolic energy. Almost all the fuel used by the musculature of the rumen itself is short-chain fatty acids. Certain other prokaryotic microbes that live in the rumen can use them too, and some fatty acids may be further broken down to methane (CH_4), carbon dioxide (CO_2) and hydrogen (H_2), which are actively expelled from the rumen as 'burps' through the mouth.

○ Could the animal oxidize free hydrogen or methane to produce energy?

● No, but the components of hydrogen or methane (H and C atoms) could have provided metabolic energy if they had remained incorporated into glucose or a fatty acid.

These gases are by-products of microbial metabolism that cannot be utilized either by their host or by other symbionts present in the rumen. Amounts thus wasted depend upon diet, but can be substantial: in one investigation, cows eating 5 kg of hay per day released over 190 litres of methane, amounting to 10% of the digestible food intake. Although almost odourless to us, these gases are usually accompanied by small amounts of the volatile fatty acids, which give cattle stables their distinctive smell. If, as happens after the animal's death, microbial fermentation continues but the waste gases cannot be expelled, they accumulate, distending the rumen. Sometimes the gas pressure thus built up is sufficient to burst the abdomen wall.

It might strike you as odd that ruminants harbour microbes that squander valuable plant carbohydrates in this way. The rumen may contain scores, sometimes hundreds of different kinds of microbes, even though the basic digestive processes could be performed by just a few species. The diversity is necessary because the microbes also inactivate or break down plant toxins (see Section 2.3). Often, only a few species of microbes can deal with the toxins produced by each kind of plant that the animal eats. Abrupt changes in forage composition can impair digestion until the appropriate microbes have become abundant enough to handle the new diet. A ruminant cannot control its own digestive capacity as quickly or as directly as non-ruminants can.

By breaking down or neutralizing potentially harmful substances before they reach the small intestine, these microbes prevent the toxins from entering the bloodstream, and relieve the animals' liver of the need to break them down. Resins, tannins and other plant toxins found particularly in mature vegetation and trees are less efficiently broken down. In large quantities, they delay the passage of food through the gut, and impair the absorption of other nutrients.

Thoroughly digested rumen contents flow through the small omasum to the abomasum (see Figure 2.11b), which is homologous to the normal vertebrate stomach. Most of the microbes are killed by contact with the stomach acid and their ruptured cells, together with the remains of the plant tissues and the dissolved products of fermentation, are subject to further digestion before passing into the intestines, where the final digestion products are absorbed as described in Section 2.5.

○   How would the chemical composition of nutrients absorbed by ruminants' intestines differ from that of nutrients released by digestion of the same material by non-ruminant herbivores?

●   The amino acids would come from digestion of the microbes themselves, as well as from the plant protein. There would be very little glucose because most of it has been converted into short-chain fatty acids (or even smaller molecules), which would be far more abundant than after digestion in a simple stomach.

Although ruminants' diet consists mainly of plant polysaccharides, they are actually chronically short of glucose, and sometimes make it from amino acids in the liver. The microbes also alter the plant lipids. In the strictly anaerobic conditions that prevail inside the rumen, many unsaturated fatty acids are saturated by adding hydrogen atoms. These modified lipids are absorbed along with other nutrients and may be broken down for energy production, or incorporated into storage triacylglycerols, or secreted in milk. So meat and milk from ruminants contain a much higher proportion of saturated fatty acids than those of most other mammals.

○   Can you relate these properties to the relative difficulty of washing up a pan in which mutton or pork has been roasted?

●   Mutton (or beef) triacylglycerols, from ruminant sheep (or cattle), contain a larger proportion of saturated fatty acids, which makes them firm, almost hard, at room temperature, while those of pork, from non-ruminant pigs, remain liquid. Hotter water, more detergent and more scrubbing are needed to solubilize the 'hard' fats from ruminant sheep or cattle.

Leaves and stems are low in protein, but ruminants deploy their symbiotic microbes to 'recycle' their own waste products, thereby supplementing the supply of amino acids derived from the diet. As in other vertebrates, the liver converts degradation products of amino acids into urea or ammonia, but instead of being eliminated through the kidney (as happens in most mammals including humans) these 'wastes' go back into the rumen as a component of saliva and by diffusing across the stomach lining. The microbes use these nitrogen-containing molecules to synthesize amino acids, which are incorporated into their own proteins and are then released by digestion and reabsorbed by the animal.

○   What other advantage would urea recycling confer on ruminants?

●   Urea excretion requires water, so urea recycling also reduces urine volume, thus saving water.

Urea recycling is particularly efficient in camels, which thus thrive on low-quality forage containing very little protein, and excrete only small amounts of urine.

As well as re-using the nitrogen of degraded proteins, symbiotic microbes also synthesize most of the water-soluble vitamins, especially those of the B group. Animals absorb them from the digested remains of the microbes, and not just the herbivore that was carrying the symbionts in its stomach: most predators eat their prey's guts, and at least a fair amount of their contents. Distasteful though it may seem, this habit makes an essential contribution to nutrition: captive lions and tigers fed only on eviscerated carcasses eventually develop vitamin deficiencies.

Several other lineages of mammals, including hippopotamuses, kangaroos (Figure 2.11c), and several kinds of monkeys (colobus, langur and proboscis monkey, Figure 2.11d) have an enlarged, non-secretory forestomach in which microbes ferment plant material before it reaches the acidic portion of the stomach. In this respect, they resemble ruminants, but they do not chew the cud, and certain kinds of microbes, notably ciliates (protoctists), are usually absent.

○ How would the absence of cud-chewing affect forestomach fermentation?

● The food is less finely fragmented, prolonging digestion time, so the forestomach has to be very large relative to the size of the body.

Hippopotamuses do not chew cud, but the first of their three stomachs is huge: its contents alone have been measured as 220 kg after a night's grazing, or 13–15% of the body mass. Hippos spend most of the day resting in pools and rivers, thus taking the enormous weight off their legs. The end-products of this prolonged digestion are smooth, viscous faeces that can be broadcast by flicking the short, bristly tail, as mature males do to establish breeding territories.

2.4.4 HINDGUT FERMENTATION

In various other herbivorous mammals, including all perissodactyls (horses, zebras, tapirs and rhinoceroses), rodents (rats, guinea-pigs and squirrels), lagomorphs (rabbits and hares), elephants and some metatherians such as the koala bear, symbiotic microbes are concentrated in an enlarged colon and/or caecum. The gut contents thus reach the microbes after the animals' own enzymes have digested them as much as possible. Figure 2.12 shows the proportions of the stomach, caecum, colon and other components of the gut in various mammals.

○ What would be the disadvantages of this arrangement compared to forestomach fermentation?

● The products of microbial digestion of cellulose cannot be absorbed unless the material re-enters the small intestine, and the bacteria themselves cannot be digested.

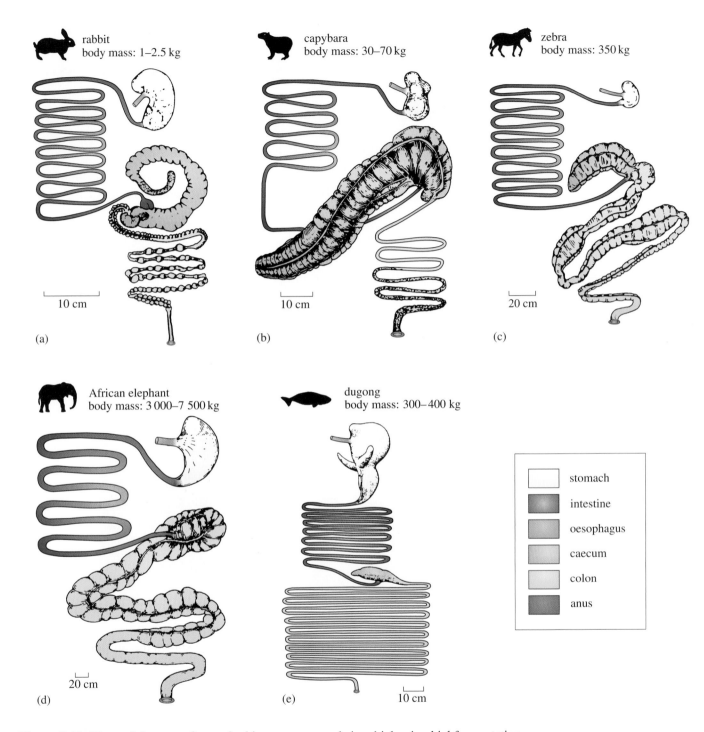

Figure 2.12 Plans of the guts of some herbivorous mammals in which microbial fermentation takes place in the colon or caecum: (a) rabbit (*Oryctolagus cuniculus*); (b) capybara (*Hydrochoerus hydrochaeris*), a large rodent similar to guinea-pigs; (c) zebra (*Equus burchelli*); (d) African elephant (*Loxodonta africana*); (e) dugong (*Dugong dugong*).

An obvious solution to this problem is intestinal reflux: in horses, material leaving the caecum probably moves backwards into the absorptive area of the small intestine before it goes to the colon and is expelled. Lagomorphs and some rodents, notably coypus, achieve much the same effect by eating their faeces, a habit known as **coprophagy**. The 'first pass' faecal pellets are soft and fibrous, and rabbits eat them as soon as they emerge, usually in the privacy of the burrow. The dark-coloured, homogenous rabbit droppings often seen on grassland are the product of the second passage through the gut.

Recent studies of wild mammals reveal that coprophagy is more widespread than was previously believed. Svalbard reindeer, *Rangifer tarandus platyrhynchus*, live and breed as far north as 80 °N, where the vegetation is very sparse and is covered with snow for nine months of the year (Figure 2.13). They supplement their meagre, indigestible diet by eating the fresh faeces of barnacle geese, *Branta leucopsis*, that migrate to breed on Svalbard during the brief summer. Experiments show that the reindeer choose goose faeces in preference to vegetation, and such 'reprocessing' of incompletely digested plants makes a significant contribution to their nutrition.

Figure 2.13 *Rangifer tarandus platyrhynchus*, grazing on Svalbard in late May.

○ What do these habits suggest about the efficiency of plant digestion in geese and reindeer?

● Geese do not digest their food as thoroughly as reindeer can, but passage through their gut facilitates further digestion in the reindeer's rumen.

Koala bears eat eucalyptus leaves, which are almost as tough and indigestible as the Svalbard reindeer's diet. The single offspring is suckled for an unusually long period, and is slowly weaned onto its mother's faeces, which both supply nutrients and colonize the young's gut with appropriate symbiotic microbes, before it tackles the adult diet.

Hindgut fermentation might seem to be a poor substitute for digestion in a ruminant forestomach, but careful observations of the composition of food ingested and faeces eliminated, and of the ecological circumstances under which animals with different kinds of digestive system prosper have revealed some advantages. For example, food passes through the gut more quickly in hindgut fermenters, taking 30–45 h in a horse compared to 70–100 h in a cow of similar body mass. Faster transit time is important if a large proportion of the forage is totally indigestible.

Silica, the component of grasses that makes their leaves and stems sharp and abrasive, is chemically similar to sand and is not digested at all. Resins and tannins are organic compounds that in principle could be converted into metabolically usable substances. Some beetles, caterpillars and other herbivorous insects can utilize them, but vertebrate herbivores cannot. These compounds simply occupy space, and in a forestomach they clog up the flow, thereby slowing down digestion and absorption of useful materials. The faster passage through the gut of hindgut fermenters enables this indigestible material to be expelled more promptly. Fragments of straw and other tough plant parts are abundant and clearly visible in the droppings of horses, rhinoceroses and elephants, but cannot be seen in the faeces of cows, sheep or deer.

Because hindgut fermenters extract energy from plants less efficiently, they need more forage to sustain themselves and produce much more faeces than carnivores or ruminant herbivores. African elephants (Figure 2.12d) defaecate 14–20 times per day, producing a total of 150 kg wet faeces containing 35 kg dry matter. This quantity is produced from about 60 kg of dry matter eaten, indicating that only about 40% is digested well enough to be absorbed. Gathering this amount of food takes around three-quarters of the elephants' time, leaving only a few hours for rest and sleep. The longest colon in Figure 2.12 is that of the dugong (2.12e), a distant relative of elephants which lives permanently in water, grazing aquatic plants in estuaries and shallow coastal waters. Weight in water is always much less than weight in air, so aquatic animals can afford to have a long, heavy gut in which large quantities of forage are digested slowly but thoroughly.

Zebras (Figure 2.12c) also have long intestines and survive seasonal droughts by eating large quantities of dry, tough plant material and digesting it incompletely but quite fast.

○   How would this diet and digestive physiology affect the teeth?

●   The teeth would wear down faster because hindgut fermenters eat more food, and more of it is likely to be very abrasive grasses.

The teeth of equids (horses, zebras and donkeys) withstand such use because the roots remain open, and the very long crown erupts slowly but continuously throughout life, thus replacing surface that is worn away (Figure 2.14a). Elephants combat tooth wear in another way: each tooth is huge, the largest weighing several kilograms. The three premolars of the 'milk' set and the three molar teeth in each jaw are used in succession instead of simultaneously: each tooth moves forward in the jaw as it is worn in use, to be replaced from behind by the next, larger tooth (Figure 2.14b). In these herbivores, which eat tough, abrasive plants, the dentition sets the maximum lifespan: old elephants, reindeer (Figure 2.14c) and donkeys die from starvation when their teeth wear down, so they cannot chew their food into particles fine enough for digestion to be efficient.

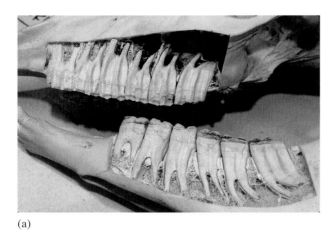

(a)

(b)

(c)

Figure 2.14 (a) Section of a horse skull to show long, continuously erupting teeth. The bone has been cut away from both the upper and lower jaws to reveal the complex roots of the molar teeth. The wear surface is visible on the lower jaw. (b) The lower jaws of a youngish African elephant. At the time of death, only a single molar tooth in each half of the jaw was in use as a grinding surface. Another tooth is in the process of formation behind each of the functional molars, but in life they were probably not yet erupted through the gum. (c) The molar teeth in the lower jaw of a young (top) and elderly (below) wild Svalbard reindeer.

The need to eat large quantities of plants helps to explain why zebras feature so prominently in safari tours: the buses usually pass around midday when most of the ruminants have retired to shady glades to chew the cud from their early morning foraging, before emerging to feed again in the cool of the evening. Especially during the dry season, when food quality is poor but tourists abundant, zebras eat almost continuously, and often do so in full sunshine, where it would be too hot for the ruminants. They are thus more likely to have their photos taken than the ruminants, which are certainly more diverse and, in most places, more numerous.

○ How would the differences in digestive physiology affect the composition of fuels circulating in the blood?

● Glucose liberated from sugars and starches digested by the animals' own enzymes is absorbed in the small intestine before the microbes get a chance to convert it to short-chain fatty acids, so the muscles and other energy-utilizing tissues of hindgut fermenters use far more glucose and less fatty acids than do those of ruminants.

Animals' digestive physiology determines many other aspects of their metabolism. Like other non-ruminants, horses use mainly glucose to fuel brief bursts of strenuous exercise, and, like human athletes, their performance in activities such as short-distance racing can be enhanced by feeding them on easily digested, starch-rich foods such as oats. The extra glucose is stored in the liver and the muscles as glycogen, which can be quickly broken down into glucose again, providing a ready supply of fuel for the muscles. The absorption of plenty of glucose also means that mares' milk contains much more sugar (and less fat) than that of cows and other ruminants. Pastoralists who herd horses on the steppes of central Asia have long fermented mares' milk to form an alcoholic drink called koumiss. Bacteria convert the sugars to alcohol in the same way as the carbohydrates in grapes, grain, potatoes, bananas or sugar cane can be fermented. Ruminant milk is much less effective for this purpose because it contains too little sugar and too much fat, so the end-product of bacterial action is yoghurt or cheese.

SUMMARY OF SECTION 2.4

1   Digestion of organic material involves mechanical shredding and churning, and enzymatic breakdown of large molecules.

2   The stomach and intestine, and associated glands, secrete digestive enzymes. Some are highly specific and attack only certain kinds of bonds in certain positions within substrate molecules.

3   Bile salts secreted from the liver emulsify lipids, thereby facilitating their digestion by lipases. The capacity for digesting waxes is low in most birds, mammals and insects, but can be much higher in animals whose diet includes large quantities of wax.

4   Efficient digestion depends upon adjusting the concentrations of food and enzymes. Water secreted and mixed with food in the mouth or stomach is reabsorbed in the hindgut. Very dilute food may be useless to animals that cannot excrete the excess water quickly and efficiently.

5   Most vertebrate herbivores depend upon symbiotic microbes to digest tough or toxic plants. A forestomach or modifications of the hindgut that accommodate microbes have evolved several times among mammals, but only ruminants chew the cud.

6   Microbial fermentation in the rumen alters energy metabolism in all the other tissues and improves protein nutrition by recycling of urea and/or synthesizing essential amino acids.

7   Intestinal reflux and/or coprophagy allow absorption of the products of microbial digestion in hindgut fermenters, thus improving nutrient extraction from plant food.

2.5   ABSORPTION AND METABOLISM

The small molecules generated by digestion of food are absorbed through special epithelial cells lining the small intestine, into the blood or other body fluid to reach tissues elsewhere. Carbohydrates are absorbed as monosaccharides (e.g. glucose or fructose), proteins as single amino acids or small peptides, and lipids as fatty acids or monoacylglycerols. Small quantities of monosaccharides and peptides pass through the gut epithelium by diffusion, but the majority, at least in mammals, are taken up molecule by molecule by **transporters** (or **carriers**), assemblages of specific proteins situated on and within the membrane of the epithelial cells on the side facing the gut contents (see Figure 2.1). Some such transporters are passive, in that they function without using energy, but **active transport** requires metabolic energy in the form of ATP and can take up substances against their concentration gradient, i.e. moving them from a more dilute solution into a more concentrated one.

In most vertebrates that have been studied in detail, the intestine has a special transporter for glucose and galactose, another for fructose, and separate transporters for each of the major categories of amino acids. The overall rate of absorption of any particular amino acid or sugar is determined by the activity of the appropriate type of transporter, their number per unit area of gut lining and the area of absorptive epithelium that is exposed to the gut contents. Comparisons between species suggest that the latter is the most important. Mammals absorb nutrients 7–10 times faster than lizards of similar body size, primarily because they have more villi, which make their intestinal surface area 4–4.5 times greater than that of reptiles. Although the mammalian body temperature is continuously higher, and they are generally more active so need much more energy, the maximum rate of transport per unit gut area is only about twice that of reptiles.

2.5.1 ADAPTING ACTIVE TRANSPORT TO DIFFERENT DIETS

Modern methods of protein separation and identification allow specific transporters to be studied individually, but from a functional point of view, it is often more useful to measure the total uptake capacity of the intestine. A long-established technique is to turn the small intestine of a freshly killed animal inside out, tie both ends and immerse it for an hour or two in a solution containing amino acids or monosaccharides, then measure their accumulation in the closed tube formed by the inside-out intestine. Figure 2.15 shows such data for glucose and proline, a common component of proteins. The tissues came from laboratory mice that had been fed for up to 2 weeks on synthetic diets containing different proportions of protein and carbohydrate.

Figure 2.15 Adaptive changes in uptake of glucose (graphs (a) and (b)) and proline (graphs (c) and (d)) in mice fed on high-protein food without carbohydrate (open circles) then switched to a high-carbohydrate, medium-protein rations (solid circles) for two weeks (graphs (a) and (c)), then back to high-protein, carbohydrate-free food (graphs (b) and (d)). In each case, the dietary change took place on day zero. Samples of mice were killed each day and the capacity of their small intestines to take up glucose or proline measured. * indicates significant difference from the values measured on day 0. Data from Diamond and Buddington (1987).

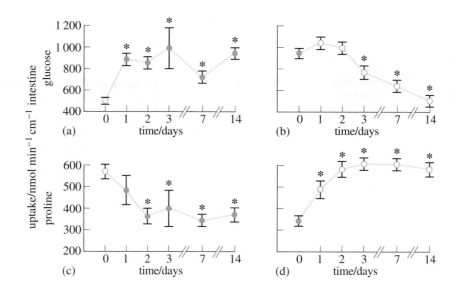

○ From the data in Figure 2.15, what happens when the proportion of carbohydrate in the diet is abruptly changed?

● When dietary carbohydrate is increased, uptake of glucose rises by at least 50% within a day (Figure 2.15a), but the reverse adjustment is slower, taking a week to complete (Figure 2.15b).

The effects of the experimental diets on the uptake of proline were more symmetrical, being almost complete within 2–3 days of the change in diet (Figure 2.15c and d).

○ What general conclusion can you draw from the data in Figure 2.15?

● When the diet and/or digestive mechanisms yield little glucose or proline in the small intestine, the appropriate transport mechanisms in its epithelium decline, and the converse.

Although reduced, the transporter systems do not disappear completely: some uptake capacity remains, even when there is apparently little for it to do.

○ Would nutrient uptake be efficient for mice abruptly switched from one diet to the other?

● No. For the first few days, the new type of food would not be absorbed (and probably not even digested) properly.

Omnivorous animals, which normally eat a wide range of different foods, maintain broader digestive and absorptive capacities. Figure 2.16 shows some data obtained by feeding the same synthetic diet to several species of carnivorous, omnivorous and herbivorous fish.

○ Are the short-term adaptations to high-protein diet experimentally induced in mice (Figure 2.15) as large as the natural differences between fish specialized to carnivory or herbivory (Figure 2.16)?

● No. The ratio of proline uptake to glucose uptake reaches 5–6 in the carnivorous fish, but the maximum ratio induced by feeding the mice on a protein-enriched diet was about 600/500 = 1.2.

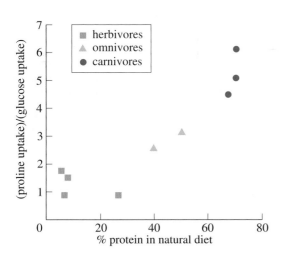

Figure 2.16 Capacity for absorbing glucose and amino acids (estimated as the ratio of uptake of proline to uptake of glucose) in the intestine of various species of carnivorous, omnivorous or herbivorous fish. At the time of the experiment, all the fish were kept in the lab and were fed the same synthetic food. The proportions of protein in the species' natural diets differed, as indicated on the horizontal axis. Data from Diamond and Buddington (1987).

As in so many physiological systems, inheritance defines the limits to physiological capacities, but within that range, actual properties can be adjusted to immediate requirements. In evolutionary biology parlance, there is a 'trade-off' between economical, thorough digestion, and the capacity for opportunistic exploitation of a wide variety of foods. Rats, mice and people are dietary generalists, but many insects, including many kinds of aphids, beetles and caterpillars, naturally feed on only one plant species and they can digest, absorb and utilize components of that diet that are useless, even toxic, to all other animals (see Chapter 5). Their food selection behaviour is so firmly tied to digestive ability that they may refuse to eat anything other than their own host plant.

GUTLESS FEEDING

The capacity for active absorption of nutrients is not limited to the cells lining the gut, and is not necessarily preceded by the secretion of digestive enzymes. The gut may be reduced or absent in animals that are surrounded by nutritive materials in solution, and substances are absorbed at the body surface, as in osmotrophic protoctists.

○ What kinds of animals would abandon digestion in this way?

● Internal parasites such as tapeworms, which live inside the intestines of other animals.

Their hosts secrete digestive enzymes, so the parasites do not do so, but they retain the capacity for active uptake of the solubilized nutrients, in many cases in competition with the host itself.

Some free-living animals, including certain marine corals, worms and clams, can take up dissolved amino acids and glucose, and possibly other nutrients, at much lower concentrations, from a few milligrams to micrograms per litre. This style of feeding may require a lot of energy for active transport, but its total energetic cost might still be low compared to that required to obtain the same nutrition by filtering particles from water or chasing after prey, then deploying digestive enzymes to break it down.

2.5.2 MINERAL ABSORPTION

Transporter systems are known for many minor nutrients, including certain vitamins, and minerals such as iron, calcium, zinc and copper, at least in birds and mammals. It has been possible to demonstrate that decreasing the amount of certain vitamins or minerals in the diet leads to increases in their rates of transport through the gut epithelium, and conversely, feeding excess of the nutrient reduces its uptake. But the abundance of transporters is often very low, in many cases, too low to measure accurately.

○ What kinds of diets and feeding habits are likely to present the least problems with mineral nutrition?

● Carnivory, especially if predator and prey are of similar chemical composition (e.g. snakes eating other vertebrates, spiders eating insects) and the prey is eaten whole.

Obtaining enough minerals is a major problem for all herbivores because most plant tissues contain very small amounts. Sodium ions are essential to all animals because of their role in the transmission of signals between cells, especially those of the nervous system. In contrast, plants do not seem to need sodium at all, so most contain almost none, and only a few species (e.g. salt-marsh and beach plants) can tolerate soils that contain more than small quantities. Calcium and magnesium are important for many intracellular processes in both plants and animals, but vertebrates need them in much larger quantities to support the growth of bones and teeth, as do shelled molluscs. Herbivorous animals have various means of supplementing diets that lack these essential minerals.

The aquatic larvae of mosquitoes feed on detritus and microbes, but the adult females must have at least one meal of vertebrate blood for their eggs to mature. Blood is believed to provide iron, sodium and other minerals that are lacking in the larval diet, as well as being a rich source of protein.

Elephants actively stir up stream beds to drink the fine mud so formed, and eat the mineral-rich bark or sapwood of certain trees, especially the baobab or bottle tree (Figure 2.17). Buffalo and other ruminants travel long distances to eat soft rocks that are rich in sodium or calcium, and they may lick the blood of injured animals, including each other. These large mammalian herbivores and smaller species such as rats, voles, rabbits, and even large herbivorous birds such as parrots, sometimes chew dried bones, especially while breeding. Smaller birds take advantage of spring rains to catch earthworms, ingesting the earth in the gut as well as worm flesh.

Omnivorous and carnivorous mammals eat their own placentas, and may eat their new-born young if seriously disturbed while suckling. Most 'herbivorous' mammals, including mice and rabbits, do the same, showing that they can manipulate and digest meat: they do not normally do so because they can deal with other foods more efficiently. However, ruminant mothers leave whole placentas and dead calves and fawns for vultures and other scavengers. The rumen microbes cannot deal with large chunks of meat and might be poisoned by it.

The shells of terrestrial and freshwater molluscs are rarely as massive as those of marine species (seawater contains plenty of calcium) and many species are restricted to chalky soils, which are rich in calcium.

Active transport is usually presented as a means of scavenging for scarce substances, as in the case of rare vitamins and minerals. But it can also be a means of limiting uptake, thus avoiding taking in too much of potentially harmful substances.

○ Which two major properties of active transport enable it to act in this way?

● (1) Active transport can be regulated according to supply and demand.

(2) There are separate transporter systems for each kind of nutrient (or small group of very similar nutrients) so uptake of one can be adjusted without affecting the others.

Figure 2.17 A baobab tree in Kenya damaged by elephants ramming their tusks into the trunk to eat the mineral-rich bark and sapwood.

Although essential in small quantities, many vitamins, especially the fat-soluble vitamins A and D, are toxic when present in excess. The same is true of many of the essential minerals, including iron, a highly reactive transition element. Vertebrate blood is unusually rich in iron because a large proportion of the red cells' contents is the oxygen-binding protein, haemoglobin, which contains iron atoms. Blood-sucking animals such as leeches (phylum Annelida, class Hirudinea), ticks (phylum Arthropoda, class Arachnida), bedbugs (phylum Arthropoda, class Insecta) and vampire bats (class Mammalia, order Chiroptera) can digest the protein component of haemoglobin and absorb the amino acids so released (together with the glucose, lipids and other nutritious components of the blood), but most of the iron itself remains in the gut and is expelled in the faeces.

○ What kinds of organisms would be unable to deal with too much iron in this way?

● Unicellular organisms, which digest all their food intracellularly.

The protoctist *Plasmodium* spends part of its complicated life cycle in the blood of mammals and birds, where it feeds by boring into red blood cells and consuming their contents. The parasite proliferates until the host's cell bursts, and the progeny escape to infect more cells. *Plasmodium*'s food vacuoles secrete not only the usual proteases, which digest most of the proteins, but also a special enzyme that builds the iron-containing proteins into insoluble, and thus non-toxic, crystals. The parasites are so small, and chemically so similar to the hosts' cells, that they are very difficult to see with a light microscope. The dark, iron-containing crystals were the distinctive feature that enabled the French army surgeon, Alphonse Laveran, to recognize them, and to suggest, in 1880, that they were associated with malaria.

Recent research has shown that drugs derived from quinine, the ancient preventative and cure for this widespread disease, work by inhibiting the enzyme that promotes crystallization of the iron-containing parts of haemoglobin. When the drug is present, the iron is released by digestion and diffuses into the rest of the parasitic cells, poisoning them.

○ Why would the drug not harm the cells of the parasite's host?

● They do not need, and do not have, the crystal-forming enzyme because almost all of their iron is locked up inside protein molecules.

The free iron that leaks from dying *Plasmodium* never becomes concentrated enough to harm the host's cells.

Unfortunately, several strains of the *Plasmodium* species that cause malaria in humans and other primates have recently developed physiological means — we do not know exactly what — of preventing quinine-like drugs from inhibiting this unique and crucial enzyme. They have thus become 'drug-resistant', and can only be suppressed effectively by much larger doses, which can harm their hosts by other mechanisms.

2.5.3 NON-ACTIVE ABSORPTION

The absorption of lipids does not involve specific transporters that utilize metabolic energy. Although most fatty acids and monoacylglycerols are larger molecules than single amino acids or glucose, they diffuse through cell membranes because they consist mainly of lipids. Until recently, all products of digestion of triacylglycerols were believed to diffuse unassisted into the gut epithelium, but during the 1990s, an assortment of carrier molecules and binding proteins were identified that facilitate the passage of long-chain fatty acids through cell membranes without utilizing metabolic energy.

Although lipids readily enter cells, conveying them between cells is more difficult.

○ How would features of glucose and amino acids that contrast with those of lipids affect their mobility in aqueous solutions such as blood?

● Glucose and amino acids would dissolve readily, but long-chain fatty acids and triacylglycerols would be as insoluble in the blood as they were in the gut contents.

Glucose and amino acids (and most vitamins and minerals) are in free solution in the blood, but special molecular apparatus is needed to escort lipids around the body. The long-chain fatty acids and monoacylglycerols are re-esterified into triacylglycerols in the absorptive epithelium and assembled, with a few structural proteins, into **chylomicrons** before being released into the blood (and, in the case of mammals, the lymph ducts). Chylomicrons can be formed very quickly and in large numbers, and may become huge by biochemical standards. The large ones are up to 0.001 mm in diameter (they average around 70 nm (7×10^{-8} m)), too big to squeeze into the space between adjacent cells of most tissues, and only a little smaller than the bore of small blood vessels.

After a fatty meal, chylomicrons may be big enough and numerous enough to produce a noticeable change in the colour and fluidity of the blood, but they only last a few minutes: adipose tissue (and some other tissues, such as muscle) synthesizes lipoprotein lipase and releases it into the tiny blood vessels that permeate the tissue. This enzyme severs the fatty acids from the triacylglycerols, fragmenting the chylomicrons.

The gut lining is never completely impermeable, and a wide range of substances can pass, at least in small quantities, from the gut to the blood with no physiological assistance at all. Most small, water-soluble molecules are quickly excreted if they are non-nutritive, and many potentially toxic organic materials are degraded (by the liver in vertebrates, or by analogous tissues in invertebrates) to harmless products that can be excreted. But heavy-metal ions such as mercury and lead, and synthetic organic compounds such as DDT and PCBs cannot be excreted, so they gradually accumulate in the body until they reach concentrations that hinder vital functions.

Damage to the nervous system, sensory organs or liver usually produces the most noticeable symptoms of such poisoning, but some absorbed pollutants have more subtle effects, on gamete formation or on the skeleton. Passive absorption of toxins in food or drinking water is becoming more of a hazard now than in the past, because mining and smelting release more heavy-metal ions into water and soil, and a much wider variety of completely new substances are being synthesized, a few of which are absorbed surprisingly well. For example, soluble derivatives of certain plastics permeate animal guts and/or gills and interfere with the hormones that control sexual maturation and sperm formation. They may accumulate in rivers and ponds, where they impair the breeding of amphibians and fish, and possibly also of people who drink the water.

2.5.4 HERBIVOROUS INSECTS

As mentioned in Section 2.5.2, many plants lack adequate quantities of nutrients that are essential to animals, especially large, active or fast-growing species.

○   How do vertebrates and molluscs avert such nutritional problems?

●   By eating a wide range of different species, and by supplementing their diet with minerals and small quantities of animal material (see Sections 2.4.3 and 2.4.4).

Such strategies are not available to many insects which are highly specialized to feed only on one component (leaves, flowers, roots, etc.) of one or a very few species of plants. One of the most meagre and monotonous diets is that of aphids: throughout their lives, they feed only by sucking the sap of green plants through highly specialized mouthparts that pierce the outer layers of stems to reach the sugar-transporting tissue (phloem) beneath, as shown in Figure 2.18.

Phloem sap is a dilute solution of sucrose and water, plus small quantities of amino acids, mostly the highly soluble amino acid glutamine, and a few minerals, mostly potassium ions.

○   Could rats, cows, bumblebees or people survive on such a diet?

●   No. Sap lacks the wide range of minerals, amino acids and fatty acids and proteins that are essential to vertebrate herbivores for synthesizing their own body fabric.

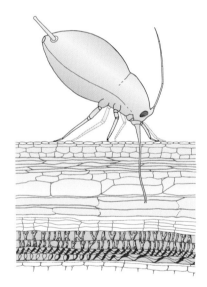

Figure 2.18 An aphid sucking from a plant stem.

Nonetheless, aphids thrive and proliferate amazingly fast. Exceptionally for insects, most species are viviparous, i.e. they give birth to well-developed young rather than lay eggs (see Figure 2.19a). For example, the greenbug, *Schizaphis graminum*, weighs about 24 μg at birth, grows to 540 μg in 10 days, and can breed at 11 days old. Aphids can have up to 15 generations in a summer and the progeny of a single female may form dense assemblages covering rose buds, pea and bean flowers and many other soft plant tissues. The insects have a voracious appetite for sap, often taking in many times their own body mass each day and making their host plant wilt. However, much of the sugar and water is quickly excreted through the anus as 'honey-dew'.

○ Why is excretion of sugar unusual?

● Most animals excrete little or no sugar because they can utilize glucose as fuel for movement and biosynthesis.

Glucose fuels the aphids' rapid growth and is incorporated into chitin, the polysaccharide that is a major component of their cuticle, but they hardly move about at all except during the winged, reproductive phase which appears towards the end of the summer. To obtain enough of other nutrients, aphids take in more sugar and water than they can use, so the excesses are eliminated, sometimes in such large quantities that on warm days, aphid-infested trees appear to drip syrup. This honey-dew is nutritious to physically active animals, and many aphids are attended by ants that 'milk' their droppings. Certain aphids that feed on fir trees are attractive to bees which collect honey-dew as well as or instead of nectar. In the Black Forest in Germany, such bees are managed for the production of 'fir honey', one of the most highly valued kinds of honey.

○ Could the ability to excrete honey-dew correct the deficiencies of protein, lipids and minerals in their diet?

● No. Elimination of excess sugar enables the insects to process larger volumes of sap from which the small quantities of glutamine and other dilute nutrients could be extracted. But the habit would not solve the basic problem of the lack of essential nutrients in the diet.

○ What kinds of organisms can synthesize a wide range of amino acids and lipids and certain vitamins from a few simple precursors?

● Microbes such as bacteria perform this role in the forestomach of ruminants (and elsewhere).

During the 1990s, the combination of high-powered electron microscopy, molecular characterization of gene structure and function, and comparative studies of a wide range of different aphid species has revealed that these insects owe their ability to thrive on an apparently inadequate diet to symbiosis with bacteria of the genus *Buchnera*. These endosymbionts live inside vesicles called symbiosomes (Figure 2.19b), hundreds of which stuff special cells called bacteriocytes (Figure 2.19c) which form a bilobed structure inside the aphid's large abdomen.

The bacteria can synthesize at least four of the amino acids that the aphids need for growth, from the glutamine obtained from the plant sap, and may also contribute vitamins. *Buchnera* enters the embryos early in development, and proliferates as their host grows. Adult aphids weighing $500 \mu g$ may contain 5.6×10^6 *Buchnera* but numbers decline sharply as breeding ends and few are left when the aphids die at the age of about 25 days.

○ How could viviparity facilitate the transmission of the endosymbionts between generations?

● The developing embryos share the aphid's abdomen with the bacteriocytes.

(a)

(b)   200 µm

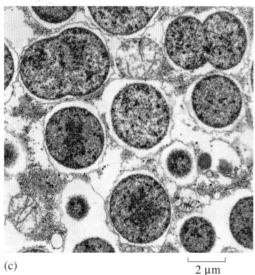

(c)   2 µm

Figure 2.19 (a) Adult and juveniles of the aphid *Schizaphis graminum*. The large female in the centre is giving birth. The juveniles attach themselves to the stem beside the mother. (b) Scanning electron micrograph of a bacteriocyte stripped of its cell membrane to reveal hundreds of symbiosomes containing *Buchnera*. (c) Transmission electron micrograph of part of a bacteriocyte to show cross-sections of *Buchnera in situ*.

This symbiotic relationship is ancient, dating back at least 200–250 Ma, and the two organisms have evolved together, so that the great majority of the more than 3000 living species of aphids harbour *Buchnera*. *Buchnera* is not found outside aphid cells, though presumably its remote ancestors were once free-living, and as yet, they cannot be maintained in artificial cultures.

Microbial symbionts also contribute to digestion and/or nutrition in a wide range of other herbivorous insects, including other hemipterans such as whiteflies, mealybugs, and cicadas, certain cockroaches, ants and beetles. Such relationships with microbes may have allowed these insects to evolve highly specialized diets and feeding mechanisms, which in turn promoted the formation of a huge range of species. Among the most economically important are wood-eating termites which harbour symbiotic flagellates, sometimes in numbers amounting to 30% of their total body mass, in a special pouch off the hindgut. Termite colonies containing millions of insects thrive on little more than wood and roots. As well as hollowing out large trees, termites destroy building and fencing timber in tropical countries and have recently spread into southern Britain as our climate becomes warmer.

SUMMARY OF SECTION 2.5

1   Absorption involves specialized cells which in vertebrates are found in the small intestine. The absorptive surface area is greatly increased by being frilled out to form villi.

2   In most animals, a large fraction of the amino acids and sugars released by digestion and many vitamins and minerals are taken up by specific transporters, some of which utilize ATP. They are located in the membrane of the epithelial cells lining the small intestine, but similar transporters may occur on the outer body surface of animals without guts. Fatty acids and monoacylglycerols enter cells by diffusion, often facilitated by carrier proteins.

3   In mice, the capacity for active transport takes at least 1 day to adapt to large changes in diet composition.

4   Many herbivores compensate for the nutritional insufficiencies of plants by eating mineral-rich soil or small quantities of animal food.

5   Unicellular protoctists that cannot avoid taking up too much iron sequester it in an insoluble form.

6   The intestine is not impermeable, and many other substances, including potential toxins, can cross its epithelium and enter the bloodstream.

7   Glucose, amino acids and short-chain fatty acids dissolve in blood but triacylglycerols form chylomicrons.

8   Most aphids harbour one species of endosymbiotic bacteria which synthesize essential amino acids and enable the insects to breed rapidly on a nutritionally meagre diet of sap. Other insects have gut symbionts that aid digestion as well as metabolism.

2.6   FEEDING OR FASTING?

Digesting and absorbing food, or even just keeping the gut fully functional, require considerable amounts of energy and materials. Although the gut epithelium (see Figure 2.1) is partially protected from digestion by its own enzymes, mechanical friction as well as chemical attack quickly wear the delicate cells, which are constantly being renewed. Some of the debris so formed is digested and its constituents absorbed, but much is eliminated with the faeces, representing a significant loss of body fabric. Mammalian faeces contain enough sloughed off cells for the individual that produced them to be identified using DNA fingerprinting techniques.

Replacement of the 'front-line' epithelial cells that secrete enzymes and absorb nutrients is also essential for adaption to changes in diet. In mammals, absorptive cells form in the 'crypt' at the base of the villi (Figure 2.1b) by division of small, unspecialized 'stem cells'. Newly formed cells enlarge and develop fully functional transporters, and migrate towards the tip, where they are eventually sloughed off. Cells from different points between the crypt and the tip of the villi can be separated and the number of glucose transporters on them estimated by measuring the binding of radioactively labelled phlorizin, a sugar-like molecule with a much higher affinity for the transport sites than glucose itself. Figure 2.20 shows the results of such a procedure from the intestinal cells of mice that had been abruptly switched between high and low carbohydrate diets.

Figure 2.20 Ratio of the density of phlorizin binding to epithelial cells from four sites along mouse villi measured at various times after a change in diet, to that measured just before the dietary change: (a) change from no digestible carbohydrate to food containing 55% sucrose (a readily digestible carbohydrate); (b) change from a high-carbohydrate diet to food containing 70% protein, 7% fat and no digestible carbohydrate.

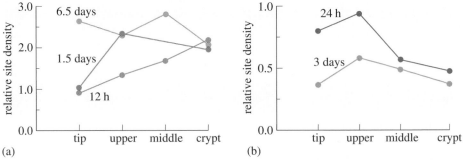

○ When do the cells start to adapt to the change in diet?

● Within 24 h. At the 12 and 24 h sample times (Figure 2.20a and b, respectively), cells in the middle of the villus and in the crypt have acquired binding capacity appropriate to the new diet, while the older cells located towards the tip are adapted to handle the old diet (i.e. relative site density = 1).

The data for the 3-day and 6.5-day samples show that, by then, all the cells are fully adapted to the new diet. The rate of formation of new cells exactly matched the timing of the decline in phlorizin binding, indicating that adaptation of the whole system is due entirely to cell replacement. The old cells cannot change their properties; they are simply replaced by new ones that matured with different abilities.

○ Would you expect the glucose uptake capacity of the whole intestine to change within 24 h?

● No. The properties of the whole intestine are attributable mainly to transporters in epithelial cells near the tips of the villi, which are most exposed to the gut contents. It takes up to 3 days for the new, fully functional cells to reach this point.

Although some cells with the appropriate capacities form within 12 h (Figure 2.20a), they have little opportunity to work when they are located near the crypt. The reverse experiment (Figure 2.20b) pointed to similar conclusions: it took the mice 3 days to acquire the ability to absorb a newly imposed high-carbohydrate diet efficiently.

○ What would happen to the nutrients in the meantime?

● They would be eliminated as faeces, probably with a fair amount of water and the remains of the enzymes that had been produced to digest them.

Not only is the food itself wasted, but digestive enzymes, water and other materials from the mouse's body are lost.

○   Are the data in Figure 2.20 compatible with those shown in Figure 2.15?

●   Yes. The time courses of adaptation to dietary change are very similar in both experiments.

○   In the light of these experiments, how would you expect wild mice to respond to novel foods?

●   They would eat only a little of a new food, gradually increasing the amounts as the mechanisms of digestion and absorption adjust to process it efficiently.

Experiments show that many wild animals do indeed eat only a little of newly encountered foods, even if to limit themselves in this way entails depleting their storage tissues. Domesticated animals that have been selectively bred to eat readily (and hence to grow as fast as possible) sometimes lack such temperance, and can be induced to eat large quantities of foods that they cannot digest properly, thereby making themselves ill.

2.6.1   REDUCING THE COST OF EATING

The experiments described in Section 2.5.1 show that switching from one diet to another entails a significant metabolic cost, but it is difficult to measure exactly how much when so many other biochemical processes are going on at the same time. A more extreme case of similar mechanisms is that of animals that eat large, infrequent meals, or whose food is available only at certain times of the year, and reduce the overall cost of digestion and absorption by partially dismantling the gut between feeds.

The energetic cost of refurbishing the gut to digest food after a long period of fasting has been most thoroughly investigated in snakes, most of which eat other vertebrates as soon as they are large enough to do so. Such prey constitute very concentrated nourishment of almost exactly the same chemical composition as the snake itself, so a few, very large meals thoroughly digested provide adequate nutrition and generate minimal waste. Many of the meals eaten by large snakes amount to 50% of the body mass, and there are records of adult anacondas and pythons swallowing prey that are substantially heavier than themselves.

Even under ideal circumstances, large pythons, boas and vipers eat only about every 1–2 months, and can fast for up to 18 months without coming to any harm. The time courses of the metabolic processes involved in digestion have been studied in the Burmese python (*Python molurus*), a non-venomous species that kills its prey by constriction, feeding mainly on mammals and large birds (Figure 2.21a). The constrictors (boas, anacondas and pythons) are the largest living snakes, and *P. molurus* can grow to a body mass of over 100 kg, but these experimental subjects were young, partially grown specimens weighing less than 1 kg.

Within 2 days of eating a meal of laboratory rats or mice amounting to 25% of their body mass, the snakes' oxygen consumption increased up to 17-fold, and remained continuously high for several days, before gradually declining over the following 2 weeks (Figure 2.21b). This increase in oxygen uptake is greater than that observed when a person or a horse goes from lying down to fast running, and means that glucose and/or fat is being consumed at a very high rate.

The protein synthesis that makes the digestive enzymes, the breakdown reactions themselves and the active transport of the products of digestion all generate additional heat. When fully active, the gut is the largest source of body heat after ATP synthesis in mitochondria.

○ How would this heat aid digestion?

● Most biochemical reactions, including enzymatic hydrolysis of proteins, fats and carbohydrates, proceed faster at higher temperatures.

So being warmer, whether from the heat produced by digestion or by other means, makes food breakdown faster and often more efficient.

Many poikilothermic (cold-blooded) animals, such as frogs, tortoises and lizards, do not eat unless they are warm enough for digestion to be efficient. But the extra heat produced in the guts can lead to overheating, which can cause permanent damage to delicate organs such as the brain. So large animals, especially those that often have to run fast and/or are exposed to bright sunshine while digestion is in progress, have ways of preventing the excess heat from reaching the brain.

The experimental pythons remained inactive during the period of observation, so the energy must have been used for the synthesis of tissues and secretions needed for digestion and absorption. Examination of specimens killed at various times after feeding showed that much of the extra energy was being devoted to fuelling reconstruction and modification of the internal organs. The stomach, intestine, liver and heart enlarged greatly, starting within a few hours of the prey being eaten, and the gut enormously increased its capacity to digest and absorb nutrients. Figure 2.21c and d show measurements of two aspects of the metabolic response to a meal. Uptake capacity was calculated as the growth of the intestine multiplied by its rate of absorption per unit area of gut, for glucose (Figure 2.21c) or lysine and proline, both products of protein digestion (Figure 2.21d).

○ From the data in Figure 2.21b–d, could the nutrients obtained from the test meal provide the fuel consumed during the period of high oxygen consumption?

● No. The highest oxygen consumption and the fastest changes in tissue mass and properties occurred before digestion was sufficiently far advanced for significant quantities of any nutrients to be absorbed.

The physiological response to feeding must have been fuelled almost entirely from body stores. The animals need sufficient reserves to rebuild their intestine and other viscera that enable them to digest and absorb the food effectively.

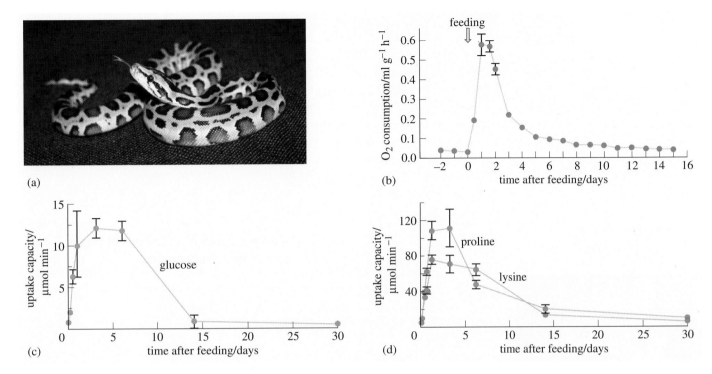

(a)

(b)

(c)

(d)

Figure 2.21 (a) A Burmese python (*Python molurus*). (b)–(d) Physiological changes measured in young Burmese pythons just before and for several weeks after a large meal. (b) Oxygen consumption of the living snakes. Uptake capacities of the whole small intestine for (c) glucose and (d) the amino acid lysine, and proline (another product of protein digestion). Data from Secor and Diamond (1995).

Big snakes apparently alternate brief periods of high energy expenditure during feeding, digestion and absorption, with long intervals in which the gut and other viscera are reduced in size and metabolic capacity. During fasting, the body is maintained at a much lower rate of energy expenditure by body stores. Of course, some energy is expended in converting the nutrients absorbed from the food into storage materials, and in breaking them down again when they are needed, but the quantity is small compared with the cost of maintaining the gut in a state of continuous readiness for frequent, small meals.

Such very long fasts are easier for large snakes than for most other animals because, being cold-blooded, their resting energy expenditure can be quite low. They also travel around very little, and rarely have to move fast, as few predators are likely to tackle them. Although large snakes are often spectacular and generate much fear among potential prey and bystanders (such as ourselves), their efficient digestion and metabolic economies between meals mean that the amount that they actually eat is tiny compared to that needed to sustain birds or mammals of similar size.

During severe illness or other circumstances in which eating is impractical, many other animals close down the gut and rely upon reserves in much the same way as large snakes do. Elderly animals and those weakened by chronic illness or defects of the mouth or gut (e.g. tooth wear, breakage or decay) reach a point beyond which they cannot muster enough energy to fuel digestion. Without the means of obtaining further sustenance, their decline continues until they die, usually, in the case of small animals, within a few hours.

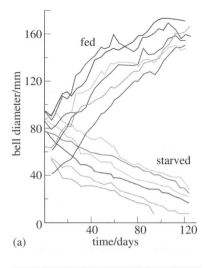

(a)

(b)

Figure 2.22 (a) Growth during regular feeding in the laboratory and 'degrowth' during starvation in the common jellyfish, *Aurelia aurita*. Each line is a record from a single jellyfish, which was either fed regularly (red) or starved (blue). Data from Hanmer and Jenssen (1974). (b) *A. aurita*. The tissues are almost transparent, except for the four ring-shaped gonads, which are pale pink.

In large animals with substantial energy reserves, the interval between the loss of capacity to feed and death may last some time, long enough to be noticed by human observers. Wild animals that do not die from predation — the fate of the majority — often appear to die of starvation, a conclusion based on the fact that *post-mortem* examination usually reveals an empty gut and little or no adipose tissue. In many such cases, starvation may have been due more to loss of the ability to handle, digest and absorb food than because none was available. The animal 'lost its appetite', but lived on its reserves for days or weeks, or in the case of large snakes, terrapins and tortoises, as long as several months.

2.6.2 STORAGE

Fluctuations in the availability of food, and in the animals' capacity to digest and absorb nutrients make some form of storage essential for most free-living animals. Many, in temperate regions most, invertebrates and lower vertebrates feed for only a fraction of the year, often as caterpillars and other kinds of larvae, then survive for long periods eating little or nothing. Although the basic mechanisms of digestion and absorption are fairly uniform throughout the animal kingdom, tissues and processes involved in storing and reclaiming nutrients are quite varied.

Many soft-bodied invertebrates seem to be able to break down almost all their tissues to provide fuel, which supports the metabolism of the surviving cells. Figure 2.22a shows some data from *Aurelia aurita*, a small jellyfish that occurs in surface waters worldwide and is often found stranded at low tide on beaches around Britain (Figure 2.22b).

○ Which of the two processes measured in Figure 2.22a is the faster?

● Growth: the jellyfish grow faster when fed frequently than they shrink in starvation.

The growth rate observed in these specimens may be close to the maximum, and might be much slower if less food were available. Even medium-sized individuals can sustain themselves for at least four months by reclaiming their tissues as fuel. These jellyfish can shrink to less than 10% of their former size and still remain active, because their simple body structure works well over a wide range of sizes. Many other soft-bodied invertebrates respond similarly to starvation, but this strategy would not be appropriate for arthropods and vertebrates. Their hard skeletons of cuticle or bone are mostly unreclaimable, so overall body dimensions cannot shrink very much. Severely wasted muscles become too weak to support the skeleton or to move the limbs or jaws efficiently, and, as explained in Section 2.6.1, depleted guts cannot deal with food properly. These more complex animals have specialized storage tissues which can sustain the animal for some time before depletion of the general body fabric (as in Figure 2.22a) becomes necessary.

The main storage tissue in larger and more complex arthropods is the **fat-body**. Its physiology has been most thoroughly studied in insects, where it stores glycogen, lipids, and, at least in juveniles, proteins. It also performs many of the metabolic functions carried out by the vertebrate liver. Glycogen and lipids are insoluble in water, so can accumulate in large quantities inside cells without promoting the uptake of too much water. The fat-body can become huge (up to 65% of the body mass) in caterpillars and grubs just before they pupate and are transformed into adult insects. In locusts or migratory butterflies about to set off on long flights, the fat-body can be the most conspicuous organ in the body, enveloping the gut, flight muscles and excretory organs.

Most kinds of vertebrate cells (neurons are the best-known exception) store small quantities of glycogen and/or small droplets of triacylglycerols as an energy reserve for their own use. Metabolically active tissue such as muscle and liver can release small amounts of protein to supply materials for rebuilding damaged tissues and for the formation of eggs, but tissue proteins are usually broken down to form glucose only in advanced starvation. Liver and muscle take up excess glucose from the blood and store it as glycogen, which is converted back to glucose and used by these and other tissues during brief periods of fasting. However, as Figure 2.23 makes clear, the quantities are quite small, usually no more than 5–7% of the tissue mass.

○ Why can't these tissues hold more storage materials?

● Because their cytoplasm is devoted to other functions, e.g. movement in the case of muscle. The necessary enzymes and structural proteins would be disrupted by large quantities of storage materials.

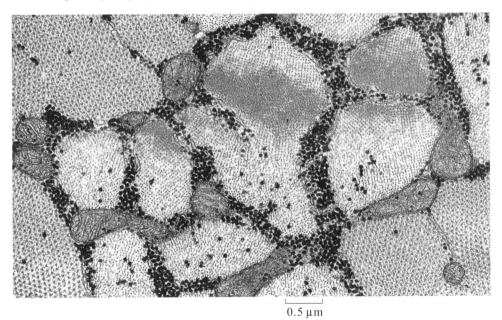

0.5 μm

Figure 2.23 Electron micrograph of a fragment of the gastrocnemius (calf) muscle of a person who has just eaten a carbohydrate-rich meal. The muscle took up the glucose and converted it into insoluble glycogen, which forms many small granules, here stained dense black. This picture also shows several mitochondria, which appear as round structures, filled with membranes. The mitochondria and the glycogen granules are packed around the contractile components of the muscle, which are seen as arrays of grey spots in this cross-section.

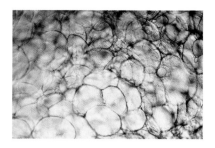

Figure 2.24 Adipose tissue from a guinea-pig. Note the round outline of the adipocytes visible in this unstained whole-mount. The yellow colour is that of the storage lipids.

Some fish, especially sharks and rays (class Chondrichthyes), may accumulate large quantities of fat in the liver, but all terrestrial vertebrates sequester most of their storage lipid in adipose tissue. This tissue consists almost entirely of adipocytes (Figure 2.24), cells that are specialized for storing lipid to be used by other body tissues. Being insoluble, triacylglycerols can be stored in an almost pure form in the single large droplet that fills most of the adipocyte.

○ What would be the advantages of having a specialized storage tissue?

● Lipids can be safely stored in far larger quantities than if they were 'loose' in the blood or in tissues such as muscle or liver which are specialized to other functions.

The quantities of adipose tissue that can be safely maintained are limited more by animals' capacity for carrying the tissue around than by metabolic factors.

Adipocytes expand by taking up long-chain fatty acids from the chylomicrons, or, especially in herbivores, by synthesizing them from glucose and other small molecules. They are unusual among animal cells in being able to undergo enormous changes in volume, up to 100-fold in some species. The adipose tissue of birds just before migration or of mammals about to enter hibernation may be up to two-thirds by mass triacylglycerols. Naturally obese animals may also have proportionately more adipocytes, perhaps two or three times as many as in continuously lean species of the same size. Polar bears are top carnivores, feeding almost entirely on seals in the Arctic, where the adults have no natural predators. They readily fatten when food is available and can fast for months while seeking prey, often travelling long distances between hunting grounds. Pregnant females may exceed 50% by mass adipose tissue before they retire inland to a maternity den where they give birth and suckle twins (sometimes triplets) for three months or more without eating anything themselves.

The arrangement of adipose tissue in most fish, amphibians and reptiles is similar to that of arthropod fat-bodies, i.e. a few large masses, usually in the abdomen, but that of mammals is partitioned into many depots spread around the body. Recent research reveals that adipocytes have site-specific properties and some are equipped to respond to local signals from the immune system, as well as, or instead of, the hormones secreted during fasting. Some (but probably not all) adipocytes also contribute to the regulation of food intake by secreting signal molecules into the blood that act directly on parts of the brain that control appetite. Adipocytes should be regarded as 'managers' of metabolic stores, rather than simply as a repository for them: they synthesize special enzymes, carrier proteins and receptors that enable them to take up, hold and release their stores in response to hormones and other signals released from other cells.

Small quantities of many vitamins and minerals are also stored in various body tissues, but amounts are very limited, often only sufficient to last for a few weeks, because almost all can be harmful in excess. As described in Section 2.5.2, iron is toxic at high concentrations, so, in spite of its physiological importance to vertebrates, it can only be stored bound to special proteins in the liver.

SUMMARY OF SECTION 2.6

1   The lining of the mammalian intestine is replaced every few days as new epithelial cells mature and pass along the villi, where they are sloughed off. The absorptive capacities of newly formed cells are adapted to changes in diet.

2   Enzyme secretion and active transport are energetically expensive. Animals that eat large nutritious meals very infrequently may save energy by partially dismantling the gut while fasting. Reassembling it after feeding requires high rates of energy usage sustained for many hours.

3   Rebuilding the gut and digestion release large quantities of heat, which speeds up digestion and metabolism but may overheat other tissues when in excess.

4   Many animals can reabsorb and break down their tissues during starvation but most vertebrates and more complex invertebrates have specialized storage tissues.

5   Glycogen is a short-term energy store often used by the tissue that sequesters it.

6   The arthropod fat-body and vertebrate adipose tissue are specialized for storing lipid for use by other tissues. These tissues can become massive, enabling animals to fast for long periods and/or travel long distances. Mammalian adipose tissue is split into many depots, some of which have specialized site-specific properties.

7   Most other nutrients are too toxic to be stored in large quantities.

CONCLUSIONS

Natural selection usually acts to thwart rather than promote the transfer of nutrients from plant to animal or from prey to predator, so there is no permanent, ideal solution to the problem of obtaining food. Obtaining and digesting food are central to the structure and habits of all heterotrophs. Continuous adaptation of diet, feeding habits, digestion and storage lead to diversification of all lineages of organisms. Digestive mechanisms determine not only their diet but also other aspects of their biology, such as the amount of time they spend feeding, their capacity for exercise, or their metabolism, including energy metabolism and (in mammals) the composition of the milk they secrete.

REFERENCES

Bertsch, A. (1984) Foraging in male bumblebees (*Bombus lucorum* L.): maximizing energy or minimizing water load?, *Oecologia*, **62**, pp. 325–336.

Diamond, J. M. and Buddington, R. K. (1987) Intestinal nutrient absorption in herbivores and carnivores, in *Comparative Physiology: Life in Water and on Land*, P. Dejours, L. Bolis, C. R. Taylor, and E. R. Weibel, (eds), pp. 193–203.

Ferraris, R. P. and Diamond, J. M. (1993) Crypt/villus site of substrate-dependent regulation of mouse intestinal glucose transporters, *Proceedings of the National Academy of Sciences, USA*, **90**, pp. 5868–5872.

Hanmer, W. M. and Jenssen, R. M. (1974) Growth, degrowth, and irreversible cell differentiation in *Aurelia aurita*, *American Zoologist*, **14**, pp. 833–849.

Secor, S. M. and Diamond, J. (1995) Adaptive responses to feeding in Burmese pythons: pay before pumping, *Journal of Experimental Biology*, **198**, pp. 1313–1325.

Slater, A. F. and Cerami, A. (1992) Inhibition by chloroquine of a novel haem polymerase enzyme activity in malaria trophozoites, *Nature*, **355**, pp. 167–169.

Vollrath, F., Downes, M. and Krackow, S. (1997) Design variability in web geometry of an orb-weaving spider, *Physiology and Behavior*, **62**, pp. 735–743.

FURTHER READING

Pond, C. M. (2000) *The Fats of Life* (2nd edn) Cambridge University Press. [This book explains in simple language the biology of feasting and fasting, fattening and slimming in wild animals as well as people.]

Pough, F. H., Janis, C. M. and Heiser J. B. (1996) *Vertebrate Life* (5th. edn), Prentice Hall, New Jersey. [A wide-ranging review of the diversity, function and evolution of vertebrates. (6th edn expected 2002)]

Schmidt-Nielsen, K. (1997) *Animal Physiology* (5th edn) Cambridge University Press. [A useful textbook of comparative physiology, with emphasis on vertebrates, packed with good ideas and useful, accurate facts, but rather poorly written.]

Stevens, C. E. and Hume, I. D. (1995) *Comparative Physiology of the Vertebrate Digestive System*, Cambridge University Press. [A beautifully illustrated account of physiological and ecological aspects of diet and digestion.]

GENETIC DIVERSITY

3.1 INTRODUCTION

In Chapter 1 of this book we discussed some of the ways in which plants and animals are adapted to the fluctuating nature of their environment, and in Chapter 2 considered diverse ways of dealing with food. How does such diversity arise? This chapter addresses the question by firstly examining how natural selection acts on differences in the phenotypes of organisms. It then moves on to consider the basis of variation in sexually reproducing organisms and how heritable variation arises. You will be able to draw on this information when comparing the costs and benefits of sexual and asexual reproduction in Chapter 4, and the long-term evolutionary consequences of asexual reproduction. Throughout Chapter 3 you will be presented with opportunities to consider how populations of species may change and some of the circumstances in which these changes result in evolution.

3.2 NATURAL SELECTION

Clearly, not all organisms do survive and go on to reproduce; so why should some succeed whilst others fail? We can begin to consider the reasons by first examining the four basic premises of the theory of evolution by natural selection. These principles were outlined by Charles Darwin in his introduction to *The Origin of Species by Means of Natural Selection*, following his joint communications with Alfred Russel Wallace in 1858:

1   More individuals are produced than can survive.

2   There is a *struggle for existence* because of the disparity between the number of individuals produced in reproduction and the number that can survive.

3   Individuals show *variation*. No two individuals are exactly the same. Those variants with advantageous features have a greater chance of survival in the struggle (*natural selection*).

4   As these selected variants produce offspring similar to themselves (*the principle of inheritance*), they become proportionally more abundant in subsequent generations.

Natural selection favours those variants in a population that leave the most offspring, who, by virtue of inheriting the same characters from their parents, should likewise be favoured by natural selection. Natural selection selectively multiplies variants between one generation and the next, so we can evaluate its effect on any particular variant by measuring how many offspring it leaves. Of course, for the offspring to reproduce themselves, they must survive to sexual maturity, so here are the two components for the recipe for success: survival (also known as viability) and reproduction (also known as fecundity).

Consider two kinds of rabbits: those with black coats that produce 20 young of which, on average, 50% survive to adulthood, and those that are grey and produce 18 young, of which 60% survive.

○ Assuming that these differences are inherited, what kind of rabbit is favoured by natural selection? To answer this question, multiply the number of young produced by each rabbit type by its survival to adulthood.

● On average, black rabbits produce $0.5 \times 20 = 10.0$ successful offspring surviving to adulthood, and grey rabbits produce $0.6 \times 18 = 10.8$ successful offspring surviving to adulthood. Therefore the grey rabbits are favoured over the black.

The product of survival and reproduction is the measure of the **fitness** of a variant, in this case the black or grey phenotype of rabbit. The outcome of natural selection is determined by the relative number of descendants left by different phenotypes, so fitness is conventionally measured with respect to the superior phenotype. The phenotype with the highest relative fitness is assigned a fitness value of 1 and the relative fitness of other phenotypes is given as a frequency value relative to this.

○ If the fitness of grey rabbits is 1, what is the relative fitness of the black ones?

● The relative fitness of the black rabbits is calculated relative to the fitness of greys (which are assigned the value 1 as they have a higher fitness than the black rabbits).

reproductive success of blacks = 10.0

reproductive success of greys = 10.8

so relative fitness of blacks $= \dfrac{10.0}{10.8} = 0.93$

In percentage terms, this calculation means that the fitness of black rabbits is 93% of that of greys. Does a difference as small as 7% matter? Such a difference may seem slight, but even small differences in fitness sustained over several generations can cause a significant evolutionary change in the relative proportions of the phenotypes in a population.

○ How many descendants could one black rabbit have over four generations? How does this number compare with the number of descendants from a grey rabbit over the same number of generations?

● After four generations, a black rabbit has $10 \times 10 \ \times 10 = 10\,000$ descendants.

A grey rabbit has $10.8 \times 10.8 \times 10.8 \times 10.8 = 13\,603$ descendants

$\left(\dfrac{3603}{10\,000} \times 100 = 36\% \text{ more than the black} \right)$.

So for a rabbit population that started off with a 50 : 50 ratio of grey : black types, a 7% difference in relative fitness can result in a ratio shift to 58 : 42 in as little as four generations. Typically, a rabbit population explosion would exhaust the food supply and cause an increase in mortality and a decrease in fecundity. These effects are what Darwin meant by the struggle for existence caused by the disparity between the number of offspring that can be produced and the number that can actually survive.

Recall from Chapter 2 that animals have many ways of improving the efficiency of dealing with food, including adaptations for catching and digesting prey, developed in response to selection pressures to reduce the costs of eating.

Note that if an organism produces a large number of offspring that survive to reproductive age, but fail to reproduce (perhaps because they are sterile), then the genetic make-up of the ancestral organism is not passed on to any future generations.

3.3 THE GENETIC BASIS OF VARIATION WITHIN SPECIES

Within a population of a species there can be great genetic variation which may be immediately apparent in morphological characters. For example, in the peppered moth, *Biston betularia*, (Figure 3.1) dark coloured, *Biston betularia carbonaria*, moths have at least one copy of the *T* allele (the dominant allele, conferring blackness) whilst pale coloured, *Biston betularia typica*, moths have two copies of the recessive, pale colour allele, *t*.

Alternative characters in garden peas, such as pod shape (inflated or constricted), pod colour (green or yellow), seed shape (round or wrinkled), and flower colour (purple or white), are directly related to single pairs of alleles.

The shell of the land snail, *Cepaea nemoralis*, may be brown, pink or yellow. The colours are determined by a locus with six alternative alleles. An individual snail has two alleles at a locus, but with more than two alternatives in the population, there are more possible combinations than for the garden pea examples above, with only two alternative alleles described. The shell colour loci are closely linked to others at which the alleles control the presence and appearance of up to five bands running round each whorl of the shell. In addition, there are six unlinked genes, each with two alleles per locus, which determine other aspects of band production including intensity, colour and suppression (absence) of some bands, and colour of the body. The morphology of an individual snail shell is determined by the interactions of alleles at many loci and Figure 3.2 overleaf shows just three of the possible phenotypes.

(a)

(b)

Figure 3.1 The peppered moth, *Biston betularia*. The typical form and the *carbonaria* form seen against the bark of a tree from (a) a rural area, and (b) an industrialized area. The relative abundances of the two forms have altered with changes in the levels of atmospheric pollution.

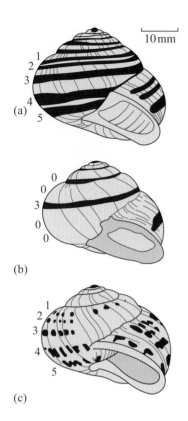

Figure 3.2 Examples of shell patterns in *Cepaea nemoralis*: (a) five-banded shell; (b) shell with bands 1, 2, 4 and 5 suppressed; (c) shell with five punctate bands.

BOX 3.1	USE OF GENETIC TERMS

Use of the terms 'locus', 'allele', 'gene' and 'character' can sometimes be confusing. The location of a gene on a chromosome is termed a 'locus' (plural, loci). Each gene can exist in one or more forms and strictly we should use the term 'allele' as a form of a gene. However you are likely to find 'allele' and 'gene' used interchangeably in some situations as in 'allele for blackness' and 'gene for blackness' in the peppered moth. The forms (alleles) of a gene are genes themselves. Notice also the association between 'gene' and 'character' (or characteristic) as in gene for the character 'seed shape' in peas. From the *Cepaea* example above, you can see that alleles at more than one locus, and hence more than one gene, may be involved in the expression of a character such as shell banding, resulting in a mid-banded shell as in Figure 3.2b.

During meiosis, the genome is restructured through independent assortment of chromosomes and crossing over between homologous chromosomes, resulting in a huge number of possible allele combinations in the gametes (discussed further in Section 3.4). The possibilities for different allele combinations at fertilization are also vast, resulting in a huge range of possible phenotypes such as shell colour and banding patterns in *Cepaea*.

Much genetic variation gives rise to differences in enzymes that cannot be recognized from morphological differences, so this genetic variation must be investigated using molecular techniques such as gel electrophoresis, immunology, and sequencing of proteins and genes.

3.3.1 THE GENE POOL

The numbers of different alleles of genes form the **gene pool** for a population of organisms. Changes in the gene pool take place as a result of natural selection and also mutation and genetic drift. Genetic drift will be considered later in this section. At the genetic level, evolution is expressed as change over time in the frequencies of alleles in populations. Remember that these alleles are expressed through the phenotype of the individuals carrying them and that natural selection acts on phenotypes.

Differences in fitness among phenotypes lead to changes in the gene pool of a population, as the less fit phenotypes and their alleles are reduced in frequency by natural selection. Natural selection also acts, via the phenotype, on new alleles produced by mutations and new combinations of alleles arising from recombination during meiosis.

It is generally easiest to study genetic systems that involve one locus and a pair of alleles. When there are two or more alleles at a locus, the character is said to be **polymorphic** (as in the shell colour for *Cepaea nemoralis,* above). However, the inheritance of the majority of characters depends on several loci, often with more than one allele at each. Then the character is said to be **polygenic** (as in the overall appearance of the *Cepaea* shell). Such polygenic characters may have many different forms (recall that in *Cepaea* there are many different shell colour and banding patterns that are determined by the interactions of several genes) or they may vary continuously so that the ratio of different phenotypes in a population is best represented by a distribution curve. Shifts in the frequencies of phenotypes may reflect a shift in the frequencies of many alleles.

Selection acting against extreme variants and in favour of the most common phenotype is termed **stabilizing selection** as it tends to maintain the underlying genotype frequencies within their existing distribution. Such selection does not bring about change and hence does not lead to evolution. **Directional selection** causes the phenotype distribution to change towards one extreme as a result of selection against the other extreme, whereas **disruptive selection** leads to a change in phenotype distribution towards both extremes as a result of selection against the intermediate phenotype (Figure 3.3).

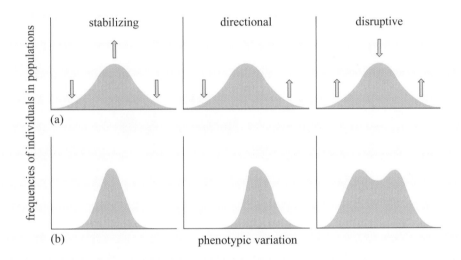

Figure 3.3   The effect of stabilizing, directional and disruptive selection on the distribution of phenotypes in a population: (a) shows the distribution as selection begins, and (b) shows the distribution after selection.

Stabilizing selection has been investigated in South American butterflies of the genus *Heliconius*. *Heliconius erato* and *Heliconius melpomene* are both distasteful to birds and deter attempts at predation with warning colourations. The colour patterns of their wings may differ at different localities, but at any one locality the wing patterns of the two species are more similar to one another (Figure 3.4). It has been proposed that this situation may represent an extended system of **Müllerian mimicry** — the mimicry (resemblance strategy) which afford unpalatable species increased protection from predators. (This topic is discussed further in Chapter 5.)

○   What would this hypothesis suggest about the fate of poor mimics whose wings are dissimilar from those of distasteful butterflies?

●   Butterflies that deviate from the usual pattern, and are therefore poor mimics, are more likely to be caught and eaten than other individuals. There is natural selection against them.

Figure 3.4 Parallel variation in three races (populations within one species that are phenotypically distinct) of *Heliconius melpomene* (yellow areas) and *Heliconius erato* (white areas). Very similar wing patterns for the two species are found in the same general areas.

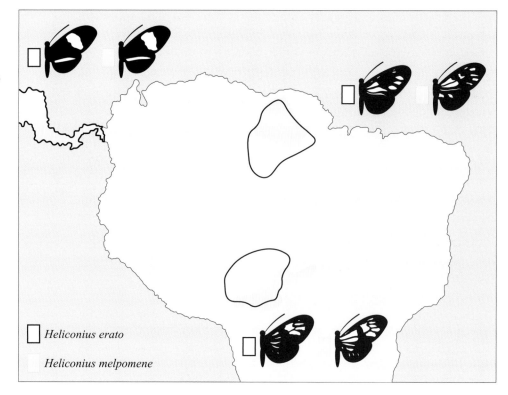

☐ *Heliconius erato*

  Heliconius melpomene

Experiments were conducted in which the wing patterns of *Heliconius erato* were altered by applying paint to the wings (with controls having the same amount of paint applied to their wings without altering the pattern). Under stabilizing selection, poor mimics would be more likely to be caught and eaten by birds, and experiments confirm this prediction. In addition, when races of a species with different wing patterns meet, there are very narrow zones occupied by both parental species. It has been suggested that stabilizing selection for the parental patterns leads to the elimination of the first generation of hybrids. These hybrids would be less fit as they are killed more often by birds.

A case of sympatric speciation, where the two parent species occupy the same geographic area, has been described, based on a model of disruptive selection. Two species of lacewings, *Chrysopa carnea* and *Chrysopa downesi*, insects of the order Neuroptera, occur in the same geographic area in the northeastern United States. *Chrysopa carnea* inhabits grasslands and meadows and produces several generations between late spring and summer every year. During the reproductive period, the adults are pale green in colour and match the light green foliage. At the end of the summer, the adults enter a resting stage, turn from pale green to reddish brown and move to the senescent foliage of deciduous trees. *Chrysopa downesi* lives in coniferous woodland and breeds once a year in early spring. The adults are dark green in colour throughout the year and are camouflaged amongst the conifers. Therefore in their natural environment, the two species are reproductively isolated by differences in habitat and seasons of reproduction. However, under laboratory conditions they can hybridize freely and produce fully viable offspring.

In hybridization experiments, it was found that *Chrysopa carnea* was homozygous for the allele designated *G1*, giving a light green phenotype whereas *Chrysopa downesi* was homozygous for the allele, *G2*, which produces the dark green colour. Heterozygotes, *G1 G2*, were intermediate in colour.

This investigation suggests that disruptive selection favoured homozygotes in different habitats — *G1 G1* in meadows and *G2 G2* in coniferous woodland. The heterozygote, *G1 G2*, is selected against because of its reduced protective colouration in both habitats. Habitat separation led to assortative mating (like phenotypes mating with like). Subsequently there was selection for differences in reproductive timing. Reproductive isolation was therefore complete, resulting in two species where there had previously been one.

Directional selection has been seen in populations of the peppered moth, *Biston betularia,* a moth that is active at night and settles during the day on tree bark which is usually covered with pale coloured lichens (see Figure 3.1). In the early part of the 18th century in Britain almost all moths were the pale *typica* form, with the genotype of almost all individuals being *t t*. When a mutation produced a *T* allele (the dominant allele conferring blackness), these dark moths were very strongly selected against by bird predation as they were highly visible on lichen-covered tree bark. However, as the air in some environments became dirtier during the Industrial Revolution, the lichen was killed by atmospheric pollutants. Dark-coloured *carbonaria* moths were better camouflaged on tree bark no longer covered by lichen, and so the frequency of *carbonaria* phenotypes increased. There was directional selection from *typica* towards *carbonaria* phenotypes.

○ If an industrial environment subsequently becomes much cleaner, what do you predict to be the action of selection on the phenotypes of *Biston betularia*?

● Lichen growth would occur again on the trunks and the direction of selection would reverse, with the frequency of *typica* phenotypes increasing and that of *carbonaria* decreasing.

This change in the direction of selection has indeed been recorded and demonstrates that selection can proceed in different directions at different times in the same location. The direction of selection may also differ in different places at the same time if the environments vary.

3.3.2 GENETIC DRIFT

In real populations, allele frequencies tend to fluctuate from generation to generation. If the population is large, these fluctuations are relatively small, but fluctuations in small populations may have relatively much larger effects on allele frequencies. These random fluctuations in allele frequencies are known as **genetic drift**.

Genetic drift is the consequence of the sampling process that occurs in reproduction. When gametes are formed, each haploid gamete receives, at random, one of the two alleles that the individual had previously inherited from its parents. In addition, only a small fraction of gametes actually succeeds in uniting through fertilization (the process of **syngamy**) and developing into organisms of the next generation. In very small populations, genetic drift can have a strong effect if, by chance, one individual produces more offspring than others, so its alleles constitute a greater proportion in the next generation. A particular allele could disappear from a small population by genetic drift.

○   What is the effect of genetic drift on the genetic variation within a small population?

●   The genetic variation is likely to be reduced as a result of chance loss of alleles.

Genetic variation between populations may arise also when a small number of individuals from an originally large population become founders of a new population, as could happen as a result of emigration to a new habitat, or as a consequence of a natural catastrophe such as drought or volcanic eruption, which wipes out much of the original population or leaves small populations geographically separated from one another. In such circumstances, the allele frequencies of the new population are those of the founders, which may or may not be representative of the original population. This sampling effect, due to small numbers, is known as the **founder effect**.

If an allele, rare in the original population, happens to be among the founders, what can we predict about its future frequency in the founder population in comparison with the original population? Assuming that it is not eliminated by genetic drift while the population is very small, the rare allele has a much greater chance of becoming common than it had in the original population.

Evidence from human populations shows that alleles present in small founding numbers of individuals may have disproportionately large frequencies of alleles that are rare in the parental population from which they were derived. The Afrikaner population of South Africa is mainly descended from a group of immigrants that landed in 1652, with almost one million living Afrikaners bearing the names of 20 original settlers. Some of these colonists carried a number of rare genes, one being that for Huntington's disease, a lethal autosomal dominant gene whose effects become manifest in middle age. Most cases of Huntington's in the modern Afrikaner population can be traced back to one original colonist.

The Afrikaner population also has a much higher frequency of the dominant allele that causes a condition known as porphyria variegata than their parent population in the Netherlands. Carriers of this allele suffer a severe, sometimes lethal, reaction to barbiturate anaesthetics. In the absence of exposure to barbiturates, the porphyria variegata allele appears to be a neutral mutation (i.e. neither selected for nor against), but the relative fitness differences of carriers and non-carriers becomes evident when the environment changes to contain (for some individuals) barbiturates.

○   Could subsequent evolution within small populations be only as a result of chance effects such as genetic drift and mutation?

●   No, the random effects of genetic drift and mutation within a founder population are important, but if there are fitness differences between individuals in the population, natural selection also takes place.

A founder population that colonizes an environment previously unoccupied by other members of that species (e.g. an island) contains a fraction of the genetic diversity in the gene pool of the parent species and all subsequent evolution proceeds from this limited genetic diversity. Mutations that are disadvantageous as heterozygotes but favourable as homozygotes have a greater chance of being incorporated in a small population. If these homozygotes are better adapted to the new environment, they are rapidly selected for, and divergence from the parent species occurs. Divergence is likely to take place much faster in a small founder population, so speciation can proceed more rapidly. Such a form of allopatric speciation (where the two populations are geographically separated) is considered to have taken place on the Hawaiian Islands, where, for example, extensive studies of the many species of *Drosophila* suggest that all the endemic species may have descended from a single fertilized female, probably from South America, colonizing the oldest islands.

SUMMARY OF SECTIONS 3.2 AND 3.3

1   The product of survival to reproductive maturity and reproduction (viability and fecundity) is the measure of fitness of a phenotype.

2   Natural selection acts on the different phenotypes within a population. It can only affect the course of evolution if these differences are heritable, i.e. produced by different genes.

3   Random fluctuations in allele frequencies occur in populations and genetic drift is likely to have larger effects in small populations.

4   The founder effect describes the effect on genetic variability of the small size of a colonizing population, which might consist of one or a few individuals. Such a population can never contain more than a fraction of the total genetic variability of the parent population. An allele that is rare in the parent population has a chance of becoming common if it is present in a founder population, provided that it is not eliminated by genetic drift when the population is small.

3.4   SOURCES OF GENETIC VARIATION

Let us now consider some of the sources of the genetic variation that we have been discussing.

In sexually reproducing organisms, **recombination** through crossing over and independent assortment of alleles during meiosis leads to genetic variability between parents and offspring. Let us first consider how variation arises through independent assortment. Study Figure 3.5.

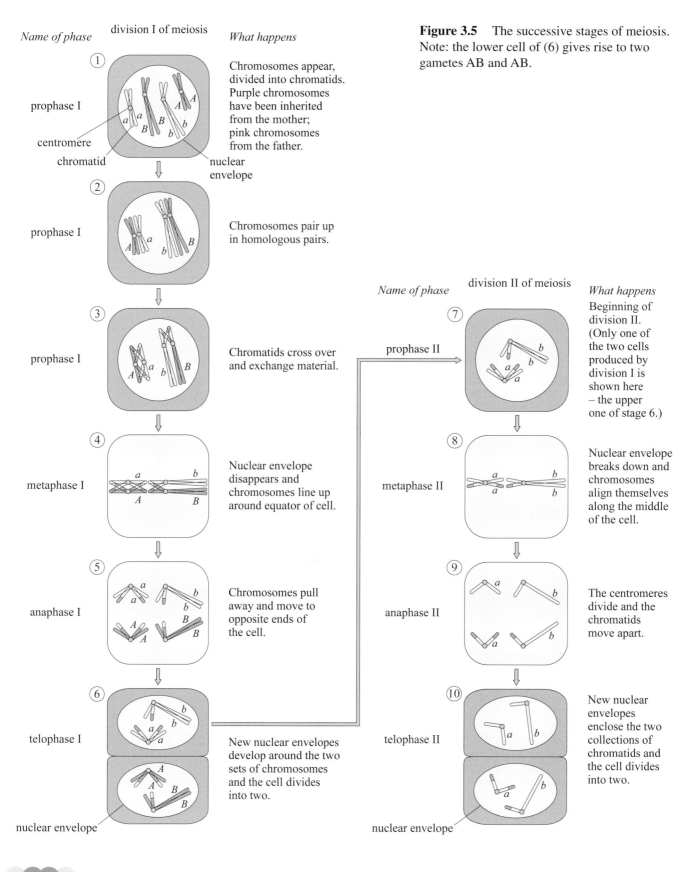

Name of phase   division I of meiosis   *What happens*

Figure 3.5 The successive stages of meiosis. Note: the lower cell of (6) gives rise to two gametes AB and AB.

① prophase I

centromere

chromatid

nuclear envelope

Chromosomes appear, divided into chromatids. Purple chromosomes have been inherited from the mother; pink chromosomes from the father.

② prophase I

Chromosomes pair up in homologous pairs.

③ prophase I

Chromatids cross over and exchange material.

④ metaphase I

Nuclear envelope disappears and chromosomes line up around equator of cell.

⑤ anaphase I

Chromosomes pull away and move to opposite ends of the cell.

⑥ telophase I

nuclear envelope

New nuclear envelopes develop around the two sets of chromosomes and the cell divides into two.

Name of phase   division II of meiosis   *What happens*

⑦ prophase II

Beginning of division II. (Only one of the two cells produced by division I is shown here – the upper one of stage 6.)

⑧ metaphase II

Nuclear envelope breaks down and chromosomes align themselves along the middle of the cell.

⑨ anaphase II

The centromeres divide and the chromatids move apart.

⑩ telophase II

nuclear envelope

New nuclear envelopes enclose the two collections of chromatids and the cell divides into two.

○ Metaphase 1 in Figure 3.5 shows one possible arrangement of the two pairs of chromosomes. What other arrangements are possible?

● Three other arrangement are possible. Figure 3.6 shows all four ways in which two pairs of chromosomes could align in a cell at metaphase I, with the arrangement in Figure 3.5 represented in Figure 3.6b (simplified, with no chiasmata shown between homologous pairs).

○ What consequences would these alternative arrangements have on the genotypes of the resulting gametes?

● The outcome of meiosis in Figure 3.5 is two types of gametes with respect to the alleles considered. However an alternative orientation of one pair of homologous chromosomes results in two different types of gametes (Figure 3.6c or d). Notice the outcome of the orientation of chromosomes in Figure 3.6a is the same as that in Figure 3.6b. The four arrangements are equally likely, so this independent assortment leads to gametes with four different genotypes, deviations from a 1 : 1 : 1 : 1 ratio being by chance alone.

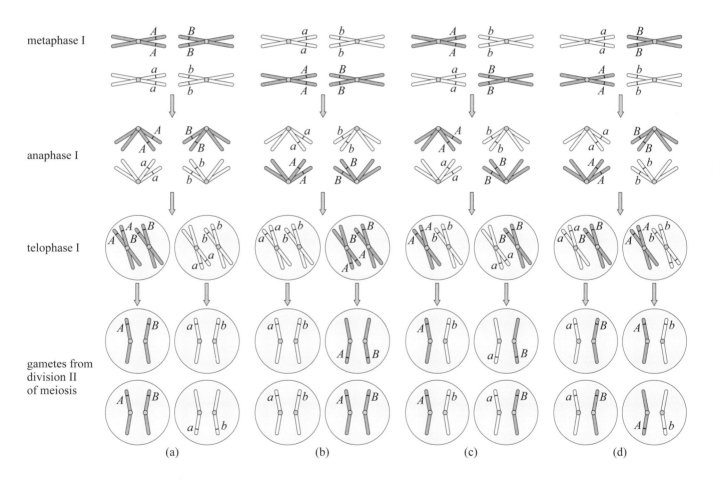

Figure 3.6   The genotypes of gametes resulting from each of the four different arrangements of chromosomes at metaphase I of meiosis.

Therefore an organism heterozygous for two pairs of alleles (i.e. alleles at two loci) situated on different chromosome pairs (i.e. non-homologous chromosomes) produces four different types of gamete in approximately equal numbers.

Let us now consider a cross between two maize plants heterozygous for grain colour and grain shape. Purple grain colour is dominant to white and smooth grain shape is dominant to wrinkled.

○ What are the phenotypes of grains from which the heterozygous parent plants developed?

● As the plants are heterozygotes, they must have developed from grains with the dominant characters purple and smooth.

Choosing the symbols *G* for purple grain, *g* for white grain, *T* for smooth grain and *t* for wrinkled grain, Figure 3.7 shows a Punnett square, a way in which the genotypes of gametes and the genotypes of the resulting offspring of the cross between plants heterozygous for both pairs of alleles are recorded. It also includes the phenotypes of the resulting maize grains.

| | genotypes of female gametes | | | |
	G T	*G t*	*g T*	*g t*
G T	*G G T T* purple, smooth	*G G T t* purple, smooth	*G g T T* purple, smooth	*G g T t* purple, smooth
G t	*G G t T* purple, smooth	*G G t t* purple, wrinked	*G g t T* purple, smooth	*G g t t* purple, wrinked
g T	*g G T T* purple, smooth	*g G T t* purple, smooth	*g g T T* white, smooth	*g g T t* white, smooth
g t	*g G t T* purple, smooth	*g G t t* purple, wrinked	*g g t T* white, smooth	*g g t t* white, wrinkled

genotypes of male gametes

Figure 3.7 Punnett square showing the result of a cross between two maize plants heterozygous for two pairs of alleles. Alleles: *G*, purple grain, *g*, white grain, *T*, smooth grain and *t*, wrinkled grain.

○   Both parent plants developed from purple grains that were smooth. What do you notice about the phenotypes of the offspring grains?

●   In addition to purple and smooth, some of the offspring grains are white and wrinkled; others white and smooth; others purple and wrinkled — three of the phenotypes are different from the parent grains.

Independent assortment of alleles during meiosis, followed by fertilization, results in expression of the recessive characters in some of the offspring.

○   How many different genotypes are there in the offspring?

●   There are nine genetically different types of offspring.

○   How many different phenotypes are produced in the offspring?

●   There are four different phenotypes.

○   In what ratios do these offspring phenotypes occur?

●   Counting the number of squares in which a phenotype occurs in Figure 3.7 gives a ratio of 9 purple, smooth : 3 purple, wrinkled : 3 white, smooth : 1 white, wrinkled.

A cross between plants heterozygous for two pairs of alleles carried on different chromosome pairs gives this $9:3:3:1$ ratio of phenotypes in the offspring, with expression of phenotypes not seen in the parents. The random nature of independent assortment and the processes that determine which gametes actually achieve fertilization mean that the ratios observed in a breeding experiment may differ from an exact $9:3:3:1$ relationship.

When we start to consider more than two pairs of heterozygous alleles the situation rapidly becomes more complex. If both parents are heterozygous for three pairs of alleles (at three loci) on three different chromosome pairs, then each produces $2 \times 2 \times 2 = 8$ genetically different types of gamete and $3 \times 3 \times 3 = 27$ different genotypes amongst their offspring. To generalize, if parents are heterozygous for N different pairs of alleles (N loci), all on different chromosome pairs, then independent assortment produces 2^N genetically different types of gametes and 3^N different genotypes amongst the offspring.

The average human has 6700 heterozygous loci carried on 23 pairs of chromosomes. If we were to assume that the 6700 heterozygotic loci are equally distributed along the 23 pairs of chromosomes, and that no crossing over occurs at all at meiosis, a human parent could produce $2^{23} = 8\,388\,608$ genetically different types of gametes, which on fertilization could produce 3^{23} different genotypes among the offspring (around 9.4×10^{10}!) The number of genetically different individuals that could arise from fertilization would be greater still. Hence independent assortment can produce huge genetic variation between parents and offspring, variation on which natural selection can act.

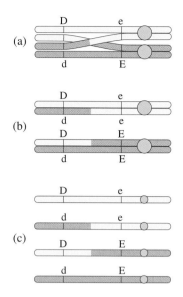

Figure 3.8 The results of crossing over between a pair of chromosomes (a) at metaphase 1, (b) after anaphase 1, and (c) the chromosomes produced by meiosis.

Independent assortment generates new combinations of alleles on different chromosomes. However, this huge potential for variation is further increased by crossing over between alleles at different loci on the same chromosome. If crossing over takes place between two heterozygous loci on the same pair of homologous chromosomes, it could produce four genetically different kinds of gametes. For example, if one chromosome of a homologous pair carries the alleles D and e and its homologous pair alleles d and E, and if there is no crossing over between these alleles, the gametes can have the genotypes De and dE only. However, if crossing over does take place between these loci, as in Figure 3.8, the resulting gametes have genotypes DE and de also.

Crossing over has produced new allele combinations on chromosomes. If an individual has N heterozygous loci, then each could produce 2^N genetically different types of gametes which could potentially produce 3^N genetically different individuals on fertilization. Therefore with about 6700 heterozygous loci in a human, potentially 2^{6700} different genetic combinations are possible in the gametes. You can see that the vast number of possible allele combinations that can arise during recombination through crossing over and independent assortment in organisms with heterozygous loci generates a huge reservoir of genetic variation for natural selection to act upon, which forms the gene pool.

This potential for genetic variation arises through reassortment and recombination at meiosis, followed by syngamy between gametes in sexually reproducing organisms. This potential does not exist for organisms that reproduce asexually. The evolution of sexual reproduction about 1500 Ma ago was followed by a period of rapid protoctist diversification. However, sexual reproduction does not appear to occur in some protoctist lineages. The advantages and disadvantages of sexual and asexual reproduction are explored in Chapter 4, but it is important to note that success, in evolutionary terms, is not confined to organisms that can reproduce sexually.

The original source of new alleles is through the **mutations** that give rise to new DNA sequences. Point mutations are changes in the sequence of base pairs in the DNA due to replication errors or chemical instability in some of the DNA bases. Mutations may also involve larger structural changes in chromosomes or changes in the number of chromosomes. Mutations may occur in any cell, but only those in cells that produce gametes contribute to genetic variation in sexually reproducing populations.

The consequences of mutations range from the sequence coding for a protein being disrupted so that the product is non-functional, to changes in control genes, to loss of sections of the genetic material or its duplication.

A point mutation may or may not have a phenotypic effect, depending on the actual alteration in the base sequence and the function of the coding sequence. Such a mutation may give rise to a serious malfunction and be eliminated, or it may improve molecular function and be selected. Many mutations are neutral, in that they are neither selected for nor against. However, the environment of a population of organisms may change with time so that such a mutation is no longer selectively neutral, and the variation it provides could confer an advantage and be selected for and so increase its frequency within a population.

Large changes in the genome may take place if chromosomes break naturally, or when exposed, for example, to chemicals or ionizing radiation. Parts of a chromosome may be lost (a deletion), or the sequence of genes, relative to one another, may change if the pieces of chromosome rejoin in a different order. Sections may also be duplicated. In addition, whole chromosomes may be lost or fuse to produce a new karyotype. Study Figure 3.9 which illustrates a number of possible structural changes and the terms used to describe them.

In an inversion, a segment within a chromosome is rotated through 180 degrees. A translocation is a transfer of segments, usually between non-homologous chromosomes.

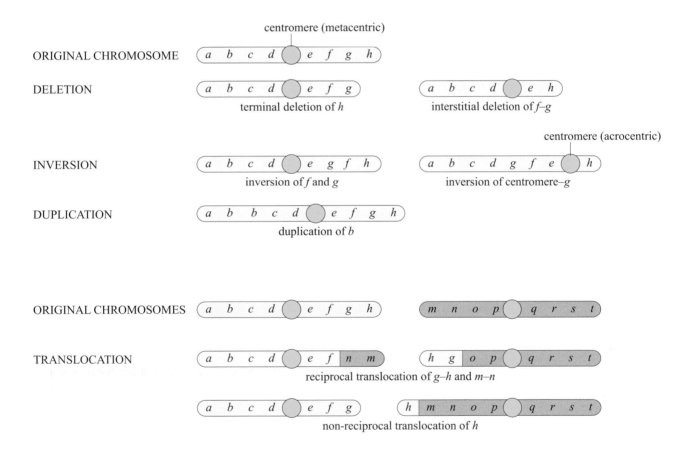

Figure 3.9 The major types of changes in chromosome structure.

Figure 3.10 The behaviour of homologous chromosomes during meiosis in an individual heterozygous for an inversion. (a) Pair of homologous chromosomes prior to meiosis. (b) Pairing at prophase I of meiosis. (c) Crossing over and exchange of genetic material. (d) Separation of chromosomes at anaphase I showing (i) a chromatid bridge, with two centromeres; (ii) a fragment without a centromere (both (i) and (ii) give non-viable gametes); (iii) two chromatids with all parts intact (which give viable gametes).

Figure 3.10 shows the irregular behaviour of the chromosomes during meiosis in a cell heterozygous for an inversion.

At prophase I some homologous regions of the chromosomes cannot align linearly, and loops may be formed. Crossing over within the inversion results in some incomplete chromosome fragments, (Figure 3.10d) and half the gametes are defective. Therefore heterozygotes with a large inversion have reduced fertility and hence reduced fitness. However, if the inversion segment is short, the probability of crossing over within the inversion is small and groups of genes within the inversion tend to be conserved. A group of genes that always remain together during subsequent meioses is known as a **supergene**. Such supergenes may conserve adaptations within a chromosome, so that they are not split up by recombination, so increasing the fitness of those individuals that carry it.

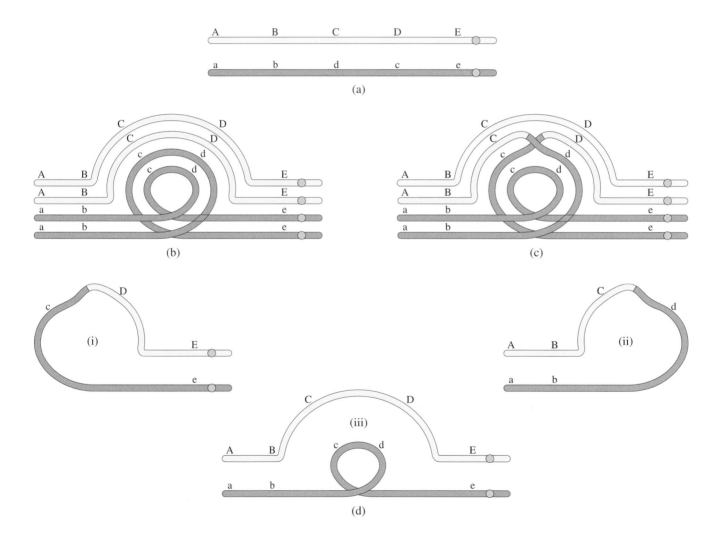

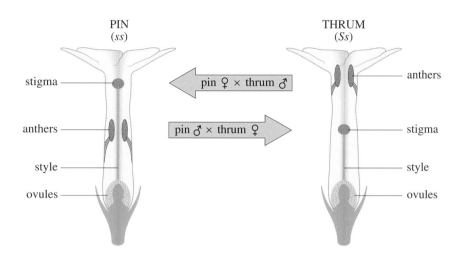

Figure 3.11 Pin and thrum plants of the primrose, *Primula vulgaris*.

One example of a supergene is found in the reproductive system of the primrose, *Primula vulgaris* (see Figure 3.11). This supergene complex includes loci determining style length, anther height, pollen size, and style and pollen incompatibilities and produces two 'super-alleles', *s* and *S*. Pin plants, with long styles and low anthers, have the genotype *s s* and thrum plants, with short styles and high anthers, have the genotype *S s*.

The mechanical and physiological differences between the two plant morphs mean that generally, pin and thrum plants cross-pollinate, a mechanism for promoting outbreeding (the fusion of gametes from different individuals). Breeding mechanisms and the genetic consequences of outbreeding and inbreeding (breeding with closely related individuals or selfing) are considered in more detail in Chapter 4.

Now study Figure 3.12 overleaf. The consequence of a translocation can be the positioning of alleles from previously non-homologous chromosomes on the same chromosome. In this figure, half the gametes are defective, so the fertility of the heterozygote is reduced. However, if genes from two non-homologous chromosomes come into close proximity in this way, the probability that they are passed on to subsequent generations as a unit is increased, so adaptive combinations of genes may remain together.

In addition to the chromosome mutations that have been described above, recent studies have shown that mutations, including deletions and inversions, may arise when transposable genetic elements encode transposases, enzymes that enable these transposable elements to 'jump' around chromosomes, altering their structure. Transposable elements appear to exist in all organisms, both prokaryotic and eukaryotic, and can move around the genome and cause mutations, for example when they are inserted into a gene sequence.

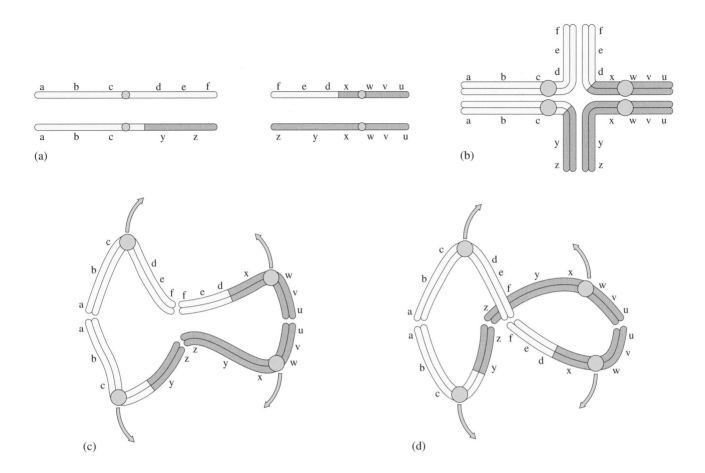

Figure 3.12 The behaviour of four chromosomes with a reciprocal translocation. (a) Chromosomes with reciprocal translocation. (b) Pairing during meiosis. (c) and (d) Alternative configurations for separation of the chromosomes at anaphase I; (c) gives rise to non-viable gametes because one chromosome segment is duplicated and another is missing in both sets of chromosomes; (d) gives rise to viable gametes as both upper and lower combinations are balanced with all parts of the two chromosomes.

Changes in chromosome numbers may come about as the result of errors in cell division. Individual chromosomes may be lost or gained, resulting in a situation known as **aneuploidy**. An organism with an extra chromosome is trisomic for that chromosome and an organism lacking one member of a pair of chromosomes is monosomic. Trisomics have been described in *Datura stramonium* (Jimson weed or thorn apple). There are 12 chromosomes in the haploid set and trisomics are known for all of them, each affecting the appearance of the seed capsule in a different way and hence generating new phenotypes. Monosomics in *Datura* are non-viable, and it is generally found that having some genes and chromosomes in numbers greater than normal is less deleterious than having them in less than normal quantities.

Let us move on to consider mutations that change the numbers of sets of chromosomes.

○ What would be the consequence of failure of cell division after anaphase II of meiosis for any resulting gametes? (You may find it helpful to refer back to Figure 3.5 to remind yourself of the outcome of a normal division II of meiosis.)

● The resulting gametes have double the number of chromosomes.

Note that diploid gametes could also arise following abnormal segregation of chromosomes at anaphase I of meiosis.

Any viable progeny arising from fertilization of such a gamete by a normal haploid gamete are triploid and sterile because their cells contain an extra set of chromosomes that cannot segregate regularly at meiosis, and the sets of three homologous chromosomes are unevenly distributed. Thus any gametes are likely to be lacking some chromosomes and have extras of others. However many plants can reproduce asexually, (which will be described further in Chapter 4), so such a sterile individual may survive. Should a further doubling of chromosomes occur, fertility may be partially restored and a viable, sexually reproducing population (autohexaploid), genetically distinct from the parent population could become established (Figure 3.13 overleaf, route A). Gene flow from the parent population is severed, so a new, **autopolyploid** ('auto' meaning 'self' and 'polyploid' having more than two chromosome sets) species has evolved; sympatric speciation has occurred.

If two diploid gametes fuse, autopolyploid cells with a tetraploid genome are formed (Figure 3.13, route B). Autopolyploidy may also arise following abnormal mitosis during development. Subsequent mitotic division of such cells may result in an autopolyploid individual. Such tetraploids often have low fertility because of complications during meiosis. As with the autohexaploids whose origin is described above, each chromosome has more than one homologous partner with which to pair. Pairing may take place between any number of homologues and is frequently followed by failure of the chromosomes to separate to give equal numbers of chromosomes in each gamete. Autopolyploids are often found to reproduce vegetatively, for example the cultivated potato, *Solanum tuberosum*, which is apparently a tetraploid that has arisen naturally from a wild diploid South American ancestor.

If a hybrid is formed between two non-matching genomes, such as two species A and B, the hybrid is generally unfit because of genetic incompatibilities. Hybrids were made in 1900 at Kew by crossing two commonly cultivated species, *Primula floribunda* and *P. verticillata*. These hybrids had the same chromosome number (18) as each of the parents, and were intermediate in appearance between them, but were sterile. In this hybrid situation, meiosis would be irregular because the chromosomes lack homologues with which to pair. However a very small number of plants were later observed to set seed and were found to have 36 chromosomes; they were tetraploids. These fertile polyploids had arisen by doubling of the hybrid chromosomes and were able to undergo meiosis normally as illustrated in Figure 3.14 overleaf (where only 6 chromosomes per parent species are illustrated for simplicity). Such **allopolyploid** tetraploids (formed from two species) can produce fertile gametes as each chromosome has only one homologue with which to pair, whereas autopolyploids have lower fertility because there are more than two homologues of each chromosome.

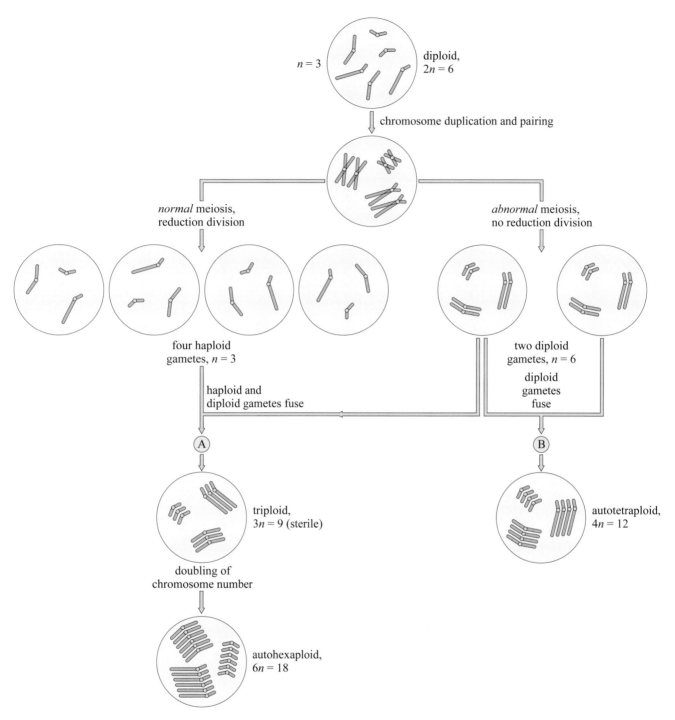

$n = 3$ · diploid, $2n = 6$

chromosome duplication and pairing

normal meiosis, reduction division

abnormal meiosis, no reduction division

four haploid gametes, $n = 3$

two diploid gametes, $n = 6$

haploid and diploid gametes fuse

diploid gametes fuse

Ⓐ

Ⓑ

triploid, $3n = 9$ (sterile)

autotetraploid, $4n = 12$

doubling of chromosome number

autohexaploid, $6n = 18$

Figure 3.13 Routes by which autopolyploidy may arise.

Notice that the allotetraploids are reproductively isolated from both parents because of the low fertility of any hybrids between them. They are effectively a new species, known as *P. kewensis*, distinct from both parents and unable to produce fertile seed when crossed with either parent. Hybridization followed by polyploidy could produce a new allopolyploid species in only three generations; this process is another way in which sympatric speciation may take place.

It has been estimated that roughly 50% of flowering plant species have originated as polyploid hybrids. However polyploidy is comparatively rare in animals, probably because it is difficult to establish in sexual, outbreeding species with sex-determining mechanisms. Polyploidy is found in some groups where asexual reproduction occurs, such as a very few insects, crustaceans, earthworms, fish, amphibians and reptiles.

Polyploid plants are often found to be larger than their diploid parents, with thicker, fleshier leaves and larger flowers and fruit. The grain yields of durum and bread wheat, *Triticum durum,* a tetraploid, and *Triticum aestivum,* a hexaploid, provide examples of desirable characters in plants cultivated for food.

A polyploid may be better adapted than either parent to a particular environment. The allopolyploid cord grass *Spartina anglica* arose around 1870 in Southampton Water following chromosome doubling of a hybrid between an American species, *S. alterniflora* and the native British species, *S. maritima. S. anglica* was found to grow particularly well in mudflats and has been widely planted to stabilize coastal environments. The distribution of both *S. alterniflora* and *S. maritima* has regressed during the last 100 years, but *S. anglica* is widespread around the coast of the British Isles.

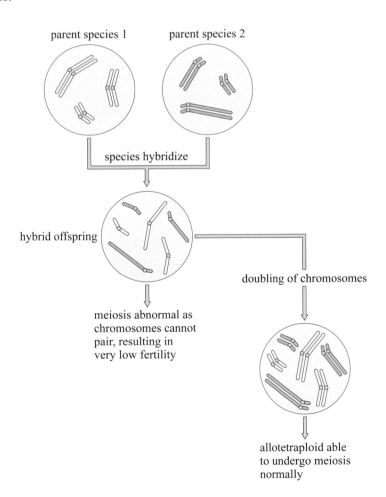

Figure 3.14 Allopolyploidy following hybridization.

SUMMARY OF SECTION 3.4

1   Independent assortment and recombination during meiosis, followed by fertilization, can generate huge genetic variability.

2   The source of new alleles is through mutations that give rise to new DNA sequences arising as point mutations or as a result of rearrangements of larger segments of chromosomes.

3   Chromosomal mutation may result in situations in which groups of genes may remain clustered together through meiosis as supergenes, or in polyploidy where the genetic changes may bring about reproductive isolation and speciation within a very small number of generations.

3.5   NATURAL SELECTION AND EVOLUTION

Charles Darwin and Alfred Russel Wallace laid the foundations for modern evolutionary thinking in their joint communications on the theory of evolution by natural selection presented in 1858. We began this chapter with the four basic premises of their theory and have examined the origin and expression of genetic variation and its effects on relative fitness when organisms are subject to natural selection. Genetic drift can change the relative frequencies of alleles in the gene pool of a population by chance. Mutation, genetic drift and natural selection may all contribute to the genetic make-up of populations which can change with time and changing environment.

Evolution is generally taken to mean cumulative change, and **biological evolution**, more specifically, the change in characteristics of descendant populations of organisms. These changes in phenotypes in populations over time may accumulate over generations to produce significant alterations and eventually new species. Today, most scientists studying evolution consider that all living organisms ultimately share a common ancestry in simple organisms that arose thousands of millions of years ago. From simple beginnings, evolution has given rise to a huge diversity of organisms, some extremely complicated, but others still unicellular. Therefore biological evolution cannot be viewed only as a process by which more sophisticated organisms replace older, simpler ones. The existence of a species in the present day demonstrates its evolutionary success, regardless of whether it has been highly modified by evolution, or like the 'living fossil' fish, the coelacanth, *Latimeria chalumnae*, it has remained apparently unchanged in morphology for many millions of years.

The process of evolution and its study integrates the ecological interactions between organisms (in the struggle) and their genetic make-ups (variation) and the effects of natural selection on the genetic composition of offspring (principle of inheritance). Recall, however, that natural selection may be stabilizing, and hence may not result in evolution, that mutation is a source of new genetic variations, that polyploidy can lead to speciation and that genetic drift can impact on gene frequencies in populations, resulting in different outcomes from that of natural selection alone.

SUMMARY OF SECTION 3.5

Evolution may take place through changes in the gene pool as a result of mutation, genetic drift or natural selection, singly or in combination.

REFERENCE

Tauber C. A. and Tauber M. J. (1977) Sympatric speciation based on allelic changes at three loci: evidence from natural populations in two habitats. *Science*, **197**, pp. 1298–1299.

REPRODUCTION

4.1   INTRODUCTION

During the course of their lives, animals and plants generally have periods of growth followed by periods of reproduction. One of the most important aspects of an organism's life history is the way it reproduces. There are two main ways in which organisms reproduce: sexually and asexually.

Asexual reproduction occurs naturally in most animal and plant phyla as well as in microbes. Indeed, alternation between sexual and asexual phases of the life cycle is common in plants and in members of some invertebrate taxa. However, obligate or strictly asexual plant and animal 'species' are rare. For example, in animals they comprise little more than one in every 1000 of the named species.

In its broadest sense, **sexual reproduction** can be defined as any process in which genetic material is transferred from one cell to another. Meiosis (reduction division of chromosomes) and syngamy are two essential features of sexual reproduction that are universal for all organisms.

As summarized in the left part of Figure 4.1, during meiosis the parent cell, which is **diploid** (carries two sets of homologous chromosomes), divides, resulting in the production of four daughter cells, each of which is **haploid** (contains only one set of chromosomes). The haploid products of meiosis are known as gametes. Gametes fuse to form a zygote during the process of syngamy (fertilization). In the course of meiosis, **recombination** occurs, as a result of the exchange of genetic material between homologous chromosomes by crossing over followed by the random allocation of one member of each homologous pair to each of the haploid gametes (Section 3.4). The essential feature of meiosis is that it 'shuffles the pack'. Usually, syngamy occurs between gametes derived from different individuals and this process, together with recombination during meiosis, has an important genetic consequence.

○   What is the genetic outcome of recombination and syngamy?

●   Offspring differ from one another and from their parents.

Each offspring is a unique product of fusion of two meiotically diversified haploid nuclei and is therefore different from either of the diploid parents from which it is descended.

In contrast, **asexual reproduction** does not involve meiosis or the production and fusion of gametes. Instead, a single individual produces exact genetic copies of itself through mitosis. These copies are called **clones** (Figure 4.1, right).

○   What are the genetic consequences of asexual reproduction?

●   The parental genome is conserved. Offspring are genetically identical to their parent and to each other, unless mutation occurs.

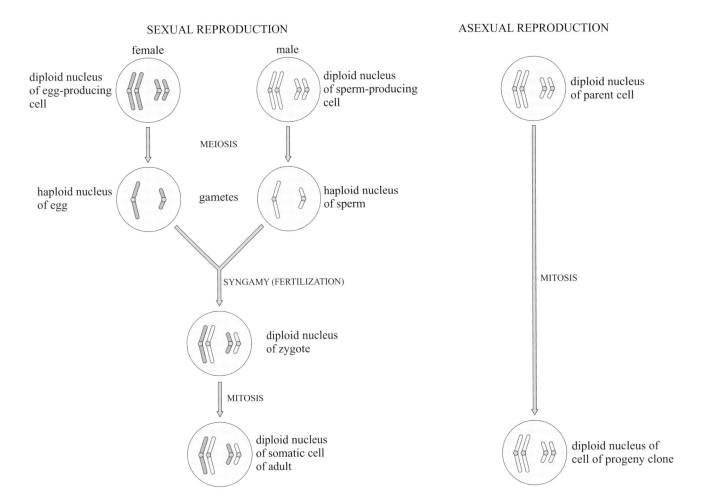

SEXUAL REPRODUCTION

ASEXUAL REPRODUCTION

Figure 4.1 The products of sexual and asexual reproduction. In sexual species (left), meiosis results in the production of four haploid gametes. (For simplicity, only one of each of the four gametes is shown.) Gamete fusion (syngamy or fertilization) results in a diploid zygote, with each parent contributing only half of the genome. The zygote undergoes mitosis to produce individuals that are genetically different from each other and from both parents. Asexual organisms (right), which reproduce by mitosis, produce identical copies of themselves (clones).

Sexual and asexual reproduction can be regarded as two extremes of a continuum. Between these extremes is a host of reproductive modes which incorporate features of both sexual and asexual reproduction.

In this chapter we will explore several aspects of reproduction in eukaryotes, beginning with some examples of the diversity of modes that exist. We will then look at the question of 'why sex?', a question that, even today, puzzles evolutionary biologists. Finally, we will examine some of the consequences of the evolution of sexual reproduction.

4.2 ASEXUAL REPRODUCTION

There is little doubt that asexual reproduction evolved long before sexual reproduction and a variety of modes persist today. Several are found in the protoctists. In this section, we examine some of the asexual reproductive modes of animals and plants.

4.2.1 VEGETATIVE REPRODUCTION

Vegetative reproduction is defined as any mode of reproduction that does not involve the production of eggs. Therefore, in organisms that reproduce in this way, the distinction between growth and reproduction is often blurred. Offspring are derived from a single parent and, because there is no meiosis or syngamy, they are clones of the parent. Several different forms of vegetative reproduction exist.

Many starfish (Echinodermata) and sea-anemones (Cnidaria), as well as undergoing sexual reproduction, sometimes reproduce by an asexual process known as **fission**. Starfish split into two and a new individual is formed from each half. Sometimes an animal can be broken up into two or more pieces, each of which grows into a new individual. This process is known as **fragmentation**, and as a means of reproduction, it depends on the organism having a good regenerative capacity. Sponges (Porifera), hydroids and sea-anemones have astonishing powers of regeneration. For example, if a sponge is macerated by passing it through a fine gauze, the separated cells come together in groups and grow into new individuals. Free-living flatworms (Platyhelminthes) can also reproduce by fragmentation: very small fragments of worm grow into new individuals.

Budding is a mode of reproduction that involves the formation of an outgrowth which, on detachment from the parent, develops into a self-supporting individual. It is common in hydras, certain flatworms and several kinds of annelids. In an adult hydra, the dividing cells are found along the column surrounding the enteron. If food is plentiful, more cells form and the extra cells migrate and accumulate at the outer surface of the column, producing a bud. The bud grows its own tentacles while still attached to the parent. Finally it separates from the parent and becomes a free-living hydra (Figure 4.2).

In plants, vegetative reproduction depends largely on the activity of **meristematic cells**, groups of cells (meristems) that are capable of dividing and developing into new tissues. Vegetative reproduction usually takes place via modified stems or roots. In strawberries, for example, a horizontal stem known as a runner grows out from one of the axillary buds on the stem of the parent plant (Figure 4.3). Later the new plant is separated by the withering of the runner.

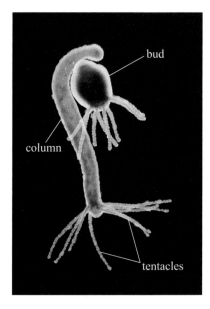

Figure 4.2 Asexual reproduction through budding in *Hydra viridis*.

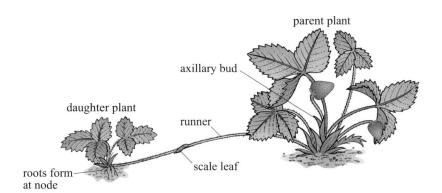

Figure 4.3 Asexual reproduction in the cultivated strawberry (*Fragaria ananassa*). A horizontal stem, or runner, grows out from the axillary bud and forms roots at the nodes (the 'joints' where leaves arise from the stem).

Vegetative reproduction may also involve the formation of some kind of storage organ which lies in the soil over winter and develops into one or more plants the following year. Such devices are known as **perennating organs** and may be formed from a modified stem, root or bud. For example, garlic (*Allium sativum*) forms a clump of cloves, which are actually underground buds used by the plant for storage. Each clove eventually develops into a new plant, complete with roots (below ground) and shoots (above ground). Another example of a plant that uses this kind of reproduction is the potato (Figure 4.4). A potato is a swollen stem and, like any stem, has both apical buds and axillary buds at leaf nodes. Each 'eye' on the surface of a potato comprises an axillary bud with its scale leaf. It is from a bud that a new plant is formed.

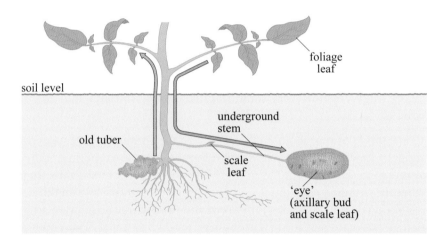

Figure 4.4   The formation and utilization of perennating organs in the potato plant. Towards the end of the growing season, the plant forms swollen tubers at the ends of horizontally growing underground stems, using food materials transported into it from the above-ground foliage leaves (blue arrow). The tubers lie dormant in the soil until the following year when axillary buds give rise to new plants. The old tuber shrivels as the food stores within it are solubilized and transported out to the regions of growth (red arrow).

Vegetative propagation from root systems also occurs in plants. The plant sends out adventitious roots (i.e. roots produced from a stem) which then develop into separate shoot systems. The creosote bush (*Larrea tridentata*) of the Mojave desert in California propagates in this way. The daughter plants form rings around the original parent, which expand in diameter at a rate of about one metre per 500 years. From the size of the rings, the Mojave desert bushes are estimated to have been propagating via the adventitious budding of root systems for up to 12 000 years.

4.2.2 PARTHENOGENESIS

Parthenogenesis is traditionally viewed as being an asexual process and sometimes the terms parthenogenesis and asexual reproduction are used as synonyms. However, classifying all parthenogens as asexual is confusing because, in some types of parthenogenesis, meiosis and syngamy take place.

○ Given that there is meiosis and syngamy in some parthenogens, why would equating parthenogenesis with asexual reproduction be confusing?

● Because meiosis and syngamy are regarded as sexual processes.

Parthenogenesis literally means 'virgin descent'. In obligate parthenogens, there are no males and new individuals are produced from a single female parent. Several different forms of parthenogenesis have been identified, which fall into two main categories: **arrhenotoky** (pronounced 'ah-renn-oh-toe-key', and derived from the Greek, meaning 'male-begetting'), which is the production of haploid males from unfertilized eggs, and **thelytoky** (pronounced 'thelly-toe-key', literally 'female-begetting'), the production of diploid females from unfertilized eggs.

Arrhenotoky is common among bees, wasps and ants (order Hymenoptera), and certain beetles (Coleoptera) and bugs (Hemiptera). Females produce haploid eggs, via meiosis, which develop into diploid females if fertilized, and into haploid males, if not (Figure 4.5). In honeybees, for example, the queen is the only sexually mature female in the colony. She receives only one insemination with sperm during her life. She stores the sperm and for several years produces eggs which she can either fertilize with stored sperm as they are laid, or not. Fertilized eggs develop into diploid females, most of which are sterile workers, but a select few become fertile queens. Unfertilized eggs develop into haploid male drones.

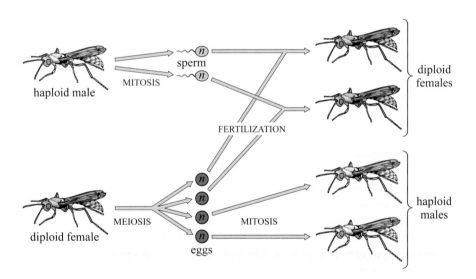

Figure 4.5 Arrhenotoky involves the parthenogenetic production of haploid males from unfertilized eggs (shown in blue shaded area) and occurs in some species of insects. Diploid females are produced through fertilization (i.e. sexually).

Thelytoky can take several different forms. In one form, each diploid female develops from a single, mitotically produced cell. There is no meiosis or syngamy. Mothers produce daughters that inherit their complete, unrecombined diploid genome. This kind of reproductive mode is called **apomixis** (also known as ameiotic parthenogenesis) and is widely distributed in both animals and plants. It is known to occur in bees and wasps (Hymenoptera), and certain bugs (Hemiptera), flies (Diptera), grasshoppers (Orthoptera), lizards (Reptilia), frogs (Amphibia) and in several crustaceans (Arthropoda), flatworms (Platyhelminthes) and roundworms (Nematoda). Figure 4.6 illustrates apomixis in the whiptail lizard (*Cnemidophorus tesselatus*).

Figure 4.6 Apomixis, the production of diploid females from diploid eggs in the whiptail lizard (*Cnemidophorus tesselatus*). Diploid unisexual (all female) *C. tesselatus* (genome MS) are derived by hybridization between two bisexual (sexually reproducing) lizard species, *C. marmoratus* (female, MM) and *C. septemvittatus* (male, SS). The diploid *C. tesselatus* females produce diploid eggs (by mitosis), in which chromosomal recombination has not occurred. These eggs develop, without sperm, into diploid offspring which are clonal, i.e. genetically identical to each other and to their mother. This parthenogenetic mode of reproduction can perpetuate clonal lineages indefinitely, yielding genetically identical females, generation after generation.

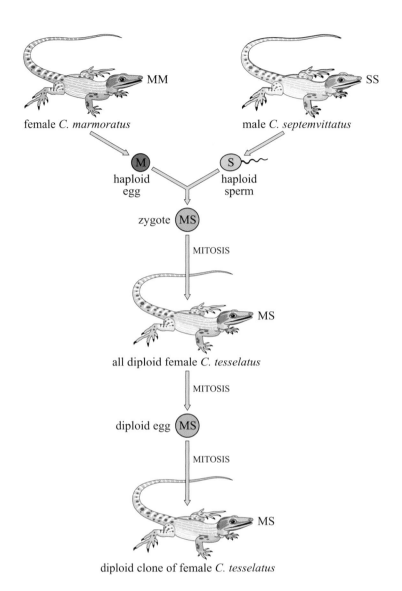

In flowering plants, apomixis is the production of seeds without normal meiosis or fertilization taking place; the seeds are generated by mitosis. For example, in citrus fruits and dandelions, an embryo develops from a diploid cell in the ovule that has not undergone meiosis. As the embryo develops, the surrounding tissues form the seed and fruit in the normal way. One advantage of apomixis in plants over vegetative reproduction is that it enables the plant to spread its offspring over a large area using the methods of seed dispersal typically available to embryos formed by sexual reproduction. Dandelions, for example, are able to disperse their seeds as far as the wind can take them.

○ In apomicts, to what extent are offspring genetically different from their parent?

● They aren't. Neither normal meiosis nor syngamy occur, so offspring are genetically identical to their parent.

A second form of thelytoky is known as **automixis** (or meiotic parthenogenesis). In automicts, females produce diploid eggs via meiosis. There are no males, so meiosis is not followed by fertilization and the consequent doubling of chromosome number. Instead, automictic females have an internal solution for doubling the chromosome number and so producing diploid eggs, which then go on to develop by mitotic division into adults. A number of chromosome doubling devices have been described. One of the most common is **premeiotic endomitosis**, in which is mitosis without cell division takes place before meiosis. This process is shown in Figure 4.7.

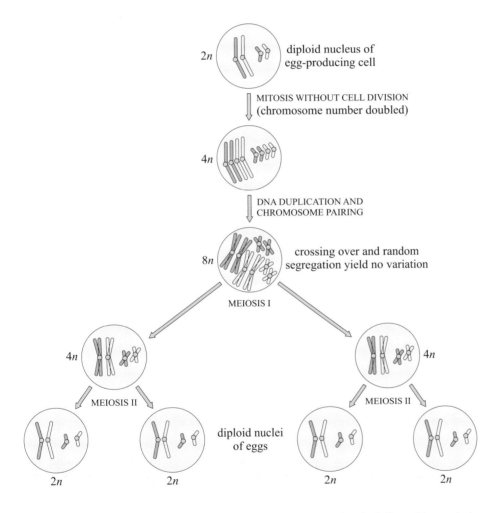

Figure 4.7   Production of diploid eggs by premeiotic endomitosis followed by meiotic chromosome duplication and cell division.

○   What is the effect of premeiotic endomitosis on chromosome number?

●   It doubles the number of chromosomes in the egg before meiosis begins. Thus at the start of meiosis the cell is $4n$, so after the chromosome doubling of meiosis and just before division I, the cell is $8n$.

At the end of meiosis II, therefore, each egg contains the diploid number of chromosomes. This mechanism of producing diploid eggs is found in the lizard *Cnemidophorus uniparens* and in at least two species of fish (genus *Poeciliopsis*, top minnows). It is also known to occur in grasshoppers (e.g. *Moraba virgo*) and in parthenogenetic earthworms (Annelida).

○ What are the genetic consequences of the system shown in Figure 4.7?

● It generates no variation. Crossing over happens only between identical chromatids (since the chromosomes are duplicated), so generates no variation. Pairs of chromosomes from different homologues in the parental diploid cell segregate, but since they are identical, no variation is introduced into the diploid eggs produced. In effect, the result is the same as that for apomixis, i.e. the egg is genetically identical to the somatic cells of the mother.

In addition to the asexual systems described above, there are several others that are difficult to classify as either sexual or asexual. One of the most common of these modes is known as **hybridogenesis**. Unlike thelytoky, in hybridogenesis males are required for successful reproduction. The uniqueness of the system lies in the fact that the males are of a different, but closely related, species. These males (species 1) mate with the females (species 2) to form a diploid hybrid female. This hybridogen (the result of a cross between two different species) then mates with a male of species 1 but during meiosis, the male's genome is excluded so that all the eggs carry only the unrecombined genome of the mother.

A classic example of fish that reproduce via hybridogenesis is seen in the genus *Poeciliopsis* (Figure 4.8). Here, crosses between two bisexual species, *P. monacha* and *P. lucida* produce an all-female hybrid called *P. monacha-lucida*, which reproduces via hybridogenesis, passing on the maternal genome unchanged through successive generations, while the paternal genome is replaced with each generation.

A second system in which males of a different species are required for successful reproduction is known as **gynogenesis**. Sperm is required to begin embryogenesis (development of the egg into an embryo) but no syngamy between egg and sperm occurs. Gynogenesis occurs in the Amazon molly, *Poecilia formosa* (Figure 4.9). *P. formosa* is derived from hybridization between the bisexual species *P. latipinna* and *P. mexicana*. *P. formosa* females produce diploid eggs via premeiotic endomitosis, so they have not undergone recombination. However, in contrast to apomixis, these eggs require sperm (from a related species) in order to develop. The sperm presumably penetrates the egg but syngamy between egg and sperm nuclei does not occur, so the sperm makes no genetic contribution to the offspring.

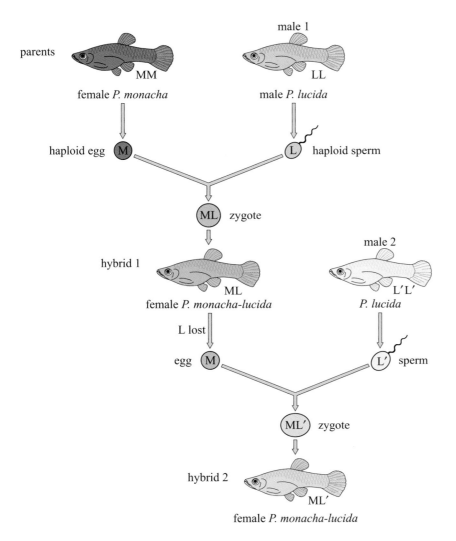

Figure 4.8 Hybridogenesis in fish. Crosses between females of the bisexual species *Poeciliopsis monacha* (containing two haploid M genomes, MM) and male *P. lucida* (containing two haploid L genomes, LL) produce a unisexual female *P. monacha-lucida* (ML). Each *P. monacha-lucida* female generated by the original hybrid cross produces haploid eggs containing only the unrecombined haploid *P. monacha* genome (M) from their mother; the *P. lucida* genome (L) of the father is lost. These *P. monacha-lucida* females then mate with other *P. lucida* males (L'L'), syngamy of egg and sperm occurs, and female offspring are produced (ML') which carry the clonally inherited *P. monacha* genome (M) from their mother and the sexually inherited *P. lucida* genome (L') from their father. In this way, the *P. monacha* genome (M) is passed on unchanged through many generations, each time combined with a new and different *P. lucida* genome.

Figure 4.9 Gynogenesis in the Amazon molly, *Poecilia formosa.* Crosses between the bisexual species *P. latipinna* (genome LL) and *P. mexicana* (genome MM) produce the unisexual female fish, *P. formosa* (genome LM). *P. formosa* produce diploid eggs without recombination. These fish mate with males of a related bisexual species and their sperm stimulates embryogenesis, but syngamy of egg and sperm does not occur. The resulting offspring (genome LM) are genetically identical to their mother and to each other and form a diploid *P. formosa* clone. (In 1% of cases, syngamy between the egg and sperm does occur, resulting in a triploid.)

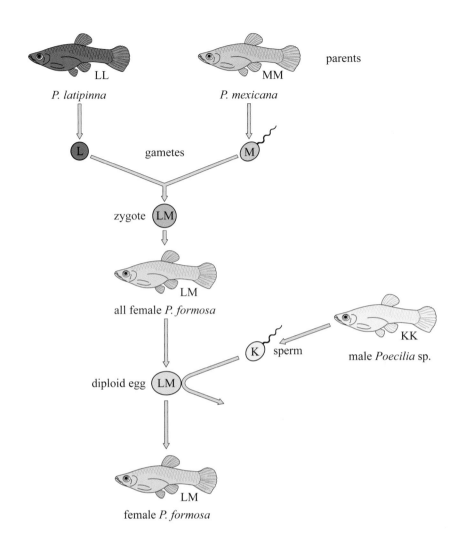

The three kinds of unisexual modes of reproduction (i.e. reproductive modes that produce only females) discussed above are compared to sexual reproduction in Figure 4.10 and in the following text.

In *apomixis* the hybrid genome (one haploid genome from an ancestral bisexual species A and another from an ancestral bisexual species B) is transmitted to the egg complete, without recombination. The egg develops without sperm into an offspring identical to its mother.

In *hybridogenesis* one ancestral genome (A) from a unisexual female (AB) is transmitted to the egg without recombination, while the other ancestral genome from the male ancestor (B) is discarded; sperm B' from another male of the same ancestral species then fertilizes the egg, producing an offspring with the original maternal (A) genome and a new paternal (B') genome.

In *gynogenesis* diploid eggs are produced by either apomixis or premeiotic endomitosis. Sperm from a related bisexual male is then required to stimulate development of the diploid egg, but makes no genetic contribution.

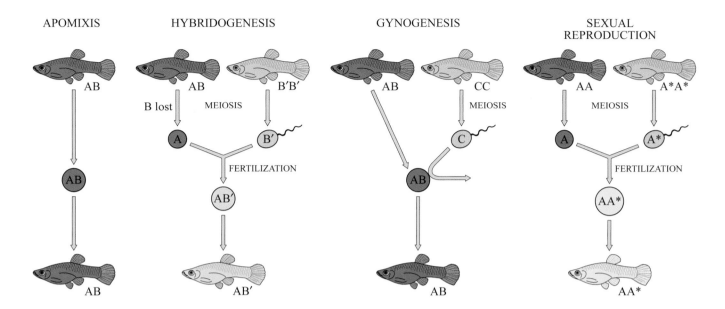

In *sexual reproduction* the mother produces a haploid egg (A) which, due to recombination, contains a unique combination of genes from *her* mother and father; the father produces haploid sperm (A*) in the same way, resulting in offspring that are highly variable.

Unisexual vertebrates of the sort discussed above are most commonly derived from a hybridization event between two species. As a consequence, their establishment in nature is subject to severe genetic, developmental and ecological constraints. They are believed by many who study them to be evolutionary dead-ends. Nonetheless, biologists investigate these animals for the same reasons that medical scientists probe disorders and diseases to define the limits of human health. Identifying the conditions in which asexual lineages prosper or fail provides a window through which biologists can view the adaptive significance of genetic diversity and sex.

Figure 4.10 Comparison between unisexual modes of reproduction and sexual reproduction. See text for explanation.

4.3   INBREEDING AND OUTBREEDING

In the introduction to this chapter, we stated that sexual reproduction usually involves the fusion of gametes derived from different individuals of the same species. If these individuals are very distantly related, the process is known as **outbreeding** (cross-fertilization, outcrossing). Much of what is dealt with in the remaining part of this chapter refers to outbreeding sex. However, it is important to understand that sexual reproduction can, in some cases, involve the fusion of gametes derived from closely related individuals of the same species, a process known as **inbreeding**. The significance of the distinction between inbreeding and outbreeding lies in their genetic consequences.

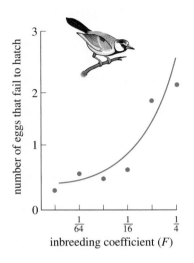

It is common knowledge that inbreeding can have genetically harmful effects. In the course of history, various families, especially royalty and aristocracy, have practised incest (mating between siblings) or frequent mating between cousins, with dire consequences. Inbreeding in humans leads to premature mortality, mental retardation, albinism and other genetic, physical and mental abnormalities in offspring. The decrease in offspring fitness as a consequence of inbreeding is known as **inbreeding depression**. In genetic terms, its explanation lies in the presence of deleterious recessive mutations in populations. Such genes are not normally expressed, because they are in the heterozygous condition. Due to their common ancestry, close relatives are more likely to carry the same deleterious gene or genes than unrelated individuals. Offspring produced by a union between two closely related individuals therefore have a high probability of inheriting two copies of a deleterious gene or genes (one copy from each parent). Deleterious recessive genes are expressed in these offspring because they are homozygous, but they are not expressed in their parents (who are heterozygous).

Figure 4.11 The effect of inbreeding on egg failure in great tits. A measure of the extent of inbreeding is given by an inbreeding coefficient, F. The higher the value of F, the higher the degree of inbreeding. As F increases, so does the number of eggs that fail to hatch. Data from Van Noordwijk and Scharloo (1981).

Long-term studies on marked populations of the great tit (*Parus major*) have shown that inbreeding depression can have strong effects on reproductive success (Figure 4.11). In song sparrows (*Zonotrichia melodia*), inbred individuals were found to be much more likely to die during population crashes than outbred individuals (Figure 4.12). Perhaps the most powerful studies of inbreeding depression have been done on flowering plants. From these studies, two general observations were made. Firstly, inbreeding effects are easier to detect when plants undergo some sort of environmental stress and secondly, they are more likely to show up later in life (Figure 4.13).

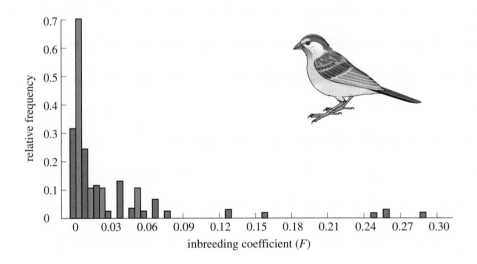

Figure 4.12 Inbred song sparrows (*Z. melodia*) are less likely to survive a population crash. Several periods of difficult environmental conditions were observed, during which many of the individuals in their population died. The red bars show the proportion (relative frequency) of birds that died with a given value of F, the blue bars the proportion that survived with a given value of F. The figure shows that 70% of the survivors had an F value of 0 (were not inbred), while only 32% of non-survivors had an F value of 0. No birds with an F value of greater than 0.05 survived. Data from Keller *et al.* (1994).

○   What can you conclude from Figure 4.13?

●   As plants get older, the disparity in flower production between outcrossed and self-pollinated plants increases, which suggests that inbreeding depression (the expression of deleterious genes) becomes more pronounced with age.

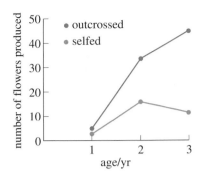

Figure 4.13 Comparison of the number of flowers produced (a measure of fitness) as a function of time for outcrossed versus self-pollinated individuals in *Lobelia cardinalis*, a perennial of the harebell family (Campanulaceae). Data from Johnson (1992).

Because of the effects of inbreeding depression, many animals and plants have evolved mechanisms that reduce its occurrence.

There are two main ways in which animals reduce the likelihood of mating with a close relative. The first is by dispersing before sexual maturity, so that close relatives are unlikely to be encountered. Male dispersal is common among mammals, whereas among birds it is more common for females to disperse. A second way is to recognize and avoid mating with close kin, which is often achieved by not mating with individuals with which an individual is reared. There is evidence, however, that for a variety of animals, including mammals, amphibians and some arthropods, kin recognition can occur without individuals having prior experience of each other.

Most plants can both self-pollinate and export pollen to the stigmas of other plants and in many such species, some self-pollination occurs. Mechanisms that decrease the incidence of self-fertilization (selfing), which is an extreme form of inbreeding, include the following:

1   **Dioecy** (pronounced 'die-ee-see'), where individual plants bear either male or female flowers, but not both.

2   In species that are **monoecious** ('mon-ee-shuss'), where male and female flowers occur on the same individual, and in those in which male and female functions occur in the same flower, the likelihood of self-fertilization may be reduced if the anthers and stigma ripen at different times or if the anthers and stigma are separated in such a way that pollen cannot reach the stigma of the flower in which it is produced.

3   Flowering plants may also prevent self-fertilization by being genetically self-incompatible: the pollen from a given flower fails to grow down the stigma of that flower or, less commonly, the embryos resulting from self-fertilization fail to develop.

Although the available evidence suggests that inbreeding does cause a reduction in fitness and that both animals and plants have evolved mechanisms to minimize its occurrence, it cannot be assumed that outbreeding is necessarily more adaptive. As mentioned already, mating with close relatives may result in deleterious combinations of alleles being expressed in offspring. However, inbreeding may also result in the conservation of advantageous combinations of alleles in the progeny, whereas outbreeding tends to break these up. This consideration has led to the idea that there may be an optimal level of outbreeding: very close relatives and totally unrelated individuals should be avoided as mates, but intermediate relatives should be preferred.

Among animals, there is some evidence for optimal outbreeding. For example, laboratory studies on the Japanese quail (*Coturnix coturnix japonica*) show that individuals prefer to associate with first cousins rather than either their siblings or unrelated birds.

In plants, inbreeding may initially result in a decline in mean fitness of the population. However, deleterious recessive alleles that have been masked in heterozygotes by dominant alleles become exposed to and eliminated by selection. In some cases, this process may result in an inbred population with a mean fitness equal to or even exceeding that of the initial outbreeding population. Factors that favour the evolution of exclusive selfing will be discussed further in Section 4.6.

SUMMARY OF SECTIONS 4.2 AND 4.3

1 Sexual reproduction has two essential features that distinguish it from asexual reproduction: meiosis and syngamy. Meiosis is the process of cell division that is intrinsic to the production of haploid gametes; syngamy is the fusion of two gametes to form a zygote.

2 In sexual reproduction, syngamy can occur between gametes derived from two different individuals that are unrelated, a process known as outbreeding, or between gametes derived from closely related individuals (inbreeding).

3 Asexual reproduction is reproduction without sex, and refers to the production by a single parent of diploid progeny that are exact genetic replicas of that parent. Wholly asexual organisms have no meiosis at all in their life cycles and reproduce by mitotically derived somatic tissues (vegetative reproduction) or mitotically derived single cells (apomixis).

4 Parthenogenesis is the development of a new individual, either male or female, from an unfertilized egg. In some parthenogenetic systems, diploid eggs are produced by one of several chromosome doubling devices.

5 Hybridogenesis has some of the features of sexual reproduction. In a diploid hybridogen, the genome derived from one parental species is transmitted to the egg without recombination, while the genome of the other parental species is discarded. The haploid egg is then fertilized by sperm of a second male of the same species, restoring the hybrid condition.

6 Gynogenetic fish result from crosses between two sexually reproducing species. The resultant hybrid female produces diploid eggs, via either premeiotic endomitosis or apomixis, and then mates with a related bisexual male. The sperm stimulates embryogenesis, but syngamy between egg and sperm does not occur and only the mother's genome is passed on to the offspring.

7 Inbreeding depression usually results from the exposure of deleterious recessive alleles to selection and both plants and animals have evolved mechanisms to reduce its occurrence.

8 In spite of the disadvantages of inbreeding depression, both plants and animals may benefit from some degree of inbreeding.

4.4   THE COSTS AND BENEFITS OF SEXUAL REPRODUCTION

By now, you will have realized that many animals and plants reproduce asexually. However, it is also true that many other organisms, including most vertebrates, insects and flowering plants must reproduce sexually or not at all. Although we are all familiar with the widespread occurrence of sexual reproduction, few of us stop to think about why it evolved in the first place. This question may seem an odd one to ask but it has puzzled evolutionary biologists for decades, because there are a number of reasons why sex should not have evolved. It is much simpler and more efficient for animals and plants to reproduce asexually. Why should two parents do the work of one? In order to understand why sexual reproduction persists in nature when a simpler alternative is available, we must identify and quantify, as far as is possible, the relative costs and benefits of sexual and asexual modes of reproduction.

4.4.1   THE COSTS OF SEXUAL REPRODUCTION

There are two main costs incurred in sexual reproduction: the cost of recombination and the cost of producing sons, which is also referred to as the cost of meiosis.

THE COST OF RECOMBINATION

The process of sexual reproduction involves the rearrangement of nuclear genomes.

○ What are the three cellular mechanisms of genome recombination?

● (i) Crossing over during meiosis, (ii) random segregation of chromosomes during meiosis and the formation of haploid gametes and (iii) the fusion of gametes during fertilization.

The effect of this 'reshuffling' is to break up genotypes and reassemble them in different arrangements, which can have two consequences. The first is that valuable combinations of particular alleles cannot be maintained by this process. The second is that deleterious combinations of alleles may arise during recombination.

One well-known case of this second effect is the human allele (Hb^S) which confers protection against malaria (Figure 4.14). Individuals that are heterozygous ($Hb^S Hb^A$), carrying one allele that confers protection and one that does not (Hb^A), are protected against malaria. However, individuals that carry two copies of the Hb^S allele (homozygous, $Hb^S Hb^S$) develop a sometimes fatal condition known as sickle-cell disease and individuals that carry no copies of the Hb^S allele (homozygous, $Hb^A Hb^A$) are susceptible to malaria. When two heterozygous individuals reproduce (sexually), one-quarter of their offspring are likely to succumb to sickle-cell disease ($Hb^S Hb^S$), one-quarter are susceptible to malaria ($Hb^A Hb^A$) and only half of them enjoy the benefits of heterozygosity ($Hb^S Hb^A$).

○ Why would it be advantageous if a heterozygous ($Hb^S Hb^A$) mother, living in an area where malaria is common, could reproduce asexually?

● Because all her offspring would be heterozygotes ($Hb^S Hb^A$) and therefore adapted to their environment.

The recombination which occurs in sexual reproduction therefore can extract a cost.

Figure 4.14 The inheritance of sickle-cell disease. Each heterozygous parent produces two types of gamete, one containing the Hb^S allele and the other carrying the Hb^A allele. When gametes combine at fertilization, three types of offspring result: half of them are protected against malaria (genotype $Hb^S Hb^A$), one-quarter are susceptible to malaria ($Hb^A Hb^A$) and one-quarter have sickle-cell disease ($Hb^S Hb^S$).

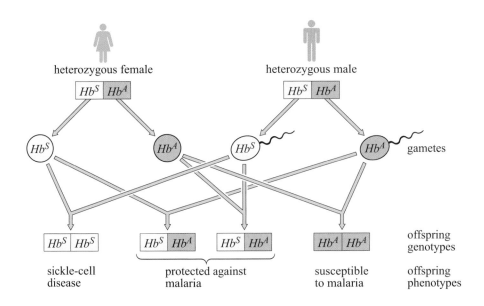

THE COST OF PRODUCING SONS/COST OF MEIOSIS

To understand why sexual females incur a cost by producing sons, we need to compare the reproduction over time, of a sexual female and an asexual female. Imagine a population founded by three individuals: a sexual female, a male and an asexual female (Figure 4.15). At this point, each individual constitutes one-third of the group. Now imagine that each female produces two offspring, after which the parents die. The sexual female produces, on average, one daughter and one son (as explained in Section 4.5.2) and the asexual female produces two daughters (since both are genetically identical to their mother and must therefore be female too). These offspring survive equally well, produce the same number of offspring themselves and their offspring have an equal chance of survival.

Figure 4.15 The cost of producing sons. F = female, M = male individuals.

Generation	Sexual reproduction		Asexual reproduction		Fraction of asexual individuals
	F M		F		$\frac{1}{3}$
1	F M		F F		$\frac{1}{2}$
2	F M		F F F F		$\frac{2}{3}$
3	F M		F F F F F F F F		$\frac{4}{5}$

From Figure 4.15 you can see that, after one generation, the sexual group consists of two individuals, one male and one female, and the asexual group consists of two females. In other words, there are four individuals in the descendent generation, of which one-quarter are males, one-quarter are sexual females and one-half are asexual females. The proportion of asexual individuals in the population has therefore risen from one-third to one-half in one generation.

○ After a further generation, how many individuals will there be in the population?

● Six: four asexual females, since each asexual mother produces two daughters, and two sexual individuals, since each sexual female produces two offspring, one female and one male.

○ What fraction of the second-generation population are asexual females?

● Two-thirds.

From these calculations, you can see that it would not be long before asexual reproduction had completely taken over. Maynard-Smith presented this argument algebraically and concluded that the clone of offspring from an asexual female would multiply at twice the rate of progeny descended from a sexual female, due to the cost to the sexual female of producing sons.

This twofold cost of sexual reproduction is sometimes referred to as the 'cost of meiosis', because the sexual female passes only 50% of her genes on to the next generation compared with the asexual female, which transmits 100% of her genes (Figure 4.16). Once again, imagine two females, one sexual and the other asexual (parthenogenetic), both of which leave two offspring. The asexual female transmits two entire copies of her genome to the next generation via her two daughters. The sexual female, on the other hand, transmits half her genome via her daughter and half her genome via her son (the other half being supplied by the father of her offspring).

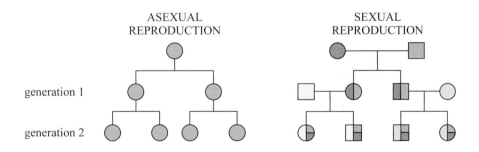

Figure 4.16 The cost of meiosis. See text for details. The circles denote females and the squares denote males.

○ How many copies of the sexual mother's genome are represented in the first generation?

● One copy (a half in each of her two offspring).

In the next generation, each of the asexual female's daughters themselves produce two daughters.

○ How many copies of their grandmother's genome are represented in the second generation?

● Four copies, one in each of the four grandchildren.

Now look again at the pedigree for the sexual female. Her daughter, carrying half of her genome, produces one daughter and one son, as does her son. In other words, she has four grandchildren.

○ How many copies of her genome are represented in the second generation?

● One copy — each grandchild has a quarter of her genome.

In one generation, the parthenogenetic female therefore replicates her genes at twice the rate of the sexual female, all else being equal. The sexual female loses out by sacrificing half her genome in meiosis, in comparison to the parthenogen, which transmits her entire genome. In addition, the sexual female produces a large egg that must contain the cytoplasm and nutrient reserves required by the zygote, because the sperm of the male contributes little of these materials. Consequently, the sexual female is providing twice as much cytoplasm and nutrients per genome copy compared to the parthenogenetic female, and suffers a 50% cost in the efficiency of genome propagation as a result. This paradox raises the important question of why a female should raise an offspring that carries only half her genes when *for the same effort* she could raise one that carries all her genes. We will come back to this topic later.

In addition to the costs described above, sexual individuals must also cope with the cost of mating itself, which is in fact a whole set of costs that are difficult to quantify. Sexually reproducing organisms invest much time and energy in securing mates and orchestrating the activity of two individuals which must cooperatively produce young. Much of the ornamentation and behaviour we observe in animals serves these functions. In general, the social interactions required for sexual reproduction cost females time, energy, a heightened probability of catching communicable disease, occasional injury by suitors and even increased predation risk as a result of the conspicuousness of attending males. For males, combat and display behaviour, as well as secondary sexual characteristics maintained by sexual selection, may constitute an additional cost.

It is not possible to sum these costs and give them a precise value, but they are clearly substantial. So, how could sex ever evolve and become predominant in a population when it incurs such heavy costs in competition with asexual reproduction, which incurs none of these costs? The only possibility is for sexual reproduction to carry considerable benefits. These benefits must not only exist, but they must be large, sometimes twofold or more, for sexual reproduction to become established and resist competition from an asexual offshoot. In the next section, we examine some of the possible benefits of sex.

4.4.2 THE BENEFITS OF SEXUAL REPRODUCTION

Although reshuffling the genome through recombination may break up valuable combinations of genes, it can also have beneficial effects.

○   How could recombination benefit an organism's evolutionary fitness?

●   Recombination produces offspring, each of which has a unique combination of its father's and its mother's genetic material. In other words, it creates variability.

The question that must now be asked is: what is so valuable about variability? After all, the maternal genotype must have done rather well to have survived to maturity and to have reproduced. Why break up a successful gene combination and incur all the costs of sex in order to gamble on novel genotypes? The answers to these questions have not yet been resolved, but several hypotheses have been suggested, which fall into two categories:

•   Sexual reproduction persists because it confers long-term benefits on *populations* or *species*.

•   Sexual reproduction is maintained because it confers short-term advantages on *individuals*.

We shall look at each of these ideas in turn.

THE LONG-TERM ADVANTAGES OF SEXUAL REPRODUCTION

R. A. Fisher was the first to suggest that the advantage of sexual reproduction lies in the capacity for sexual populations to make a rapid evolutionary response to environmental change. Figure 4.17 illustrates how this process can happen. Suppose that a sexual and an asexual population both have genes A and B at two loci. Two mutations, A' and B', arise in different individuals and are advantageous in the environment where the two populations live. The asexual population eventually consists of $A'B$ and AB' individuals, because in this population, there would be no way for an $A'B'$ individual to arise unless the B gene mutated to B' in a descendant of an $A'B$ individual or the A gene mutated to A' in a descendant of an AB' individual. If mutations are rare, production of an $A'B'$ individual may take a long time. However, in a sexually reproducing population, after A' and B' have arisen in different individuals, recombination can bring them together in the offspring of a mating between these individuals. Recombination would therefore allow favourable mutations to appear together in the same individual sooner than they would if they had to occur sequentially in a single asexual lineage. If they conferred an added advantage when they occurred together, then they would spread through the sexual population more rapidly than through the asexual one. From this reasoning, it follows that a sexual species can evolve faster than an asexual one.

Although Fisher's argument seems plausible, the rate of mutation must be fast in order for it to work. If favourable mutations occur rarely, each becomes fixed in a population (all individuals carry it) before the next one arises and so both sexual and asexual populations evolve at the same rate. New mutations always arise in individuals that already carry the previous mutation (because the previous mutation is fixed in the population and therefore appears in every member of the population). In the above example, the *B'* mutation arises in an *A'B* individual in both sexual and asexual populations. However, if favourable mutations arise frequently then Fisher's theory does work.

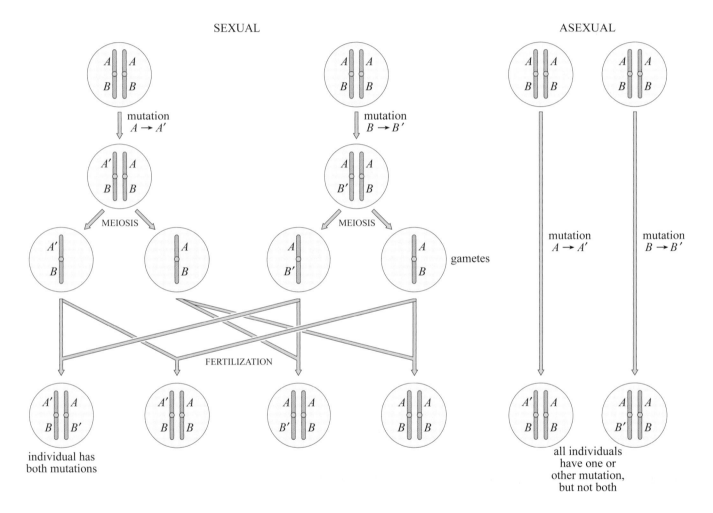

Figure 4.17 Advantages of sexual reproduction: sex accelerates the rate of evolution because favourable mutations can be brought together in the same individual much faster than in an asexual population.

Muller also pointed out that sexual populations are not only able to evolve faster but are better able to *resist* evolutionary change too. Most mutations damage fitness, and when such a mutation occurs in an asexual line, all descendent individuals are stuck with it; it is not possible for an individual free of the deleterious mutation to appear. Muller evoked the image of a ratchet wheel, clicking inexorably forward with each deleterious mutation accumulated, with no way ever to eliminate errors. At any given time, Muller envisaged a population that included individuals that carry no mutations, individuals that carry one mutation, individuals that carry two mutations, and so on (Figure 4.18a). Because the population is asexual, Muller thought of the groups as distinct sub-populations. The number of individuals in each group may be small, depending on the size of the whole population. The members of the group with zero mutations on average would enjoy the highest fitness; but if this group is small, then chance events may prevent all individuals reproducing. If this happens, the zero-mutation group dies out, and individuals of the one-mutation group now have the highest fitness (Figure 4.18b). The only way the zero-mutation group can reappear is if an individual in the one-mutation group sustains a mutation that returns the mutant allele to its original form (a back-mutation), which is an unlikely event. The one-mutation group, if it is small, may also be lost by chance in a single generation, leaving the two-mutation group as the highest-fitness individuals (Figure 4.18c). The loss of a small group by chance can occur through genetic drift (Section 3.3.2) and the loss of a group through drift is much easier than its recreation by back-mutation. As the 'ratchet' clicks away, the highest-fitness groups are lost, one by one, from the population, so that over time, the fitness of the population declines. The burden imposed by the accumulation of mutations is known as **genetic load**. When the genetic load becomes too high, the population becomes extinct.

Sex breaks the ratchet, because recombination allows sexual strains to 'edit' the genotype. In a sexual population, two individuals with deleterious mutations may produce, by recombination, an individual with no deleterious mutations.

Further research showed that the most critical parameter of Muller's ratchet was population size. In populations of less than ten individuals, genetic drift is a potent mechanism of evolution and the ratchet turns rapidly. In populations of more than 1000, drift is weak and the ratchet does not turn. Some evidence that Muller's ratchet actually operates in organisms is provided by studies on invertebrates that normally alternate between sexual and asexual generations, e.g. aphids. If the experimenter intervenes to prevent sex, repeated asexual reproduction may be accompanied by an accelerating decline in fitness in the asexual lines, apparently due to the accumulation of deleterious mutations.

○ Why is the view that sex is of value because it accelerates the rate of evolution of species or populations open to criticism?

● Because it provides no explanation of how sexual reproduction can become *established* in a population in the first place.

Because of the twofold advantage to females of reproducing parthenogenetically, whenever a parthenogen arises in a sexual population, it can replace the sexual population that gave rise to it simply by the rapid spread of parthenogenetically transmitted genes. Only in the long term do sexual forms supplant their asexual competitors because they evolve more rapidly. However, any population that reproduces sexually must resist invasion by parthenogens in the short term, and it can do so only if there is some short-term *individual advantage* to sex.

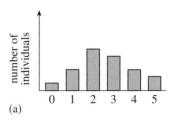

(a)

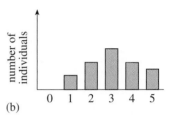

(b)

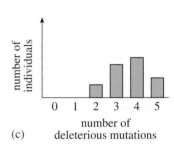

(c)

number of deleterious mutations

Figure 4.18 Muller's ratchet. Asexual populations accumulate deleterious mutations. Each of the histograms (a)–(c) shows a snapshot of a hypothetical finite asexual population. In any given generation, the class with the fewest deleterious mutations may be lost (by genetic drift).

SEX AND INDIVIDUAL ADVANTAGE

Evidence that there must be some short-term advantage to sex and that casts some doubt on the importance of rapid evolution of populations in the maintenance of sex comes from an argument put forward by Williams in 1975, which is known as 'the balance argument'. Many plants, aphids, sponges, rotifers and water fleas (*Daphnia*) can reproduce both sexually and asexually, depending on conditions. Many of these species time their sexual reproduction to periods of environmental uncertainty, and reproduce asexually when conditions are more stable, i.e. they are cyclical parthenogens. Williams' point is that when an individual such as an aphid reproduces sexually, it must be advantageous to that individual, otherwise the aphid would have reproduced asexually (since it has a 'choice'). Both sexual and asexual reproduction must have 'balanced' advantages to maintain them in the species life cycle, otherwise the inferior method would be lost. The persistence of occasional sex in these species therefore suggests that the costs of sex are met with benefits in individual fitness.

Since the balance argument was first raised by Williams, there have been several mechanisms proposed for the maintenance of sex in populations in the short term. We will consider two of these: sib-competition models, suggested by Williams, Maynard Smith and Bell, and the Red Queen hypothesis, which was put forward by Seger and Hamilton. Both hypotheses focus on the advantages associated with producing genetically variable offspring.

SIB-COMPETITION MODELS

The essential feature of sib-competition models is that individuals produce a large number of offspring which compete with one another for limited resources. One hypothesis that relies on competition between siblings is Bell's 'tangled bank model', which is based on a reference to a diverse, multi-species environment, described in Darwin's *The Origin of Species*. Darwin realized that if conditions were the same everywhere, a few species would come to dominate any habitat. Yet, when he surveyed an area of about a square metre of his own lawn, he counted over 20 different species of plant. Darwin's description of a tangled bank emphasized the fact that, within a small area, many different microhabitats exist, which differ with respect to factors such as shade, moisture, exposure to wind, suitable germination or nesting sites, availability of mates, etc. So, within each patch of habitat, there is a spectrum of resources that can be partitioned among individuals in that patch.

If the habitat is underpopulated, it may not matter just how an organism is specialized to deal with the environment. However, if the habitat is crowded, small differences among individuals in resource utilization may begin to matter. Organisms that reproduce asexually may be at a disadvantage in a crowded, heterogeneous habitat because they are superior in only one microhabitat. They produce multiple clones of themselves, each of which competes for the same resources. Under these conditions, siblings compete among themselves and the more individuals there are, the more intense this competition.

In contrast, sexual species produce offspring with different genotypes which are able to exploit small-scale differences in the environment. Because their genes differ, sexual organisms can utilize the resources available to them without competing directly with one another. This phenomenon is known as **frequency-dependent selection** because the advantage of a trait depends on how many other individuals have it. In crowded habitats, where competition is important, frequency-dependent selection leads to a situation where there is a balance between the numbers of organisms with alternative traits: if individuals with a certain rare trait have an initial advantage, the number of offspring carrying that trait increases. But as soon as they begin to compete with one another, the value of the trait drops until there is no advantage. In other words, rarer types do better than common ones (because competition is less intense) but their advantage disappears as the density of once-rare types increases.

A second model that relies on sib competition is known as the **lottery model**. Here again, the environment is considered as a series of patches, but there is heterogeneity *between* patches rather than within them. Each patch is colonized by progeny from several parents but only one individual — the one best adapted to that particular patch — survives to reproduce. Since the offspring of sexual parents have varied genotypes, the progeny from a single individual can survive on several different types of patch. Offspring from asexual parents, on the other hand, can only survive on patches similar to the parental patch. Under this hypothesis, each patch can be considered as having a single winning lottery number. A sexual parent has many different lottery tickets with different numbers (different offspring genotypes). An asexual parent, on the other hand, holds numerous tickets with the same number. The probability is therefore greater that the sexual female has the ticket with the winning number for each patch.

The sib-competition and lottery models are concerned with the advantage of sex in dealing with spatial heterogeneity and focus on the unpredictability of the physical environment. In contrast, the second hypothesis we will discuss focuses on variation in an organism's biotic environment and considers how individuals deal with heterogeneity over time.

THE RED QUEEN HYPOTHESIS

The **Red Queen hypothesis** for the maintenance of sex states that sexual reproduction enables individuals to escape from parasites. The coevolution between parasites and hosts is thought to generate environmental change at a speed that renders sex advantageous in the short term. The 'environment' for the parasite is the host's resistance mechanism; for the host, the 'environment' consists of the parasite's method of penetrating its defences.

The Red Queen hypothesis was originally formulated by Leigh Van Valen in 1973 to explain the fact that, over evolutionary time, species are continuously becoming extinct and replaced by other species. The hypothesis took its inspiration from the scene in *Through the Looking Glass* by Lewis Carroll in which Alice and the Red Queen are running as quickly as they can and yet make no progress: however fast they move, they cannot outrun their surroundings. So, for proponents of the Red Queen hypothesis, life is an evolutionary race: you must sprint as fast as you can just to keep up, never mind getting ahead. The hypothesis in effect states that because the relative importance of factors such as predation, competition and parasitism varies over time, species have to keep changing in order to 'stay in the same place'.

So, how does the Red Queen hypothesis relate to host–parasite evolution and the maintenance of sex? Most parasites are strain-specific. For example, one variety of wheat may be susceptible to one strain of rust (a fungus) but resistant to other variants of that species of parasite. Specialization of this kind is possible because many parasites have a short generation time compared to their hosts. The parasite therefore has many generations to evolve new ways to overcome the host's defences before the host reproduces. Each version of a parasite evolves specializations to overcome the defences of one set of its host alleles. Strain specificity of parasites typically results from a match between its host's surface protein and the parasite's binding protein.

To understand how parasite–host coevolution may be important in the maintenance of sex we can examine a simple genetic model where the host and parasite species are both haploid and each has two alleles (1 and 2). One parasite allele (*P1*) is adapted to penetrate hosts with the *H1* allele (e.g. it codes for a protein that binds to the host's surface protein encoded by the allele *H1*). The other parasite allele (*P2*) is adapted to penetrate hosts with the *H2* allele.

If a parasite carrying the *P1* allele is more common in a population, then the host carrying the *H2* allele (which is not affected by *P1*) is favoured and increases in frequency. The fitness of parasites with *P1* as a consequence declines, as more hosts become resistant to it. *P2* then becomes more common, resulting in a decrease in fitness of *H2* individuals (since they are susceptible to *P2*). Once *H2* individuals become rare, *H1* individuals increase in number and the fitness of *P2* declines. *P1* becomes more common and the cycle starts again. (See Figure 4.19a.) You can see that this kind of selection can generate cyclic changes in gene frequency (Figure 4.19b); as a genotype increases in frequency, its fitness decreases.

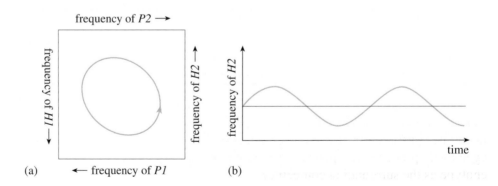

(a)   ← frequency of *P1*   (b)

Figure 4.19 (a) Relationship between the frequencies of genotypes of hosts (*H1* and *H2*) and parasites (*P1* and *P2*). Changes in the relative frequencies of each of the four genotypes over time are indicated by following the loop round. (b) Plotted against time, the frequency of each genotype oscillates cyclically; here the frequency of *H2* is plotted, starting from the point on the loop in (a) marked by an arrowhead.

So how does sex confer an advantage in these circumstances? The unique genotypes of offspring produced by sexual reproduction present novel challenges to many aspects of the environment, including diseases. In an asexual population, all individuals would be the same, so a parasite that has evolved specializations to overcome the defences of one set of host alleles can spread rapidly. For example, new pure-bred strains of barley in Britain have a useful life of only 2–3 years before parasitic fungi ruin crops. Only by producing offspring with different combinations of alleles can a parent prevent the uncontrolled spread of a specialist parasite among its progeny; in a sexual population, recombination ensures that at least some of the offspring produced are resistant to a common form of a parasite and therefore enjoy high reproductive success. The parasite must adapt continuously in order to circumvent the host's defence and the host must continuously adapt in order to resist invasion by the parasite. Sexual reproduction makes this evolutionary process possible by generating novel genotypes of both host and parasite through recombination.

○ Why is the coevolution between parasites and hosts described above, an example of frequency-dependent selection?

● Because as any gene combination becomes frequent in either the host or the parasite population, it loses its fitness advantage. A rarer genotype enjoys a reproductive advantage.

The sib-competition model and the Red Queen hypothesis can be tested by examining the predictions they make. For example, the sib-competition model states that sexual species have an advantage because genetically variable siblings have slightly different resource requirements and thus compete with each other less than the genetically uniform competing progeny of asexual species. Some direct evidence for this hypothesis came from a study by Antonovics and Ellstrand, on the sweet vernal grass, *Anthoxanthum odoratum*. They planted small 'test' cuttings of the grass and surrounded each cutting with competitors (Figure 4.20). Test cuttings were produced either sexually (by seed) or by vegetative reproduction and were surrounded by competitors that were the same genotype as the test individuals produced vegetatively (taken as vegetative shoots from the same parent plant). The test plants produced sexually were therefore 'rare' phenotypes (differing from each other and from all surrounding plants). The vegetatively produced test plants were 'common', as they all had the same genotype as the surrounding competitors.

Figure 4.20 Planting design for an experiment to test the sib-competition model. Individuals of the common genotype are shown as blue circles, and those of the rare genotype are shown red. Green boxes denote 'test' individuals. The four test individuals (two of the common and two of the rare genotype) were each surrounded by six individuals of the common genotype.

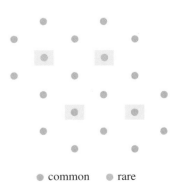

● common ● rare

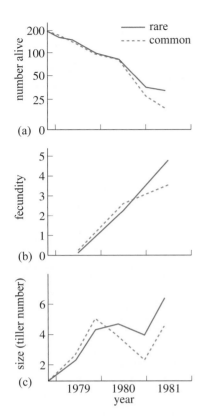

(a)

(b)

(c) 1979   1980   1981
          year

Figure 4.21 Comparison of the rare and common genotypes from the experiment illustrated in Figure 4.20. (a) Age-specific survival (number alive), (b) fecundity (number of inflorescences per surviving individual) and (c) size (expressed as number of shoots, or tillers) of rare and common individuals. Data from Antonovics and Ellstrand (1984).

○ Look at Figure 4.21. What do the data show with respect to rare and common genotypes?

● The number of plants alive, fecundity (number of inflorescences per surviving individual) and size of plants with the rare genotype were greater than for those with the common genotype at the end of the experimental period.

○ What do these results suggest?

● Individual grass plants have a higher fitness if grown in competition with grass plants of different genotypes (as would be the case if siblings were produced sexually) than with those of the same genotype (i.e. with asexually produced siblings).

○ Is this result consistent with what the sib-competition model predicts?

● Yes, the result supports the hypothesis that one evolutionary advantage of sexual reproduction is that it produces rare or unique genotypes and thereby reduces competition between siblings.

One prediction of the Red Queen hypothesis is that animals and plants that are subject to a high exposure to parasites are more likely to be sexual. In 1992, Lively investigated whether this prediction is true using the freshwater snail, *Potamopyrgus antipodarum*. This snail, which lives in lakes and streams throughout New Zealand, is the host of over a dozen species of parasitic trematode worms (Platyhelminthes). The trematodes effectively castrate their hosts by eating their gonads, which of course prevents reproduction. There is therefore strong selection for parasite resistance in the snails. Most populations of snails contain two types of females: obligate sexual females, which produce a mixture of male and female offspring, and obligate parthenogenetic females, whose daughters are clones of their mothers. The proportion of sexual to asexual female snails varies from population to population and so does the frequency of trematode infection. Lively took samples of snails from 66 lakes, determined the sex of each snail and whether it was infected by parasites. He used the frequency of males in each population as an indicator of the number of sexual females. Figure 4.22 shows his results.

○ What does the graph show?

● It shows that the frequency of males in populations of a host snail is positively correlated with the frequency of trematode parasites. In other words, males are more frequent in populations in which more snails are infected, so sexual reproduction must predominate in these more heavily parasitized populations.

Many unicellular and nearly all multicellular organisms indulge in sex. Yet why sex evolved and how it is maintained in nature remains a mystery. Among animals and plants, asexual lineages have evolved many times, but almost all

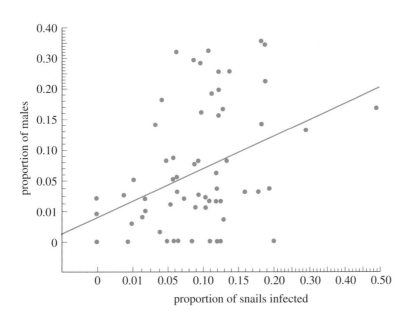

Figure 4.22 The relationship between the frequency of males in each population of host snails (*P. antipodarum*) and the proportion infected with parasites. Data from Lively (1992).

extant asexual lineages have arisen very recently, implying that asexual populations have high extinction rates. Thus, sex does appear to have a group-level advantage in the long term, but it is still not clear why asexual reproduction does not replace sexual reproduction in the short term. The hypotheses that have been discussed in this chapter are a handful of over 20 that have been proposed in an attempt to explain the evolution and maintenance of sex. They remain afloat today and inspire a great deal of research and the question of why sex exists remains an intriguing puzzle in evolutionary biology.

SUMMARY OF SECTION 4.4

1   Two costs of sexual reproduction are commonly recognized: the cost of recombination and the cost of producing sons, also referred to as the cost of meiosis. In addition, there are also the costs incurred in finding and fertilizing a mate.

2   To offset these costs, sexual reproduction must also confer benefits if it is to persist. Two types of benefits have been discussed: long-term benefits associated with more rapid evolution of species or populations, and short-term benefits to individuals.

3   Rapid evolution of species or populations in the long term may be facilitated by the more rapid fixation of combinations of advantageous mutations in sexual populations or by the reassembly, by recombination, of mutation-free genotypes (a solution to Muller's ratchet).

4   There are several theories about why sex arises and persists in the short term. They rely primarily on the advantage of sex to individuals in a changing environment. Some theories focus on changes in the organism's physical environment (sib-competition model, lottery model) whereas others focus on changes in the biological environment (Red Queen hypothesis).

4.5 THE CONSEQUENCES OF SEXUAL REPRODUCTION

The existence of sexual reproduction does not necessarily imply the existence of different sexes. In outbreeding organisms, sex is the process of shared parenthood where two individuals combine genetic material by the fusion of two haploid gametes to form a diploid zygote. Sexes, male and female, are two different types of individuals of the same species and successful reproduction requires the parental pair to include one of each. It is not entirely obvious why there are distinct males and females, because sex without sexes does in fact exist and is common among the fungi. However, in the great majority of organisms, males and females are defined by the type of gamete they produce: females produce relatively large eggs while males produce tiny sperm, a condition known as **anisogamy**. This difference in the size of the gametes has no bearing on the evolutionary basis of sexual reproduction *per se*, since the genetic consequences of sex are the same, whether or not the gametes differ in size. It is however important to understand why anisogamy evolved, because it provides the basis for many of the differences between males and females.

4.5.1 THE EVOLUTION OF ANISOGAMY

It is generally assumed that anisogamy evolved from isogamy, a condition in which there is no size difference between gametes. Imagine a multicellular organism which is able to devote some of its energy to the production of gametes. Each individual produces haploid gametes which can unite with any other gamete they encounter, since there are no males and females, simply gametes. When two gametes fuse, their nuclei, each containing their complement of chromosomes, unite to form a diploid zygote which develops into a new individual. Now imagine the process goes one step further. In order to be of genetic value, syngamy must occur between gametes derived from different parents, which means that they must be able to recognize whether or not they come from the same parent. In some fungi, members of a species can be separated into two **mating types**, arbitrarily designated + and −. A zygote can only result from a union between a + and a − type. Like cannot fuse with like, so zygotes are always the product of two different parents.

In order to sustain itself while it finds another gamete and to sustain the resulting embryo, each gamete must contain a quantity of nutrients stored in its cytoplasm and it must also possess some means of reaching a gamete with which it can fuse. There are two alternative ways in which individual gametes can achieve these requirements. One way is to decrease its size in favour of number and motility, which increases the chance of a gamete finding another gamete. The other way is to decrease number and motility and increase size, which ensures that each gamete has an adequate amount of cytoplasm to support early embryogenesis.

Since the organism has a finite amount of energy to devote to gamete production, gamete number cannot increase without a corresponding decrease in size, and vice versa. Gametes are therefore subjected to two antagonistic forces.

○ How could both size and number of gametes be maximized?

● By having two contrasting kinds of gametes; one large gamete with a substantial supply of nutrients to give the zygote a good start and a second, small motile gamete which has a better chance of finding another gamete with which to fuse.

This condition exists in most multicellular eukaryotes and is a good example of a trade-off (Chapter 1) between size and number of gametes. In animals, eggs are larger than sperm, produced in relatively small numbers and are relatively immobile. Sperm are small, produced in large numbers and are motile. In plants, the egg cells (female gametes) are large, few in number and costly, whereas pollen grains, which carry the male gametes, are small and plentiful.

Although the actual course of events leading up to the evolution of anisogamy is still much debated, dimorphism in gametes represents the basis of a diverse array of differences between males and females. In animals, this dimorphism leads to further division of labour between the sexes, incorporating parental care, competition for mates and mate choice. In flowering plants, such extreme specialization does not occur. Flowers having only male or female gametes may be produced (e.g. hazel, *Corylus avellana*, which has separate male (pollen-producing) catkins and minute female flowers), and such unisexual flowers may be borne on separate individuals. However, the majority of plants have bisexual flowers and no division of labour between the sexes.

4.5.2 THE SEX RATIO

In the great majority of sexually reproducing organisms that exist as separate sexes, sons and daughters are produced in roughly equal numbers, giving rise to a 1 : 1 sex ratio. Fisher in 1930 was the first to explain why, under natural selection, approximately equal numbers of males and females are produced. Imagine a population in which females are predisposed to producing female offspring. The result would be that males would have a better chance of mating than females, since there would be a surplus of females in the population. Therefore parents that are genetically predisposed to producing sons at this point would leave a greater than average number of grandchildren. Consequently, the genes that predispose parents to producing sons would spread in the population and male births would become more common. As the sex ratio approached 1 : 1 again, the advantage to having sons would be lost. The same argument would apply to having females: in a population with an excess of males, a female-producing genotype would be favoured. In this way, selection acts against any departure from a 1 : 1 sex ratio or, put another way, a 1 : 1 sex ratio is said to be **evolutionarily stable**, while a biased sex ratio is not.

Fisher's argument is based on an important assumption: that parents invest equally in each sex. When parents need to invest more in one sex compared to the other, we may expect a consistent difference in the numbers of males and females produced. For example, what happens if two males can be produced with the same effort it takes to produce one daughter? The parents would do better to raise sons rather than daughters, unless a daughter's reproductive prospects are as good as those of both sons put together. In this case, the sex ratio reaches equilibrium when twice as many males as females are produced. At this sex ratio, males leave, on average, half as many offspring as females, but equilibrium exists because males are only half as expensive to produce. Such considerations led to a modification of Fisher's original sex-ratio theory. The more general principle is that parents should, on average, invest equally in the production of offspring of each sex. A sex ratio of 1 : 1 is the special case of this general principle when sons and daughters are equally costly.

The chromosomal mechanism of sex determination in birds, mammals and insects (Section 4.5.3) results in sex ratios that are fixed at equality at meiosis. There is, however, increasing evidence that biased sex ratios do occur in nature, most arising as a result of non-genetic mechanisms. The extended period of pre- and post-natal parental care, for example, provides an opportunity for mammals and birds to manipulate the sex ratio by differential elimination of, or investment in, the two sexes. For example, in the common grackle (*Quiscalus quiscula*) male and female eggs are produced in roughly equal numbers but, by the time they fledge, females outnumber males by 1.6 : 1. The cause is the difference in the amount of parental care required by each sex. Males require a greater energetic investment by their parents than females in order to fledge successfully. However, parents devote equal amounts of parental care to both males and females and, as a result, there is greater mortality among males.

There is also evidence of manipulation of the sex ratio before birth in many animals, which Trivers and Willard suggested could occur if the fitness of sons and daughters varied, depending on the condition or circumstances of their mother. For example, in red deer (*Cervus elephas*) females (hinds) live in groups which are defended by a single male. Group of hinds establish a dominance hierarchy. The more dominant hinds have priority access to food, so are stronger and can better provide for their offspring. Their offspring, in turn, grow up to be stronger than average. Under these circumstances, selection favours the production of more sons by high-ranking females and more daughters by low-ranking females. High-ranking females would be expected to produce more-successful sons, low-ranking females would be expected to produce sons that fail to breed. In fact, this outcome is what is observed: the sons of dominant females have a higher reproductive success than the sons of subordinate females (Figure 4.23a). As a result, dominant females invest more in sons (have more sons) and subordinates have more daughters (Figure 4.23b), a situation called **condition-dependent sex allocation**. The physiological basis for this manipulation is unknown, but because sex is determined by the sperm and because dominant females are not selectively aborting embryos, it seems that individuals are able to discriminate against female-producing sperm before they reach the egg, perhaps by altering the chemical environment within the Fallopian tubes.

A second circumstance in which primary sex ratios would become biased is under conditions in which an individual competes against a limited part of the rest of the population. Fisher's theory assumes 'population-wide' competition for mates so that a typical male would expect to produce an average number of offspring equal to the total number of offspring produced by the population divided by the

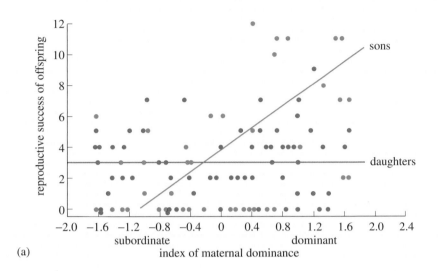

(a)

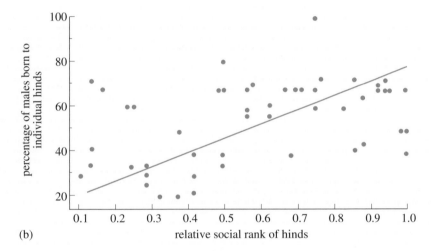

(b)

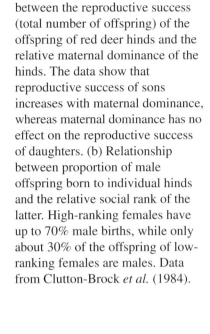

Figure 4.23 (a) Relationship between the reproductive success (total number of offspring) of the offspring of red deer hinds and the relative maternal dominance of the hinds. The data show that reproductive success of sons increases with maternal dominance, whereas maternal dominance has no effect on the reproductive success of daughters. (b) Relationship between proportion of male offspring born to individual hinds and the relative social rank of the latter. High-ranking females have up to 70% male births, while only about 30% of the offspring of low-ranking females are males. Data from Clutton-Brock *et al.* (1984).

number of males in the population. The same is true for females. In some instances, this condition does not apply and individuals only compete against a limited part of the rest of the population, a situation known as **local mate competition**, which was first proposed by Hamilton in 1967.

Certain families of viviparous mites are an extreme case of such competition. In this group, brothers inseminate their sisters while they are still inside their mother. As a result, the mother needs to produce only one or two males in a brood in order to ensure all her daughters are inseminated; the sex ratio is therefore female-biased. For instance, in the mite *Pyemotes ventricosus*, a brood contains, on average, four males and 86 females. The males don't compete against the whole population for mates; instead, they compete only against their brothers. Mothers reduce this fruitless competition by producing fewer sons.

4.5.3 SEX DETERMINATION

Given that the process of sexual reproduction in all multicellular organisms begins with the coming together of a large non-motile egg from a female and a small motile sperm from a male, the question we should now ask is: what determines the sex of an individual?

In species with separate sexes (dioecy, Section 4.3), the most widespread mechanism of sex determination is genetic; an individual's sex is determined at the time of conception by the chromosomal constitution inherited from its parents. In many mammals, birds and insects, the sex of an individual is determined by a pair of **sex chromosomes**, one of which is inherited from each parent. Sex chromosomes are inherited in the same manner as the autosomes, i.e. they segregate at meiosis so that each gamete contains only one of the pair.

In addition to genetic sex determination, dioecious species may also have **environmental sex determination** (ESD) whereby the sex of an individual can be determined as a consequence of environmental effects experienced early in life. ESD is common among reptiles and fish.

GENETIC SEX DETERMINATION

There are generally two kinds of genetic sex determination: heterogamy and haplodiploidy. **Heterogamy** is the simplest sex-determining mechanism, with a consistent genetic difference between males and females. Both sexes inherit two sex chromosomes, one from each parent, and one sex is designated XX (female) or ZZ (male) and the other XY (male) or ZW (female) (see Table 4.1). The sex that inherits two X (or Z) chromosomes is known as the homogametic sex while the sex that inherits one X (Z) chromosome and one Y (W) chromosome is known as the heterogametic sex. Heterogamy is widespread, occurring in some of the dioecious flowering plants, invertebrates such as insects, nematodes and arachnids and also in most vertebrates. Which of the sexes is heterogametic and which is homogametic appears to be random across different lineages. Both male and female heterogamy occur in some groups (e.g. the insect order Diptera, lizards and amphibians), only male heterogamy occurs in others (e.g. mammals, arachnids and nematodes) and only female heterogamy occurs in yet others (birds, snakes and the insect order Trichoptera).

The second kind of genetic sex determination, **haplodiploidy**, is found in many species of bees and wasps, mites and ticks, thrips and some beetles. In these species, females are diploid (XX) and inherit two sex chromosomes, while males are haploid, have only one sex chromosome and are designated XO. (See Section 4.2.)

One of the main areas of research into genetic sex determination revolves around the question of what actually determines whether the heterogametic sex is male or female. Researchers have gone some way towards answering this question in the fruit-fly, *Drosophila melanogaster*. Male *D. melanogaster* are normally XY and females XX, which at first suggested that the Y chromosome may have a male-determining function. However, controlled breeding experiments ruled out this

Table 4.1   Different systems of sex determination in vertebrates.

Vertebrate group	Genotypic sex determination		Temperature-dependent sex determination
	XX/XY (male heterogamy)	ZZ/ZW (female heterogamy)	
mammals	+		
birds		+	
reptiles			
crocodilians			+
turtles	+	+	+
squamates			
lizards	+	+	+
snakes		+	
amphibians			
frogs	+	+	+
salamanders	+	+	+
fish			
teleosts (bony fish)	+	+	+

possibility, because mutant flies of the genotype XXY are fertile females, while XO flies (with a single X chromosome and no Y chromosome) are male, albeit sterile. More recently, molecular studies have demonstrated that the sex of flies is determined by the ratio of the number of X chromosomes to the number of sets of autosomes. The X chromosome carries genes for femaleness and the autosomes carry genes for maleness and the sexual phenotype results from a balance between the two. A 1 : 1 ratio of number of X chromosomes to sets of autosomes is required for a female to develop, because it is this ratio that activates the gene for femaleness (*Sxl*). Any other ratio results in the development of a male because *Sxl* is inactive.

The situation is quite different in mammals. As in *Drosophila*, males are XY and females XX but, in contrast to *Drosophila*, the possession of XXY sex chromosomes leads to the development of a male phenotype (a condition in humans known as Klinefelter's syndrome) while XO individuals are female (known in humans as Turner's syndrome).

○ What does the relationship between genotype and phenotype in these disorders suggest?

● The Y chromosome plays an important role in determining maleness.

To understand how the Y chromosome fulfils this role, it is necessary to consider briefly the development of male and female characteristics in the mammalian embryo. At first, embryos appear to develop in an identical fashion, regardless of whether they are XY or XX. Even when the genital ridges (the rudiments of testes and ovaries) are first formed, they appear to be indistinguishable from one another. However, a little later on, the genital ridges of XY embryos show the first signs that they are developing into testes, not ovaries. Fetal testes produce hormones that stimulate male development. The absence of these hormones results in the development of females. These finding have led to the idea that a 'switch' operates in the genital ridge to direct its subsequent development in either the male or female direction and that the Y chromosome carries a gene that brings about this switch. This gene has been given the symbol *SRY* in humans and *Sry* in mice (sex-reversal on Y) and, when it is switched on, it initiates the release of testis-determining factor (TDF) and the subsequent development of a male. Research has shown that when *Sry* is inserted into genetically female XX early embryos of mice, it induces them to develop into males.

While the identification of *SRY/Sry* has ended the search for the 'testes-determining' gene in mammals, the mechanism does not seem to be the same in other vertebrates. In birds, reptiles and fish, the sex-switching gene appears to be present in both males and females, suggesting that the sex of individuals is determined by a different genetic mechanism. The exact nature of this mechanism is unknown. In birds, females are the heterogametic sex (ZW) while males are homogametic (ZZ), which is the converse of that found in mammals. However, the equivalent of XXY males and XO females have not been found in birds, so it is not yet known whether the W chromosome contains genes that promote female development, or whether the sex of birds is determined by the number of Z chromosomes. In reptiles, amphibians and fish, both the XX/XY and ZW/ZZ mechanisms are known to occur (Table 4.1).

4.5.4 ENVIRONMENTAL SEX DETERMINATION

Many groups of fish and reptiles lack sex chromosomes. They depend on non-genetic triggers to guide sexual differentiation. Among these species, the gender of an individual usually depends on the environment it experiences as an embryo. This kind of sex determination is known as environmental sex determination (ESD). In some cases of ESD, the determining factor is the temperature to which the embryo is exposed (temperature sex determination, TSD) while in other cases the animal's social environment determines its sex.

Temperature-dependent sex determination occurs in some lizards (but others have sex chromosomes, which can be of either the XX/XY or the ZZ/ZW type), whereas it is absent in snakes (which all have genetic sex determination of the ZZ/ZW type). Many species of tortoises and turtles have TSD while others have sex chromosomes. Among crocodiles and alligators, sex chromosomes are unknown and TSD is the rule (Table 4.1).

With TSD, hatchlings incubated at low temperatures are exclusively of one sex, while those incubated at high temperatures are of the other sex. Incubation across a narrow band of intermediate temperatures results in individuals of both sexes. Which sex develops at a particular temperature depends on the group of animals.

Figure 4.24 illustrates the four patterns of sex determination in response to temperature: in (a), females develop at low temperatures and males at high temperatures (found in certain lizards and in alligators); in (b), males develop at low temperatures and females at high temperatures (characteristic of many turtles); in (c), females develop at low and high temperatures and males at intermediate temperatures (geckos, some turtles and crocodiles); in (d), temperature has no significant effect on sexual development (some lizards and turtles and all snakes).

It is known that the temperature-sensitive period is at about the time when gonadal development occurs. In the loggerhead turtle (*Caretta caretta*), there is considerable mass difference in the urinogenital system at male-producing compared to female-producing temperatures, suggesting that TSD could affect sexual phenotype by controlling the rate of growth.

Among animals that have temperature-dependent sex determination, the sex remains fixed once it is set. However, the same is not true in species where sex determination is behaviourally controlled. In most cases, animals that have behaviour-dependent sex determination are hermaphrodites (Section 4.6). For example, in some species of fish, an individual's social environment determines whether it takes on a male or a female role, and it is sensory stimuli, rather than chromosomes, that direct sexual differentiation. How animals accomplish this gender switch is not fully understood, but current research suggests that the transformation, which under some circumstances can take only minutes, must result from signals originating in the brain. All vertebrates have neural connections between the brain and the gonads. Perhaps changes in the animal's social environment stimulate these nerves, which alter the hormonal environment within the gonads, which in turn induces a change in sexuality.

SUMMARY OF SECTION 4.5

1   Male and female sexes are defined by the difference in the size of their gametes. The prevalent theory holds that distinct sexes evolved because it is advantageous, on the one hand, to produce numerous gametes (sperm) and, on the other, to produce large gametes (eggs) because the zygote's survival is enhanced by large size.

2   The sex ratio is usually 1 : 1 because the reproductive success of all males in a population must equal the reproductive success of all females. If the population sex ratio deviates from 1 : 1, natural selection favours individuals that produce more offspring of the rarer sex.

3   Biases away from a 1 : 1 sex ratio do occur in nature, either as a result of manipulation of primary sex ratios or because of unequal investment in the two sexes in offspring that require parental care.

4   There are two major categories of sex determination: genetic and environmental. Within these categories, there are many contrasting mechanisms that differ even in quite closely related groups.

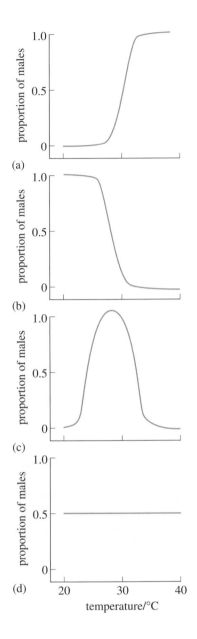

Figure 4.24 Four alternative patterns of sex determination in reptiles in response to incubation temperature.

4.6 HERMAPHRODITES AND ORGANISMS THAT CHANGE SEX

Not all animals, and very few plants, consist of separate male and female individuals. Most plants and many animals, both vertebrate and invertebrate, are **hermaphrodites.** The word hermaphrodite has its origins in Greek mythology, and refers to organisms that are capable of producing both male and female gametes. **Simultaneous hermaphrodites** possess the functional sexual organs of both sexes and can be both mother and father at the same time, as in a large number of invertebrates, including many earthworms and snails, as well as many plants. Among vertebrates, hermaphroditism is normal only among fish, which are usually **sequentially hermaphroditic**; that is, an individual functions as a female first and then a male, or vice versa.

In animals, simultaneous hermaphrodites produce both eggs and sperm, but many are unable to use their own sperm to fertilize their own eggs and instead engage in the mutual exchange of gametes, each individual passing eggs or sperm to the other. Less commonly, they are capable of self-fertilization. One of the main selective forces believed to have promoted the evolution of self-fertilization in animals is difficulty in finding a mate. Sessile animals, which cannot move about in search of mates, animals that live at low population densities and so have a low probability of finding a mate, or internal parasites, which typically live in an environment that is isolated from other members of the same species, are usually self-fertile. For such animals, the ability to fertilize one's own eggs in the absence of a mate is a great advantage.

Many plants can both self-pollinate and export pollen to the stigmas of other plants. Fisher first pointed out in 1941 that a partial selfer automatically has a strong selective advantage over an exclusive outcrosser, because it can transmit its genes in three ways: through its egg cells, through its pollen by selfing, and through its pollen as a sire of outcrossed progeny (Figure 4.25).

○ How does an exclusively outcrossing individual (such as individual B in Figure 4.25) transmit its genes?

● Through its egg cells and through outcrossed pollen.

On average, the ratio of genes transmitted by partial selfing and by outcrossing is 3 : 2, so partial selfing has a 50% advantage.

A second, frequently cited advantage of partial selfing (or full selfing) in plants is **reproductive assurance**: a plant is almost certain to produce some seeds by selfing, even if they are of low fitness. Reproduction by outcrossing, on the other hand, depends on a sufficient supply of pollinators and a high population density of the plant species. Selfing is common in plants that grow in harsh environments, where pollination frequency is low or unpredictable, and on islands, where populations are sparse for some time after colonization.

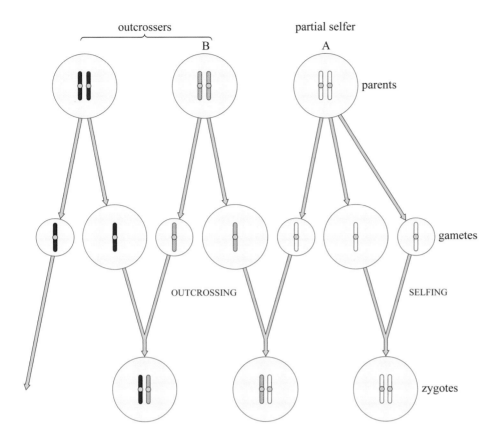

Figure 4.25 The advantage of selfing. The parent plants produce two types of gamete: pollen (small circles) and egg cells (large circles). Individual A is a self-fertile hermaphrodite; individual B is self-incompatible. In the zygote population, there are three copies of each chromosome from A (pale purple) for every two from B (mid-purple).

Given these substantial advantages to selfing, one might expect that all plants would be self-fertile. However, not all are.

○   What are the genetic disadvantages of selfing, which is an extreme form of inbreeding?

●   Offspring are usually of low fitness, due to inbreeding depression (Section 4.3). In the long term, selfing would result in the loss of the evolutionary advantages of sex.

Little is known about the incidence of self-fertilization in animals. Among gastropods (snails), members of the genera *Helix* and *Cepaea* are completely self-sterile, while *Rumina*, another land snail, typically self-fertilizes in the wild. The white-lipped land snail, *Triodopsis albolabris*, never fertilizes itself when kept in pairs, but does so after being kept in isolation for several months. However, the reproductive success of cross-fertilizing pairs is 86 times greater than self-fertilizing individuals, suggesting that for this species at least, self-fertilization incurs severe fitness costs.

Hermaphrodites that are not self-fertile may also have some advantage over dioecious (separate sexes) animals that live at low densities. *Any* two individuals that meet each other can mate, because each produces both male and female gametes. Mating in many hermaphrodites involves the mutual exchange of gametes, each individual passing sperm to its partner. Several species of coral reef fish of the family Serranidae are simultaneous hermaphrodites. In one species, the black hamlet (*Hypoplectrus nigricans*), each individual has a large ovary and a relatively minute testis. When spawning, they form pairs for a day or more and the two partners take turns to be males and females. One fish produces a batch of eggs which its partner fertilizes externally; the other fish then produces eggs which the first fish fertilizes. This alternating pattern is repeated many times until both fish have exhausted their egg supply.

○ What is the advantage of this system?

● Since each fish needs only a small testis to produce sufficient sperm to fertilize the eggs of its mate, the allocation of resources to the production of male capability is much less than in species in which sexes are separate and where allocation of resources to male and female function is equal. Furthermore, since every individual can function as *both* sexes, the species does not incur the cost of having sons. Black hamlets therefore appear to gain many of the benefits of sexual reproduction but pay few of the costs.

Several species of fish consist of individuals that are capable of producing both male and female gametes, but not at the same time (i.e. they are sequential hermaphrodites). Some begin life as males and become females later, while others change sex in the reverse direction. It seems that body size is one factor that is important in determining the direction of change, but its exact role depends on the mating system of the species. For example, in fish, large size in both females and males can be advantageous. Larger females produce more eggs than smaller individuals. Because females produce large eggs, their fecundity increases with body size. However, the same is not true for males. Since sperm are cheap to produce (in terms of energy and materials), even a very small male produces enough sperm to fertilize thousands of eggs. The advantage of being large for males depends on whether larger males can dominate smaller males and prevent them from mating. If so, only large males can realize their full reproductive potential, since small males are dominated by larger individuals and prevented from breeding. Figure 4.26 illustrates hypothetical relationships between reproductive success and body size in male and female fishes.

Both graphs (a) and (b) show that female reproductive success increases with size. For males, graph (a) shows that males only achieve a high reproductive success when large, while graph (b) shows no effect of size on reproductive success: males have an equal reproductive success regardless of size.

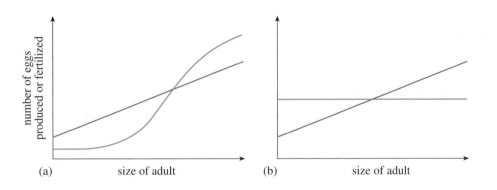

Figure 4.26 Hypothetical relationships between reproductive success (expressed as number of eggs produced or fertilized) and adult body size in females (red lines) and males (blue lines) for fishes that change sex. See text for explanation.

○   Given the hypothetical relationships illustrated in Figure 4.26, what would be the best strategy for an individual capable of changing sex?

●   If male reproductive success increases with size (graph (a)), then individuals should be female first and only become male once they reach the critical size that allows them to breed without being dominated by larger males. If there is no relationship between male size and reproductive success, i.e. there is no disadvantage to being small because males have equal mating success regardless of size (graph (b)), then individuals should be male first and become female when they are large and can produce a large number of eggs.

In plants, the reproductive success of an individual is often dependent on its size or age. Figure 4.27 plots the fitness of a hypothetical male plant and a hypothetical female plant against their respective size or age. If these curves intersect, as shown in the figure, then the best strategy for the plant is to specialize as one sex when small (young) and the other when large (older). In fact, there are a number of plant species where sex change as a function of size (or age) occurs. Whilst small (young), plants are males but when they reach a large size (older) they become female or hermaphrodites. An example of a plant that develops in this way is the jack-in-the-pulpit (*Arisaema triphyllum*), a perennial herb common in deciduous forests of the eastern USA.

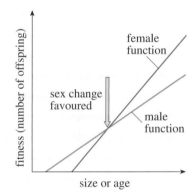

SUMMARY OF SECTION 4.6

1   There are two kinds of hermaphrodites, simultaneous and sequential. Simultaneous hermaphrodites may or may not be capable of self-fertilization.

2   Some animals and plants switch sex once during their lifetime, from male to female, or vice versa. Whether it is advantageous to begin as one sex or the other depends on how reproductive success as a male or as a female changes with an individual's size or age.

Figure 4.27 Relationship between fitness and age or size when male and female function are age- or size-dependent and favour a change in sex.

REFERENCES

Antonovics, J. and Ellstrand, N. C. (1984) Experimental studies of the evolutionary significance of sexual reproduction, I. A test of the frequency-dependent hypothesis, *Evolution*, **38**, pp. 103–115.

Bell, G. (1982) *The Masterpiece of Nature: the Evolution and Genetics of Sexuality*, Croom Helm, London.

Clutton-Brock, T. H., Albon, S. D. and Guinness, F. E. (1984) Maternal dominance, breeding success and birth sex-ratios in red deer, *Nature*, **308**, pp. 358–360.

Fisher, R. A. (1930) *The Genetical Theory of Natural Selection*, Clarendon Press, Oxford.

Hamilton (1967) Extraordinary sex ratios, *Science*, **156**, pp. 477–488.

Johnson, M. O. (1992) Effects of cross and self-fertilization on progeny fitness in *Lobelia cardinalis* and *L. siphilitica*, *Evolution*, **46**, pp. 688–702.

Keller, L., Arcese, P., Smith, J. N. M., Hochachka, W. M. and Stearns, S. C. (1994) Selection against inbred song sparrows during a natural population bottleneck, *Nature*, **37**, pp. 356–357.

Lively, C. M. (1992) Parthenogenesis in a freshwater snail: reproductive assurance versus parasite release, *Evolution*, **46**, pp. 907–913.

Maynard-Smith, J. (1978) The evolution of recombination, in *The Evolution of Sex*, R. E. Michod and B. R. Levin (eds), Sinauer Associates, pp. 106–125.

Muller, H. J. (1964) The relation of recombination to mutational advance, *Mutation Research*, **1**, pp. 2–9.

Seger, J. and Hamilton, W. D. (1988) Parasites and sex, in *The Evolution of Sex*, R. E. Michod and B. R. Levin (eds), Sinauer Associates, pp. 176–193.

Trivers, R. L. and Willard, D. E. (1973) Natural selection of parental ability to vary the sex ratio of offspring, *Science*, **179**, pp. 90–92.

Van Noordwijk, A. J. and Scharloo W. (1981) Inbreeding in an island population of the great tit, *Evolution*, **35**, pp. 674–688.

Van Valen, L. M. (1973) A new evolutionary law, *Evolutionary Theory*, **1**, pp. 1–30.

Williams, G. C. (1975) *Sex and Evolution*, Princeton University Press.

FURTHER READING

Gould, J. L. and Gould, C. G (1997) *Sexual Selection: Mate Choice and Courtship in Nature*, Scientific American Library. [A richly illustrated book that explores the evolutionary origins and consequences of sexuality in animals.]

Michod, R. E. and Levin, B. R. (1988), *The Evolution of Sex*, Sinauer Associates. [A collection of papers by experts on a wide range of different organisms.]

Williams, G. C. (1975) *Sex and Evolution*, Princeton University Press. [A general discussion of the origins and implications of sexual reproduction in the light of Darwin's theory of evolution.]

DEFENCE

5.1 INTRODUCTION

You are probably familiar with the physical defences of organisms that help to protect them against predation, but there is a lot more to defence than tough hides and sharp spines. In this chapter, we focus on the molecular and cellular defences that enable plants and animals to protect themselves, at least to some extent, from potentially damaging attacks on their bodies, by both smaller and larger organisms.

Amongst the animals, we focus on defence against infection and parasitization by smaller organisms. Striking similarities in the defence mechanisms of animals that evolved millions of years apart are shedding light on the *coevolution* of animal **hosts** and their **pathogens**. The term 'host' is applied to any organism that harbours other organisms in or on its body, irrespective of whether any harm or benefit accrues to the host. The same species can be both a host and a pathogen. In this chapter, we focus on animal host defences against pathogens, a collective term for those organisms whose proliferation in the bodies of the host is usually associated with pathological effects, such as tissue damage, obstruction, chronic inflammation, fever or toxicity.

Animals also have to defend themselves against being eaten by larger carnivorous animals. The huge diversity of physical, behavioural and molecular defences against carnivory prevents us from attempting a comprehensive review in this chapter, but we do consider a special case among the insects. Instead our main focus is on plant defences. We consider a range of plant defences against herbivores (whose strategies for eating plants were discussed in Chapter 2), which include animals as diverse as giraffes, beetles and snails.

In both the animal and plant examples the themes we emphasize are the costs of defence, trade-offs between defence and other biological functions such as reproduction, and the importance of coevolution in host–pathogen and plant–herbivore interactions. We also discuss an example of coevolution, in which herbivorous insects defend themselves against predation by utilizing chemical defences derived from the plants on which they feed. We provide a number of lines of evidence for coevolution, including comparative and experimental data. The experimental method also shows how the cost of defence can be estimated. We will consider ways in which organisms minimize the costs of defence by utilizing mechanisms that are switched on only when and where required.

In summary, the main themes of this chapter are:

1   The diversity of molecular and cellular mechanisms of defence against pathogens and herbivores.

2   The uniformity underlying the diversity of these defence systems.

3   The ability to maintain pre-formed defences and switch on additional defences, and the implications for metabolic cost.

4   The coevolution of species involved in defence and counter-defence interactions.

5   The examination of different lines of evidence in support of these themes.

5.2 ANIMAL DEFENCES AGAINST PATHOGENS

The most effective defence against pathogens would, of course, be to prevent their entry into the host in the first place. Many animals have evolved physical barriers of various kinds to protect themselves from invasion, such as a tough outer skin or shell, a thick coating of mucus and fine hairs in the respiratory tract which trap microbes, or cilia that beat and create a current which repels them (Figure 5.1). Behavioural reflexes such as coughing, sneezing and vomiting, or grooming actions, also expel pathogens from the body. But once these defences have been breached and pathogens penetrate the host's tissues, then cellular and molecular mechanisms for destroying or immobilizing pathogens become vital.

Figure 5.1 Electron micrograph of the outer surface of an epithelial cell from guinea-pig trachea (windpipe) (magnification × 10 000) showing the extensive border of cilia and even finer projections from the cell surface called microvilli. Although these structural defences are effective against a range of pathogens, the influenza virus gets into cells in the respiratory tract by attaching to the cilia and microvilli.

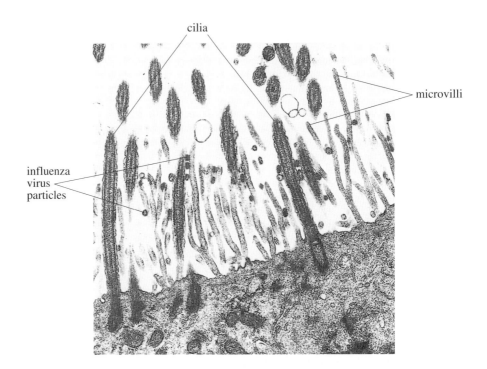

5.2.1 THE EVOLUTION OF IMMUNE SYSTEMS

A wide range of pathogenic microbes, protoctists and animals have evolved life histories in which all or part of their lives are spent within the body of a larger animal (or plant), gaining nutrients and shelter from their host. As you know from Chapter 2, species throughout the animal kingdom are hosts to a huge number of microbes, most of which do no harm, while others are directly beneficial or even essential to their host's existence. Here we are concerned only with **host–pathogen interactions** in which the host diverts energy and materials from other functions to generate defensive cells and molecules directed against pathogens that would otherwise reduce its fitness. Host species have evolved elaborate defences against the pathogens that most commonly invade them and, in turn, their pathogens have evolved counter-defences. Thus, this process of coevolution is a dynamic and ongoing interaction — a subject to which we return in Section 5.5.

The molecular and cellular defences evolved by animals against their pathogens are referred to collectively as **immune defences**. The study of extant animal species suggests a tentative relationship between the complexity of these defences and the evolutionary age of animal phyla. However, we must be cautious about this approximation because biologists cannot tell when defensive molecules and cells evolved in the past, since they are not preserved in fossils. Furthermore, evidence for the sequence in which different animal phyla diverged during millions of years of evolution is not yet conclusive. So we must base our description of these defence mechanisms on what can be found in the small fraction of present-day species that have been studied.

The simplest immune defences have been found in invertebrate phyla characterized by simple body plans, such as the Porifera (sponges, Figure 5.2a, overleaf), Cnidaria (e.g. jellyfish, Figure 5.2b) and the Platyhelminthes (e.g. flukes, Figure 5.2c), which are generally agreed to be among the most ancient of the animals. More complex immune defences are found in invertebrates with more elaborate body plans, which seem to be of more recent evolutionary origin, such as the Echinodermata (e.g. starfish, sea urchins, Figure 5.2d), Mollusca (e.g. snails, mussels, limpets, Figure 5.2e), Annelida (e.g. earthworms, leeches, Figure 5.2f) and Arthropoda (e.g. insects, crustaceans, spiders, Figure 5.2g). The invertebrate immune defences that have been most investigated are those of groups such as snails and insects that destroy crops or transmit pathogens to humans. Although relatively few species in each of the invertebrate phyla have been studied extensively, striking similarities in their defence mechanisms have been identified and will be described under *innate immunity* (Sections 5.2.2–5.2.5).

A significant shift in the complexity of immune defences appears to have come about as vertebrate (phylum Chordata) animals evolved. The innate defence mechanisms resembling those of the most complex invertebrates were retained, but some additional defence mechanisms not found in invertebrates evolved. These 'extra' immune defences can be detected today in the jawless vertebrates (e.g. lampreys and hagfish; class Agnatha), whose ancestors may have been among the first animals to evolve backbones. This additional layer of defence mechanisms is referred to as *adaptive immunity* and is described in Section 5.4.

The range of mechanisms encompassed by adaptive immunity is even more extensive and diverse in the jawed vertebrate classes, such as the Amphibia (e.g. frogs, newts and toads) and the Aves (birds), and is particularly complex in the Mammalia. Among the vertebrates, most is known about the immune defences of humans, laboratory rodents, domestic mammals, and birds such as chickens, although one amphibian (the clawed frog, *Xenopus laevis*, Section 5.4.4) has also been extensively studied, as have various species of commercially important fish. As with innate immunity, there are strong similarities in the adaptive immune defences of widely divergent animals, which may be evidence of common evolutionary pathways or convergent evolution.

Figure 5.2 (a) Venus flower basket (phylum Porifera); (b) jellyfish (*Aurelia aurita,* phylum Cnidaria); (c) fluke (phylum Platyhelminthes); (d) sea urchin (phylum Echinodermata); (e) limpet (*Patella* sp., phylum Mollusca); (f) medicinal leech (*Hirudo medicinalis,* phylum Annelida); (g) black widow spider (*Latrodectus* sp., phylum Arthropoda).

Vertebrate defence mechanisms present such a complex and coordinated array of interacting cells and molecules that they are referred to as the vertebrate **immune system**. However, it is very important to emphasize that the greater simplicity of the immune defences found in invertebrates does not mean that they are less effective. Invertebrates account for over 90% of the animal species on earth. The earliest evolved about 800 million years ago and they have shared their habitats with bacteria for the whole of their evolutionary history. Indeed, many of them fed on detritus and bacteria. The success of invertebrates at evading destruction by pathogens testifies to the effectiveness of their ancient immune defences, which form the foundation of the more complex vertebrate immune systems (Beck and Habicht, 1996).

Before studying the major features of animal defences against pathogens, it is worth considering the selection pressures underlying their increasing complexity over evolutionary time. The increasing size and complexity of vertebrates is one factor. The requirement to transport nutrients and oxygen around a larger body mass led to the evolution of a fast-flowing circulatory system, which spread pathogens around the body. Another factor is that animals colonized a greater range of habitats, particularly in the transition from sea to land.

○   How might the exploitation of new habitats and the evolution of the capacity to ingest large prey have selected hosts with more complex defences against pathogens?

●   As Chapter 2 made clear, an increase in the diversity of food sources also increases the risk of ingesting a more diverse range of pathogens, particularly for carnivorous species whose prey may already be infected.

Furthermore, the evolution of *endothermy* — the ability of mammals and birds to raise their body temperature above ambient temperature — presented pathogens with warm bodies in which they could proliferate faster. As longevity increased, animals had to defend themselves against pathogens for years (a point discussed further in Chapter 6), so the evolution of more elaborate immune defences was favoured. In turn, pathogens evolved more sophisticated counter-defences which enabled them to survive attacks from increasingly complex immune systems. The interaction has promoted the evolution of increasingly diverse pathogen species, ranging from the smallest viruses to huge parasitic animals such as tapeworms 10 m long.

This way of looking at evolution might suggest that pathogens simply adapted to exploit gradual changes in animal structures and life histories, but you should keep in mind that pathogens have also been a powerful driving force for evolutionary change in their hosts. For example, the evolution of viruses may have increased the selection pressure for adaptive immunity on vertebrates, since the mechanisms of innate immunity are primarily directed towards detecting and attacking bacteria, protoctists and fungi.

5.2.2 Innate immunity

Innate means 'inborn' in the sense that innate responses do not have to be learnt by experience, but are an intrinsic feature of the organism. **Innate immunity** (or natural immunity in some textbooks) is the collective term given to a range of molecules and cells which are the first line of defence against pathogens in the host's body. They exist *before* pathogens are ever encountered — hence the term 'innate' immunity — and are found in some form throughout the Animal Kingdom. Indeed, they are the only mechanisms available to invertebrates to attack their internal pathogens. Innate defences are primarily triggered by and directed against unusual sugars and other small carbohydrates, usually associated with proteins, which commonly occur on the outer surface of pathogens, particularly bacteria and fungi (Fearon, 1997).

Many of the genes that contain the coded instructions for these innate defence mechanisms are highly **conserved,** a term which indicates that these genes (or their protein products) have been detected with similar sequence structures in many different animal phyla, and a few have even been found in certain bacteria, protoctists, fungi and plants. There is evidence for three different processes which may account for the extent of conservation among genes involved in the innate defence against pathogens. We can summarize them briefly as follows: (i) some of the genes appeared early in evolution and were retained virtually unaltered as species diverged; (ii) others represent examples of *convergent* evolution, in which random mutations in different phyla and subsequent natural selection independently produced similar genes; and (iii) some conserved genes may even have originated in viruses and were incorporated into the DNA of different phyla during viral infections. The ubiquity of these genes testifies to their effectiveness in generating protective innate immunity.

A characteristic feature of innate immunity is that the defensive response against a particular pathogen is about the same intensity no matter how many times that species or strain of pathogen has invaded the host in the past. Innate immunity does *not* adapt to repeated exposure to the same pathogens. (As you will see in Section 5.4, this property is in sharp contrast to the additional defence mechanisms evolved by vertebrates, which *do* adapt to the pathogens encountered within the lifetime of the host.)

As you study the more detailed descriptions of innate defences that follow, consider the substantial cost they impose on the host in energy and material resources. However, this cost is outweighed by the survival advantage from effective defences against potentially lethal pathogens. A form of 'trade-off' is being made every time an immune response takes place (a point we return to in Section 5.5).

5.2.3 Innate molecular defences

Innate defences based on molecules circulating in the host's body can be grouped into three functional categories: those involved in (i) wound closure; (ii) **agglutination**, i.e. sticking pathogens together in clumps; and (iii) **cytotoxicity**, literally 'cell poisoning', but the term refers to any mechanism that causes structural or metabolic damage to pathogens.

Wound closure is of obvious importance in preventing loss of body fluids and the entry of more pathogens. Species from invertebrate phyla as diverse as the Arthropoda, Annelida and Echinodermata have all been found to contain specialized cells that congregate in wounds and produce chemical **coagulants**, which cause body fluids to gel and plug the wound. These invertebrate coagulants perform a similar function to the clotting factors in vertebrate blood plasma, but they can seal wounds even more rapidly.

All animals studied to date also produce **agglutinins**, a functional term for a variety of molecules capable of binding pathogens together in clumps by forming cross-links between short-chain carbohydrates in the pathogens' surface. Among the most important and ubiquitous of the agglutinins are the lectins, examples of which can be found in bacteria, protoctists, every animal phylum and many plants.

○ What benefit might be derived by the host from the ability to agglutinate pathogens quickly once they have entered the body?

● Sticking pathogens together impedes their dispersal around the body and immobilizes them close to the entry site. It also makes it more difficult for them to take up nutrients by diffusion and stops them moving about to feed. A mass of trapped pathogens is also a concentrated source of chemical signals, which trigger other defensive mechanisms in the area.

Cytotoxic molecules are capable of puncturing some bacteria and the cells of animal pathogens, thereby inflicting potentially fatal structural damage. Among the most widely distributed of the cytotoxic molecules in both invertebrates and vertebrates is **lysozyme**, an enzyme that splits the bonds between unique sugar- and protein-containing molecules (peptidoglycans) found only in bacterial cell walls. Further evidence that similar cytotoxic defences are widespread in animals has come from the isolation of small cytotoxic molecules known collectively as **antimicrobial peptides** (they are all chains of less than 100 amino acids). These peptides have been shown to damage a wide range of bacteria, fungi and protoctist parasites in their hosts, although the majority are antibacterial. Among the most widespread are the cecropins, originally isolated from the moth *Hyalophora cecropia*, but since detected in many other animals including pigs. A cecropin-like molecule, which may have a role in defence against competing bacteria, has also been isolated from the bacterium *Helicobacter pylori*. Other antimicrobial peptides include magainins found in amphibian skin and gut ('magainin' is derived from the Hebrew for 'shield'), and defensins isolated from certain insects, molluscs, snakes, birds and mammals. Plant defensins with antifungal activity have also been identified.

Pharmaceutical companies are devoting large research budgets to deriving new drugs from these and other naturally occurring antimicrobial molecules (e.g. squalamine found in sharks), and to isolating equivalents in vertebrates that could be produced in commercially viable quantities (Ganz and Lehrer, 1999). This research is driven partly by the alarming rise in bacterial resistance to long-established and widely used antibiotics such as penicillin (derived from a fungus), which have been over-used in treating bacterial infections in humans, and partly by the need for new antiviral drugs, for example to combat HIV, the virus that leads to AIDS.

Some of the coagulating, agglutinating and cytotoxic molecules involved in innate immunity circulate in their active form at approximately constant concentrations throughout the animal's body fluids (i.e. they are *systemic*, widespread). Defence mechanisms with these characteristics are referred to as **constitutive defences** (from the Latin *constituere*, 'to assemble, already put in place'). For example, lysozyme in mammals is found in extracellular fluid throughout the body and in secretions such as sweat, tears and saliva. Some of the molecules involved in constitutive defences can also arise locally in tissues where pathogens are proliferating. An **induced defence** may take some hours to reach its maximum level, since the synthesis of new effector molecules is stimulated by the presence of pathogens.

○ Induced defences that require increased synthesis of defensive molecules take longer to exert their effect on newly invading pathogens than do constitutive defences. Why might it be advantageous to have both?

● There must be an energy and material cost to the host associated with generating defence mechanisms, particularly in the absence of an infection. This process diverts resources from other functions and potentially reduces fitness. The optimum survival strategy may be to have some constitutive defences always 'at the ready', and reinforce them by induced defences only when and where pathogen invasion actually occurs.

However, an extremely rapid induced defence can be achieved by **cascade reactions**, in which a series of pre-formed but inactive molecules are activated in sequence — a process that takes just seconds. The first-stage molecules in the cascade are activated either by contact with pathogens, or by the changes in calcium ion concentration and pH that follow tissue damage, or by triggering molecules produced by cells involved in immune defences. Once a few of the first-stage molecules are activated, they in turn activate many more of the precursors of the second-stage molecules, which in turn activate still more third-stage molecules and so on (Figure 5.3). Some of these intermediate molecules, as well as the cascade end-product, have defensive functions. Local activation ensures that the end-products are formed close to pathogens or sites of tissue damage.

○ What are the principal advantages of induced defences based on cascade reactions?

● Cascades build up very rapidly since all the precursors for all the intermediates are pre-formed in the circulation. Once triggered, the number of molecules recruited into the cascade at each stage increases, amplifying the response. When the pathogens have been destroyed, the first-stage molecules are no longer activated and the cascade reaction stops.

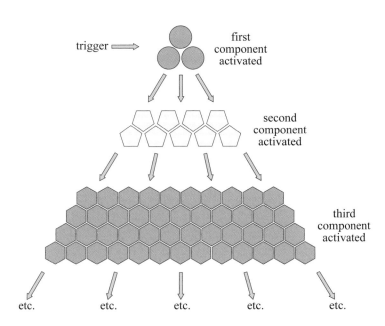

Figure 5.3 Schematic diagram of the first few stages in a cascade reaction.

A cascade reaction found in several invertebrate taxa, including the Arthropoda, Annelida and the tunicates (subphylum Urochordata, phylum Chordata), is the **PpO cascade**. The last step in the sequence is the conversion of prophenoloxidase (PpO) to phenoloxidase, an enzyme that inflicts structural damage on microbial pathogens. The PpO cascade bears a striking similarity to the **complement cascade**, the main defensive cascade reaction of innate immunity in vertebrates. Intermediate molecules formed in both these cascades attract phagocytes and agglutinate pathogens. The final molecule in the complement cascade is a cylindrical protein called the *membrane attack complex*, which is inserted in the membrane of target cells, creating a pore (Figure 5.4). It can also breach bacterial surfaces, allowing access for other defensive mechanisms.

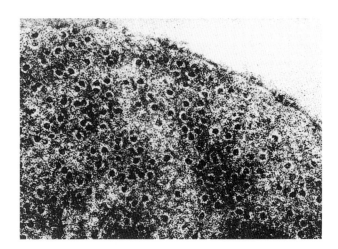

Figure 5.4 Holes punched through the surface of the bacterium *Escherichia coli* by membrane attack complexes, the end-product of the complement cascade (magnification × 300 000).

○ What happens to a cell that has been punctured many times?

● Cytosol is more concentrated than extracellular fluid, so initially the punctured cell swells up and bursts as fluids rush in through the pores from the more dilute surroundings. The cell dies as its metabolic processes are disrupted and its contents leak out.

Another example of a rapidly induced antibacterial peptide is 'hidden' in the structure of a molecule found in the nervous system of a wide range of vertebrates and some invertebrates. Proenkephalin is a precursor molecule, which can be cleaved into several active fragments inside nerve cells. One fragment, a peptide called enkelytin, damages the cell walls of bacteria, raising the fascinating possibility that nerve cells can generate their own 'antibiotics' locally in response to bacterial infection. The sequence of amino acids in enkelytin has been determined in leeches, mussels and laboratory rodents (from the phyla Annelida, Mollusca and Chordata, respectively) and it seems to be highly conserved — 98% of the sequence is identical in the species studied (Stefano *et al.*, 1998).

5.2.4 INNATE CELLULAR DEFENCES

Bacteria, protoctists, fungi and plants rely on molecular defences to protect themselves from pathogens, but animals have evolved specialized defensive cells in addition to their defensive molecules. The key to innate (and indeed adaptive) immunity in animals lies in the evolution of a family of cells which, in many invertebrates and all vertebrates, are called **leukocytes**. Cells with functional similarities to leukocytes can also be found in the simplest invertebrates.

Leukocytes are the source of many (though not all) of the defensive molecules described in the previous section. They are often referred to as white blood cells, which could imply (incorrectly) that they are only found in the bloodstream. Although several types of leukocytes do spend part of their lives circulating in blood, they occupy a much wider territory in the body. Some leukocytes are motile and can 'burrow' between cells, penetrating deep into the host's tissues. They are found in the greatest concentrations where tissues are in contact with the external environment, for example in the gut lining (as already described in Chapter 2) and in the respiratory, urinary and reproductive tracts, and they congregate in areas of infection or parasite infestation.

In vertebrates, solid masses of leukocytes are found in membrane-bound structures such as the spleen and thymus gland in many vertebrate classes, Peyer's patches in the mammalian gut wall, the Bursa of Fabricius in birds, and lymph nodes throughout the mammalian body (Figure 5.5). Leukocytes also circulate in the lymphatic system, a branching network of capillaries as extensive as the vascular system. Some invertebrates also have organized structures containing leukocytes, as well as freely-circulating populations of defensive cells.

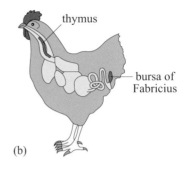

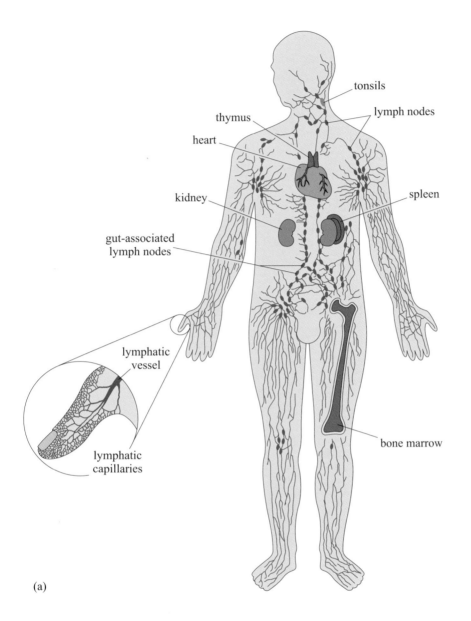

(a)

Figure 5.5 (a) Diagram of the human lymphatic system. (b) Chicken lymphatic system, showing the Bursa of Fabricius, an organ packed with leukocytes in the cloaca, the common exit of the intestinal and reproductive system in birds.

Following contact with pathogens, and in the presence of the correct activating signals and adequate nutrients, leukocytes flood into an infected area and are induced to proliferate locally by cell division. Leukocytes can be distinguished into several functional groups. By far the most important in innate immunity are the **phagocytes**, i.e. leukocytes capable of phagocytosis (Figure 5.6, overleaf). Phagocytes occur in all animals, including the sponges, whose ancestors may have been among the earliest animals to evolve. Most sponges, like some protoctists, such as *Amoeba*, feed by a process identical to phagocytosis and phagocytes ingest and kill single-celled pathogens in the same way.

nucleus

bacteria

(a)　　　　　　　　　　(b)　　　　　　　　　　(c)

Figure 5.6 Phagocytosis is central to innate immune defences in animals. (a) Electron micrograph of a phagocyte from a tunicate, the sea squirt *Ciona intestinalis*, containing three bacteria (magnification ×850). (b) Electron micrograph of a human phagocyte engulfing a *Leishmania* sp. parasite (shown in mauve) (magnification ×1300). (c) Phagocyte membrane engulfing a red blood cell from another species (magnification ×10000).

○ How is the pathogen transported into the phagocyte?

● The outer membrane of the phagocyte flows around the pathogen and gradually encircles it, drawing it into the cell wrapped in a vesicle (bag) of membrane and cytosol.

The ability of phagocytes to engulf their targets is greatly enhanced if the pathogen is coated with molecules to which the phagocyte membrane can bind. Agglutinins such as the lectins are one category of molecules that help phagocytes to 'get a grip' on their targets. Once inside the phagocyte, membrane-bound organelles called **lysosomes** fuse with the vesicle and discharge their contents. Lysosomes contain a range of molecules that generate a so-called **respiratory burst** when the lysosome empties into the vesicle surrounding the pathogen. Oxidizing chemicals, including superoxide and hydrogen peroxide (the active constituent of some kinds of bleach), together with the potentially toxic messenger molecule nitric oxide (NO), attack the surface of the pathogen, destroying its cell membrane. Lysosomal enzymes then break down pathogens into their constituent molecules, some of which may be utilized by the cell.

Some pathogens are too large for a phagocyte to engulf and others 'hide' inside the host's own cells, but even in this location, they are vulnerable to a range of defence mechanisms collectively called **cell-mediated cytotoxicity**. The term signifies that all these mechanisms require direct cell-to-cell contact between leukocytes and pathogens or the host's own cells if they are harbouring pathogens inside. Cell-mediated cytotoxicity also utilizes a respiratory burst, generated by leukocytes when they are in close contact with a pathogen or an infected host cell. The contents of lysosomes, other toxic molecules held in granules within certain leukocytes, and hydrolytic enzymes are secreted onto the target cell's surface. Some vertebrates, including the mammals, also have leukocytes that can synthesize a protein (perforin) whose cylindrical tertiary structure forms an open pore in the target cell's outer membrane, in much the same way as already described for membrane attack complex, the end-product of the complement cascade.

If larger bacteria, protoctists and animals enter the body, they may be surrounded by thousands of the host's leukocytes, forming a capsule of defensive cells (Figure 5.7). The contents of lysosomes, together with other toxic molecules, are transported to the leukocytes' surface and emptied into the capsule where they inflict structural damage on the pathogen. Even if it is not killed, encapsulation may ensure that it cannot reproduce or disperse to other sites.

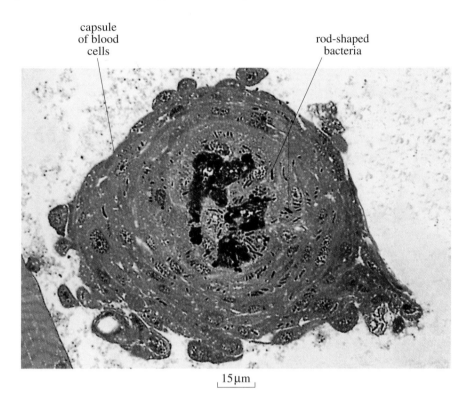

Figure 5.7 Encapsulation of bacteria by leukocytes in the blood of a caterpillar of the cabbage white butterfly *Pieris brassicae*.

Leukocytes are also involved in regulating and directing immune responses through the synthesis and release of **cytokines**, the collective term for short-range signalling molecules involved in coordinating and promoting immune defences. Two important groups of cytokines — the tumour necrosis factors (TNFs) and the interleukins — have been found in many groups of animals. TNFs were originally detected in the inflammation around tumours in mammals (hence the name), but they have since been found in areas of infection in many vertebrates and TNF-like molecules have been detected in some invertebrates. TNFs enhance phagocytosis, attract leukocytes into an infection site and contribute to cell-mediated cytotoxicity. In mammals, at least one TNF and several interleukins are also involved in mobilizing energy supplies from adipose tissue to fuel the immune response. The interleukins are even more widespread and have been detected in protoctists, representatives of all invertebrate phyla tested and all classes of vertebrates studied to date. They are primarily involved in stimulating leukocyte proliferation and activation.

5.2.5 PATHOGEN RECOGNITION AND SELF/NON-SELF DISCRIMINATION

The mechanisms of innate immunity are particularly effective against bacteria, the most ancient kinds of pathogens on earth. What is it about bacteria and other pathogens that betrays their presence in the host's body and elicits an innate immune response? How do leukocytes reliably identify their targets against a background of the host's own cells and molecules? The key to this crucial recognition event is sugar! The cells and molecules of innate immunity detect the presence of unusual sugar-like molecules not present in animal tissues, or unique short-chain carbohydrates or combinations of sugar molecules with proteins or lipids (glycoproteins and glycolipids), which commonly occur only in the structures of bacteria, fungi and some other pathogens. For convenience we will refer to these 'signature' molecules as **pathogen carbohydrates**. Cells and molecules involved in innate defences have evolved receptors or binding sites that fit these pathogen carbohydrates.

○ Which pathogen 'signature' molecule was mentioned earlier in this chapter and what is the innate response to it?

● Peptidoglycan, which occurs only in bacteria. The bonds between adjacent molecules of peptidoglycan are cleaved by the enzyme lysozyme.

Another example is lipopolysaccharide (LPS), a component of all Gram-negative bacterial cell walls.

Both the PpO and complement cascades are triggered by carbohydrates unique to the outer layers of pathogens, and they are also powerful activators of phagocytes.

There are no more than a few tens of unique pathogen carbohydrates, but they are very common in the surface structures of pathogens. Their ubiquity enables the cells and molecules of innate immunity to focus a relatively narrow range of defensive mechanisms against a wide variety of different pathogens, all of which display similar 'signature' molecules in their structures. Innate immunity is often described as 'non-specific' because a broad-spectrum attack is mounted indiscriminately against any cell that displays pathogen carbohydrates. Not surprisingly, leukocytes have receptors for these molecules which are also highly conserved. For example, the leukocytes of most vertebrates have receptors that bind to LPS, and so do the leukocytes of at least one invertebrate, the horseshoe crab (*Limulus polyphemus*).

Selection pressure has also ensured that the host genes involved in innate immunity do not usually encode receptors that bind to the molecules of the animal's *own* body. Except in certain disease states, the mechanisms of innate immunity are blind to 'self' because they lack receptors that can bind to the host's molecules.

○ Under what circumstances would destruction of the host's own cells contribute to defence against pathogens?

● When pathogens are replicating inside the host's cells, as is the case with all viruses. (Some very small bacteria, e.g. the mycobacteria that cause tuberculosis or leprosy, and the protoctist malarial parasite, *Plasmodium*, have adapted to life inside host cells.)

However, intracellular pathogens betray their presence when their unique molecules appear on the surface of the host cell. Many viruses 'bud' new virus particles from their host cell's surface (Figure 5.8) and digested fragments of pathogen are transported to the surface of phagocytes for expulsion.

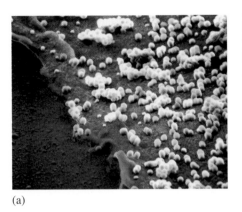
(a)

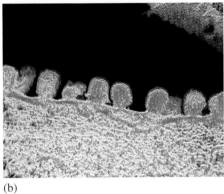
(b)

Figure 5.8 Influenza virus particles 'bud' from the surface of a human lung epithelial cell in which the virus is replicating. (a) Scanning electron micrograph, magnification approximately $\times 11\,600$; (b) Transmission electron micrograph, magnification approximately $\times 50\,000$.

Specialized leukocytes have evolved the ability to recognize and destroy 'infected-self' cells, using all of the innate mechanisms of cell-mediated cytotoxicity described earlier. In vertebrates, these leukocytes are given the dramatic title **natural killer cells** (or NK cells for short), but there are equivalents in some invertebrates. NK cells may also have a role in destroying host cells that have transformed into malignant tumours. They are part of innate immunity because they circulate in the body throughout life in more-or-less constant numbers and they do not become more effective killers after contact with pathogens. In addition, a TNF binds to and destroys infected host cells. Leukocytes also synthesize **interferon**, a local defence in an area of virus infection. This protein 'interferes' with the ability of viral genes to use their host cell's mechanisms for protein synthesis, thereby preventing the construction of new virus particles in infected cells and their release and spread to neighbours.

Innate immunity has another feature arising from the ability to distinguish self from non-self. It has long been known that sedentary or sessile invertebrates such as sponges, corals and sea squirts have an innate ability to use immune defences to destroy the cells of other individuals of their own species if they grow too close to each other. This property has been demonstrated experimentally, e.g. by binding clumps of two genetically different sponges together (Figure 5.9), and is termed **graft rejection**. Adjacent sponges attack each other's cells where they are touching, using immune defence mechanisms as though defending against invading pathogens.

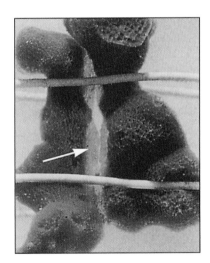

Figure 5.9 The pale orange area of damage caused by graft rejection is clearly visible where two segments of sponge from the same *Callyspongia* species, but from different colonies, have been held in contact with plastic-coated wire.

○ What selection pressures might have led to the evolution of graft rejection in sessile animals?

● When suitable habitats are scarce, it would be advantageous for each animal to defend its 'territory' by rejecting the cells of other individuals who might crowd it out.

Most free-living invertebrates and all vertebrates also display graft rejection when a graft from another genetically distinct individual of their own species is experimentally introduced. Since there is no apparent selection pressure to explain why free-living animals might have evolved this ability, it has been speculated that graft rejection is a vestige of their distant ancestry as sessile animals.

Graft rejection demonstrates an important feature of animal cell membranes — they too, like the pathogens, must display 'signature' molecules which are unique to each genetically distinct individual, even within the same species. These 'self-signature' molecules are unique proteins that have been given the collective title **histocompatibility antigens** ('histo' means 'tissue' and 'antigens' is a term given to any molecule that elicits an immune response). The study of histocompatibility antigens on the surface of human cells was given huge impetus in the 1960s when the first human heart transplants ended in graft rejection. Differences between the histocompatibility antigens of the grafted heart and the recipient's body triggered a massive immune response against the donated tissue. Among humans, only identical twins have identical histocompatibility antigens, and so accept grafts from each other. Each individual is **self-tolerant**, i.e. immune defences are not triggered by the presence of the organism's own histocompatibility antigens.

The success of modern transplant surgery relies partly on finding donor organs from individuals whose histocompatibility antigens differ as little as possible from those of the graft recipient, and partly on suppressing the recipient's immune response with drugs. Graft rejection in vertebrates is far more rapid than its equivalent in the invertebrates because the additional layer of defence mechanisms known as adaptive immunity (described in Section 5.4) also attacks the graft. Graft rejection tells us something else about the surface of leukocytes: they must — in addition to the receptors that bind to pathogen carbohydrates — also have receptors that recognize the histocompatibility antigens of the host and of other individuals from the host's species.

The central role of leukocytes in innate immunity is now clear: they are capable of self/non-self recognition, they detect unique pathogen carbohydrates, they destroy infected host cells and invading pathogens by phagocytosis and cell-mediated cytotoxicity, and they synthesize and release key molecules in the innate defence against pathogens. These molecules include cytokines which attract and activate more leukocytes to join an immune response, and many of the coagulants, agglutinins, interferons, cascade molecules and antimicrobial peptides described earlier.

Summary of Section 5.2

1   Host species throughout the animal kingdom have evolved complex arrays of defences against pathogens, which include physical barriers, reflexes such as coughing and behaviours such as grooming. If these barriers are breached, then the first (and in invertebrates, the only) defence against pathogens is the molecular and cellular mechanisms known as innate immunity.

2   Innate immune defences pre-exist in the host animal *before* it comes into contact with pathogens for the first time; constitutive defences are permanently activated whereas induced defences increase locally or exist in a precursor form and are activated by the presence of pathogens.

3   Molecular defences include wound closure and coagulation, agglutination of pathogens, antimicrobial peptides and enzymes, oxidizing chemicals and other toxic molecules, pore-forming proteins that puncture cell membranes, and molecules that interfere with pathogen replication. Some of these molecules are generated in induced cascade reactions.

4   Cellular defences involve different types of leukocytes: some destroy pathogens by phagocytosis, others engage in cell-mediated cytotoxicity, and collectively they synthesize and secrete many of the molecular defences listed above.

5   Many of the genes for molecules involved in innate immunity are highly conserved between widely divergent animal phyla, which may indicate a common origin in shared ancestors.

6   Innate immunity relies on broad-spectrum defensive mechanisms, which are targeted against unique pathogen carbohydrates commonly found in the surface structures of pathogens. Innate immune mechanisms are non-specifically effective against all pathogens that contain these molecules.

7   The effectiveness of the innate immune response to invasion by a particular pathogen is more-or-less constant, no matter how many times the same pathogen is encountered (i.e. it does *not* adapt during an exposure).

8   Innate defences are self-tolerant and are not directed against the host's own cells unless they betray the presence of intracellular pathogens. Unique histocompatibility antigens on host cells are recognized as 'non-self' if grafted into another member of the same species, provoking graft rejection.

5.3 PLANT DEFENCES AGAINST HERBIVORES AND PATHOGENS

5.3.1 EVOLUTIONARY OVERVIEW OF INSECT–PLANT INTERACTIONS

Figure 5.10 Bramble leaf mining by moth larvae of the golden pygmy moth (*Nepticula aurella*).

In this section, the attention switches from animal to plant defences, in particular the chemical defences of plants against herbivores. Before immersing ourselves in the details of plant defences, it is worth considering the extent and longevity of the interactions between plants and one of their major groups of natural enemies — plant-feeding (herbivorous) insects. Flowering plants and insects are two very diverse groups of macroscopic terrestrial organisms. Whilst some plant chemical defences have probably evolved in response to other organisms (e.g. fungal pathogens), the herbivorous insects constitute a major selection pressure, which fossil evidence shows has been operating over millions of years. For example, rocks in the Dakota formations laid down 97 million years ago (during the Cretaceous period), contain the fossilized remains of the most diverse mid-Cretaceous flora known. This flora includes more than 400 flowering plant species, associated with coastal swamp, flood-plain lakes and ox-bow channel deposits. Traces of insect damage, such as leaf mining by moth larvae, were found, similar to that shown in Figure 5.10. The state of preservation of the mines was quite extraordinary, with minute details such as egg-laying sites, faecal pellets and internal structure of larval and pupation chambers clearly visible. This information is important in furthering our understanding of the life histories of moths and other herbivorous insects living during the major period of flowering plant radiation.

By the mid-Cretaceous there was abundant evidence for several types of interaction between insects and plants, including leaf mining and gall formation (Figure 5.11).

The important general point is that plants and herbivorous insects have been intimately associated for millions of years. In the case of the Dakota formations this period may be equivalent to at least 100 million generations — a substantial platform for coevolution.

5.3.2 OVERVIEW OF PLANT CHEMICAL DEFENCES

As an introduction to plant chemical defences we will consider the group of nitrogen-containing compounds collectively referred to as **alkaloids**. Thousands of flowering plant species (about one-fifth of all species tested) are known to contain alkaloids. The abundance of alkaloids is higher amongst particular plant families (e.g. the Solanaceae, which includes the potato and tomato), parts of plants (e.g. seeds) and parts of the world (e.g. tropics).

Many of the alkaloids are implicated in plant defence against a range of herbivores and pathogens. When present at toxic concentrations, the alkaloids adversely affect the physiology of the attacking organisms in a variety of ways, including interfering with growth and development of insects, altering blood

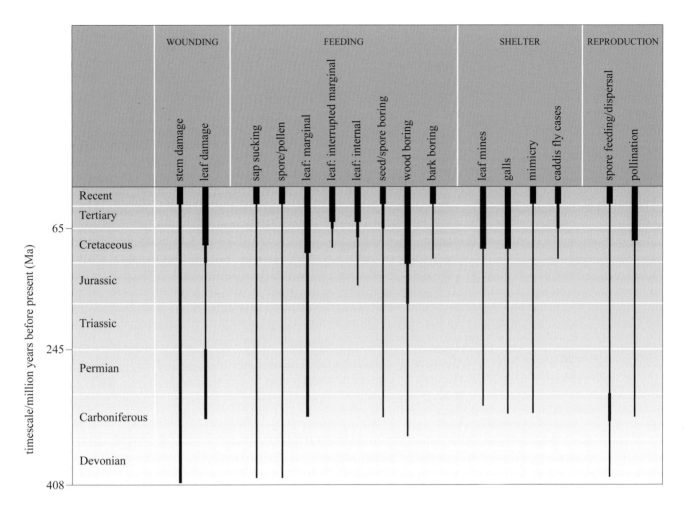

Figure 5.11 Occurrence of plant–insect interactions in the fossil record. Thin lines indicate presence or presumed presence, medium lines indicate common evidence, thick lines indicate abundant evidence.

pressure and respiratory rate in vertebrates and affecting neurotransmitters (chemicals released by nerve cells that signal to other cells). Humans have learnt how to exploit the alkaloid diversity of plants, including many familiar substances that act as drugs at low concentrations, such as morphine, caffeine, nicotine and quinine. Humans have also learnt how to detoxify the chemicals, e.g. through cooking, and to remove (e.g. decaffeinate) and synthesize them in the laboratory.

Alkaloids are derived from certain amino acids, such as tryptophan and lysine, via a series of chemical reactions which we will not discuss here. Figure 5.12 shows the tobacco plant (*Nicotiana tabacum*) and opium poppy (*Papaver somniferum*) from which the alkaloids nicotine and morphine, respectively are derived. The biochemistry of alkaloids illustrates a general principle which is that basic uniformity, in this case the structure of the precursor amino acids, can be manifested in a diversity of different chemical defences. For example, alkaloids derived from the amino acids phenylalanine and tyrosine occur in many families of monocotyledonous and dicotyledonous plants.

Figure 5.12 (a) *Nicotiana tabacum* and (b) *Papaver somniferum.*

(a)   (b)

Compounds such as alkaloids have come to be known as **secondary chemicals** (or **compounds** or **metabolites**) because they are not part of the 'primary' metabolism of the plant (Figure 5.13). Ehrlich and Raven first suggested in 1964 that secondary chemicals had evolved in plants as defence against herbivores and pathogens. A previous explanation was that plant secondary chemicals are waste products of plant metabolism, whose role in defence is purely incidental. Alkaloids are now implicated as an important part of the innate defence system of many plants.

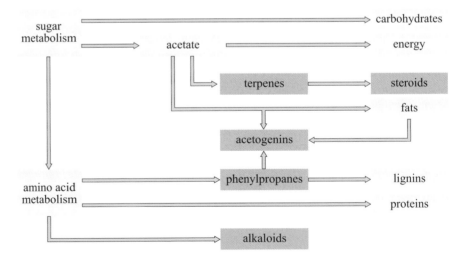

Figure 5.13 Metabolic relationships of the major groups of plant secondary compounds (in dark mauve boxes) to the primary metabolism of plants. Adapted with permission from Whittaker, R. H. and Feeny, P. P., 'Allelochemics, chemical interactions between species', *Science* **171**, p. 757. © 1971 American Association for the Advancement of Science.

Various hypotheses arise out of the **plant defence theory** of Ehrlich and Raven. In particular it is predicted that (i) plants that receive higher levels of damage from herbivores should invest more in defence; (ii) the higher the cost of defence the fewer defences employed; and (iii) that defences should be allocated to parts of the plant that benefit the most (Krebs, 1994). We will investigate these hypotheses in the next section (5.3.3) and discuss the meaning of cost later (Section 5.5), showing how to test experimentally whether selection pressures such as herbivory might lead to greater investment in defences.

5.3.3   EXPLANATIONS FOR THE TYPE, DISTRIBUTION AND ABUNDANCE OF PLANT DEFENCES

The various hypotheses arising out of the plant defence theory of Ehrlich and Raven have been restated in two more recent forms — the **plant apparency theory** and the **resource availability hypothesis** ('hypothesis' and 'theory' are used as originally stated, although the latter might equally be called a theory).

The plant apparency theory (developed in 1976 by Feeny and Rhoades & Cates) stated that the differences in defences between plant species depend on the apparency of those species. Apparent plants were defined as those easily found by herbivores or pathogens because they are locally abundant and/or widely distributed and/or long-lived.

○   Which tree species in Britain are highly apparent?

●   Common, widespread trees would be good examples, such as oak or sycamore.

In considering the evolution of defence, the definition of apparency also takes into account how long a species has been in a particular area. For example, in Britain, oaks have been abundant for thousands of years (since the last glaciation) whilst sycamore was introduced by people about 500 years ago.

A prediction that emerges from the apparency theory is that highly apparent plants and less apparent species evolve chemical defences of two different types. These two types of innate defence have been grouped as quantitative and qualitative. **Quantitative defences** include chemical defences such as tannins (complex substances that give tissues a bitter taste and upset digestion) or resins produced in large amounts, and physical defences such as thick cuticles, thorns and seed coat resistance, in which the *quantity* of defence is important. **Qualitative defences** are primarily chemical such as cyanogenesis (the production of hydrogen cyanide) and alkaloid defences. Qualitative defences are active in small amounts and relatively inexpensive (in terms of energy costs) to synthesize. It is predicted that apparent species would produce primarily quantitative defences and unapparent species would produce primarily qualitative defences.

○   Why should unapparent species produce qualitative defences?

●   Unapparent species are less easily found and therefore should experience lower rates of herbivore attack. Consequently, the selection pressures result in reduced investment in defence. As we will see in Section 5.3.4, some low-cost (qualitative) systems also include induced ones that can be switched on and off.

Examples of unapparent species include annual plants. It has been shown that a higher percentage of these plants have alkaloid defence systems compared with apparent species such as oak trees, which contain quantitative defences such as tannins. This result has been supported using a statistical method that takes account of the relatedness of species and therefore their likelihood of sharing a particular trait due to common ancestry. This method demonstrated that plant families with a high number of species containing tannins also had a high number of woody species but a low number of species containing alkaloids.

The resource availability hypothesis was put forward by Coley and colleagues in 1985 to explain certain features of plant defence unexplained by apparency theory. In this case resource availability in the environment was proposed as the major determinant of both the amount and type of plant defence. **Plant resources** are those substances required for growth and reproduction, i.e. mineral nutrients, water, carbon dioxide and light. In an environment with limited resources, plants with an inherently slow growth rate are favoured over those with a fast growth rate. Slow growth rates in turn favour large investments in anti-herbivore defence, due to the reduced metabolic cost of growth. This trade-off is also consistent with the apparency theory because slow-growing plants often live longer and are therefore more apparent. Support for the resource availability hypothesis has been provided by field data. For example, tree species of similar apparency in nutrient-poor soils in Cameroon contain twice the concentration of chemical defence compounds as species growing in similar rainforest vegetation but on richer soils.

A note of caution is appropriate here. The above hypotheses focus on differences *between* species. However, there is considerable variation *within* species that does not depend on resource availability. For example, cyanogenic and acyanogenic (not cyanide generating) forms of white clover (*Trifolium repens*) are known. Furthermore, an individual of one species may contain different types of defence. Whilst combinations of physical and chemical defences are well known, there are also some interesting examples of combinations of chemical defences. Bracken (*Pteridium aquilinum*), a fern species that occurs throughout the world, owes some of its success to its combination of tannin and cyanogenic defences, i.e. a quantitative and a qualitative defence. The growing tips and young leaves have higher concentrations of cyanogenic substances whereas the tannins increase in concentration through the growing season (Figure 5.14).

○   Describe the changes shown in Figure 5.14 in tannin and cyanide concentration in bracken through the season.

●   Tannin increases steadily in concentration from 2% dry weight in June through to about 5% dry weight in September and then drops in October. In contrast, the concentration of cyanide drops from about $30\,mg\,100\,g^{-1}$ dry weight in May to less than 5 mg by June and thereafter fluctuates at low levels.

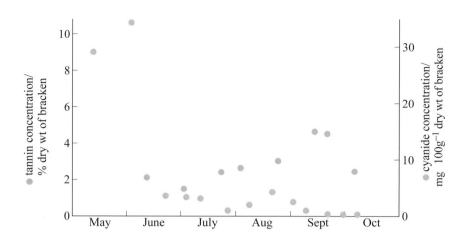

Figure 5.14 Changes in concentration of tannin (blue circles) and cyanide (orange circles) through the season in bracken, *Pteridium aquilinum.* Based on Rhoades and Cates (1976).

5.3.4 INDUCED PLANT DEFENCES

You have seen that animals have innate defence mechanisms that are activated (induced) by contact with pathogens. Plants also have induced defences. Evidence from the field and laboratory suggests that a variety of plants can respond to various types of stimulus such as physical damage by switching on or amplifying existing defence systems. For example, the levels of tannins in various tree species in the Kruger National Park (South Africa) increase in response to browsing by giraffes. The triggers for release or activation of chemical defences include not only physical damage from herbivores but also pathogen (e.g. fungal) activity and external chemical stimuli such as ozone.

There has been a large amount of work on the possible mechanisms underlying induced defence, from details of the molecular genetics through to the movement of defence molecules within the plant. Much of this work has been undertaken on a few commercially important species such as tomato (*Lycopersicon esculentum*) and tobacco (*Nicotiana tabacum*), both of which produce alkaloids. Like the pathogens that attack animals, plant pathogens release various elicitor molecules that cause the formation of lesions in the leaf. Studies on cultures of tobacco cells have shown that the plant responds with a *cascade* of biochemical signals (as in the animal examples), including salicylic acid production, which is detectable after 3–4 hours, reaching a maximum after 20–28 hours. Increased woody material deposition at the site of attack, which strengthens the wound against further lesions, is detectable 4 hours after elicitation reaching a maximum between 12 and 96 hours.

○ Compare and contrast, with reference to Section 5.2.3, the cascade defence reactions of plants and animals.

● Both involve induced defences, with the first stage activated by tissue damage (or related phenomena) followed by a series of stages. In both cases, the end-product is formed around the site of tissue damage. A major difference is in the overall time of the cascade reactions. The total time in animals may be tens of seconds whilst in plants it may take hours.

There is a variety of abiotic environmental conditions that can also produce the wound-induced response of plants. Ozone elevates enzymes associated with general plant defence, inducing plant signal molecules such as ethylene gas and salicylic acid, and activating genes and biosynthetic pathways associated with pathogen infection. In urban areas, ozone levels on the ground increase in hot weather in association with pollution events such as heavy traffic. The high ozone levels could therefore either act with pathogens to increase the plant defence levels or induce resistance without the effects of pathogens. Light is also known to induce defence systems in plants. About 75–100 phototoxins (molecules that become toxic in the presence of light) have been recorded. They have diverse biochemical origins and have been extracted from higher plants across a wide range of plant families. The phototoxins are non-specific in their targets and may combat viruses, bacteria, fungi, nematodes and herbivorous insects.

SUMMARY OF SECTION 5.3

1   Plants have evolved a wide range of physical and chemical defence mechanisms, in response to a variety of herbivores and pathogens. Interactions between some groups of herbivorous insect and plant species have occurred over tens of millions of years.

2   Alkaloids are important plant secondary compounds implicated in defence against a range of herbivores and pathogens. The plant defence theory was the first to suggest the defence role of secondary chemicals like alkaloids.

3   The plant apparency theory and the resource availability hypothesis can explain the diversity of plant chemical defences, i.e. why certain plant species have different types and amounts of defence, leading to the idea of qualitative and quantitative defences.

4   Induced defence, an example of a qualitative defence, has been found in various plant species. The principles of the mechanisms, in particular the cascade response, are similar to those in animals.

5.4 ADAPTIVE IMMUNITY

In this section, we return to cellular and molecular defence mechanisms in animals to consider the most sophisticated version of defence against pathogens. **Adaptive immunity** is found only in the vertebrates, where it interacts with and greatly enhances the mechanisms of innate immunity already described in Section 5.2. We can speculate that the selection pressure driving the evolution of this additional defensive capability may have been the increasing success of pathogens in adapting to and evading innate immunity in vertebrate hosts.

The mechanisms of adaptive immunity are rudimentary in the jawless vertebrates (class Agnatha, e.g. hagfish, lampreys), which first appeared about 400–500 million years ago. They are more developed in jawed vertebrates, but the cartilaginous fish (class Chondrichthyes) show less elaborate adaptive defences than do the bony fish (class Osteichthyes). Some reptiles (class Reptilia) have relatively simple adaptive immunity (order Crocodilia, e.g. the crocodiles and alligators), whereas others (e.g. order Squamata, the lizards and snakes) show more sophisticated mechanisms, comparable to those found in amphibians (class Amphibia), where the frogs and toads (order Anura) have been the most studied. The largest range of adaptive defence mechanisms have been demonstrated in birds (class Aves) and the placental mammals (subclass Eutheria). As with studies of innate immunity, adaptive immunity has been extensively characterized in relatively few species and there are gaps in current understanding of the evolution of these defensive mechanisms.

5.4.1 SMALL LYMPHOCYTES AND THEIR TARGETS

The most important cells in adaptive immunity are a group of leukocytes called the **small lymphocytes**, which are not found in invertebrates. They can be distinguished into three major types or 'lineages' known as the **B cells** (because they mature in the *b*one marrow in most vertebrates and in the *B*ursa of Fabricius in birds, Figure 5.5b), and the **helper T cells** and **cytotoxic T cells** (both of which mature in the *t*hymus gland). They have very different functions, as you will see shortly, but they have one thing in common — they all have receptors on their surface membranes that enable them to bind to pathogens or their toxic products. The first step in activating the defensive capability of these cells is for their receptors to bind to pathogen molecules.

The receptors on small lymphocytes are not responsive to the widespread and unique pathogen carbohydrates that trigger innate immunity. Instead they bind to tiny clusters of 10–20 amino acids (the cluster sometimes includes sugar molecules) known as **epitopes**. None of the individual molecules in an epitope are unique to pathogens, in fact they all occur in the tissues of the host, but the *combination* of those molecules in that precise physical relationship *is* unique to the pathogen. Each type of pathogen has some unique epitopes not found in the host's tissues or even in closely related pathogens. This capacity enables the adaptive immune system to do something that innate immunity cannot— distinguish each type of pathogen from all others with exquisite precision on the basis of its unique epitopes. Some epitopes are found in molecules on the pathogen's surface and others occur in its internal structures.

Any molecule that has one (or more) epitopes in its structure is called an **antigen** (Figure 5.15)— a term which signifies that the molecule is capable of triggering an adaptive immune response. The receptors on small lymphocytes are called **antigen receptors**. We are not concerned here with the structural differences between the antigen receptors of B cells, helper T cells and cytotoxic T cells; our focus is on their functional similarities. They can all be synthesized in an astonishing number of different three-dimensional shapes in the part of the molecule (the binding site) which exactly fits an epitope with a complementary shape. However, each individual small lymphocyte synthesizes receptors with just one shape, which means that each cell can only 'recognize' a single complementary epitope (Figure 5.16, overleaf). Before a vertebrate has been exposed to any antigens, its small lymphocytes exist in 'naive' **clones**, each of at most a few hundred cells with identical receptors able to recognize the same epitope.

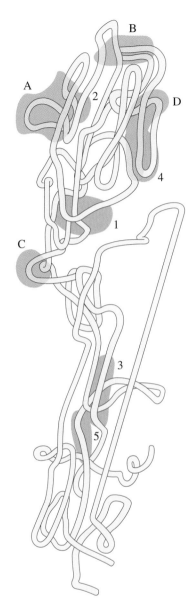

Figure 5.15 Schematic diagram of the haemagglutinin molecule, a protein antigen that occurs on the surface of the influenza virus, showing the locations of nine epitopes (colour-coded areas) in its structure. Pink-shaded epitopes are recognized by antigen receptors on B cells; blue-shaded epitopes are recognized by T cells.

Figure 5.16 Diagram of small lymphocytes in different clones with different receptors binding (or not binding) to epitopes.

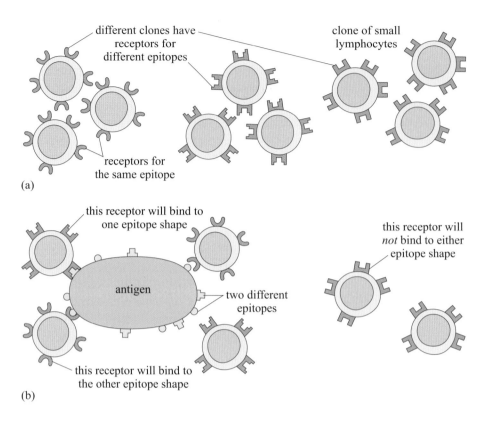

(a)

(b)

○ Look at Figure 5.15 again. How many small lymphocyte clones with different antigen-receptor shapes would be required to ensure the earliest possible detection of the influenza virus?

● At least nine (five T cell clones and four B cell clones), because in this one antigen molecule, which is itself only a small part of the influenza virus, there are nine different epitopes.

Collectively, all the clones of small lymphocytes within a single vertebrate carry a *repertoire* of antigen receptors with differently shaped binding sites. There may be an approximate inverse relationship between the size of the **antigen receptor repertoire** and the evolutionary age of the vertebrate classes. The largest repertoires have been found in eutherian mammals, including *Homo sapiens*, where an estimated 10^8 (100 million) different receptor shapes—and thus 10^8 different clones of small lymphocytes—are generated during a lifetime. Compare this number with the average receptor repertoire of about 10^5 (100 thousand) in frogs, and you begin to see what we meant when we referred to adaptive immunity becoming more elaborate in more advanced animals. If you think of how many different types of pathogens an organism could be exposed to in its lifetime, you can see why animals that have evolved huge receptor repertoires have successful defences against a very wide range of pathogens. As a host species increases its exposure to more diverse pathogens, perhaps because it extends its habitat or increases its food sources, then selection pressure tends to promote enlargement of its receptor repertoire. Later in this section we will describe the genetic rearrangements that enable vertebrates to generate such large numbers of different receptor molecules.

Most small lymphocytes circulate in the body without ever encountering their 'target', i.e. the one epitope their receptors could bind to. But collectively they provide the host with the ability to recognize any epitope on any of the pathogens it is likely to encounter during its lifetime. The large antigen receptor repertoire enables adaptive immunity to be highly *specific* in the host's defence, because even closely related pathogens can be distinguished by their unique epitopes.

○   How does innate immunity differ from this mechanism?

●   The receptors on the cells involved in innate immunity recognize the carbohydrates which are found in many different pathogens. As a consequence, the innate receptor repertoire is relatively small (a few tens of different shapes) and innate immunity is relatively *non-specific* because it attacks different pathogens indiscriminately.

You may be wondering what advantages there might be for vertebrates in having the exquisite recognition capability of adaptive immunity *in addition* to the broad-spectrum defences of innate immunity. The answer lies in the defining property of adaptive immunity from which it takes its name. The effectiveness of the adaptive immune response to invasion by a particular pathogen *increases* each time the host encounters the *same* pathogen again. Adaptive defences 'adapt' within 2–3 weeks of the first exposure, so the host can mount an even faster and more strenuous attack if a second exposure occurs. Thus, the defence against commonly encountered pathogens becomes increasingly effective, to the point where the host may even become **immune**, i.e. no longer susceptible to infection with that pathogen.

The adaptation to a particular pathogen involves a huge proliferation of the few hundred small lymphocytes whose receptors could bind to it during the first exposure. For example, in laboratory rodents it has been estimated that within the first four days of an infection, each small lymphocyte activated by contact with the pathogen (and given other promoter signals by cytokines) divides repeatedly to generate an enlarged clone of approximately 64 000 identical daughter cells, each carrying receptors that bind to that pathogen (Figure 5.17, overleaf). **Clonal expansion** on such a scale gives some idea of the energy and material cost of an immune response.

Clonal expansion continues over 2–3 weeks, so the adaptive response against a newly encountered pathogen builds up relatively slowly. Once the pathogens that triggered this primary response have been eliminated, most of the clone cells die, but a proportion survive. These long-lived survivors are known as **memory cells**. If the same pathogens invade the host a second time, the memory cells form the basis of a much faster and more effective secondary response. Any subsequent exposures result in even larger clones of surviving memory cells and a faster adaptive response. However, because clonal expansion only occurs among those small lymphocytes that have actually encountered the pathogens to which their receptors can bind, responsiveness to all other pathogens remains unchanged. This feature of adaptive immunity is described as **immunological memory**, since it appears as though the vertebrate host's immune system can 'remember' which pathogens it has encountered before. Immunological memory is more highly developed in the endothermic vertebrates than in the ectotherms.

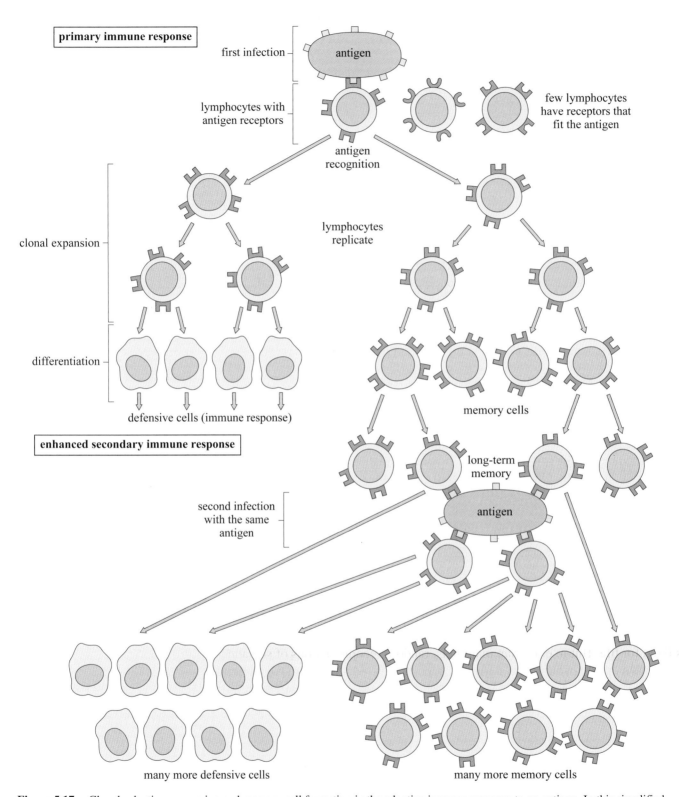

primary immune response

first infection

lymphocytes with antigen receptors

few lymphocytes have receptors that fit the antigen

antigen recognition

clonal expansion

lymphocytes replicate

differentiation

defensive cells (immune response)

memory cells

enhanced secondary immune response

long-term memory

second infection with the same antigen

many more defensive cells

many more memory cells

Figure 5.17   Clonal selection, expansion and memory cell formation in the adaptive immune response to an antigen. In this simplified diagram, the antigen has several copies of a single epitope, so only one clone of small lymphocytes is activated. In reality, naturally occurring antigens (e.g. in a pathogen's structure) have many different epitopes and activate all the corresponding small lymphocyte clones.

○ Why is immunological memory a better defence strategy than having all the small lymphocyte clones permanently expanded to their maximum size?

● It provides an energy-efficient defence. Host animals would have to grow much larger to accommodate thousands or millions of expanded clones in their bodies, and most of the huge cost in energy and materials of wholesale clonal expansion would be wasted effort because the majority of clones never encounter the epitopes to which they could bind.

Thus, the evolution of adaptive immunity provides an economical method of recruiting additional defence mechanisms to reinforce innate immunity, but only for those pathogens that have actually penetrated the host's outer barriers.

5.4.2 THE GENERATION OF RECEPTOR DIVERSITY

Next we return to the question of how so many different antigen-receptor shapes are produced within a single animal, while its small lymphocytes are restricted to just one shape each. The account here is a brief introduction to a process called **somatic recombination**. Somatic recombination is not universal among the vertebrate classes (evidence for it has not been found in sharks and other cartilaginous fish), but it underlies the large receptor repertoires of most vertebrates. The starting point is a few hundred alternative receptor genes in the animal's *germline* DNA (i.e. the DNA inherited from its parents via their gametes) in the stem cells, which give rise to new small lymphocytes by cell division. The number of alternative receptor genes varies in different vertebrate classes, but that need not concern us here. As each lymphocyte develops, enzymes cut the DNA and recombine (splice together) a few randomly selected receptor genes in a novel relationship. The process is random so different lymphocytes generate different receptors. Variations in exactly where the cuts and joins occur create more than enough unique combinations to account for the huge number of different antigen-receptor shapes that these 'shuffled' genes encode.

Somatic recombination is so-called because it occurs in the *somatic* DNA of cells giving rise to small lymphocytes — 'somatic' is a term applied to all cells *except* the gametes. In most vertebrates, it occurs during a limited period early in development; thereafter, the size and composition of the receptor repertoire is fixed for life. But in eutherian mammals, random recombinations of somatic genes goes on occurring throughout life, continuously creating new and unique codes for new antigen receptors. The random nature of this process may even generate receptors that bind to the epitopes of new pathogen strains arising through mutation in the future.

○ Does rearrangement of somatic genes in the small lymphocytes of an individual have any impact on the adaptive immune defences of future generations?

● No. The novel somatic gene combinations created by rearrangement in a vertebrate's lymphocytes cannot be passed on to the next generation because they do not exist in the germline DNA of the animal's gametes. Thus, no matter how effective the adaptive immunity of an individual becomes during its lifetime, this enhanced ability is not inherited by its offspring.

○ Can you foresee a potential threat to the host arising from the *random* rearrangement of antigen-receptor genes and hence the random generation of new antigen-receptor shapes?

● It is inevitable that a proportion of the antigen receptors generated by random somatic recombination have shapes that bind to clusters of amino acids on the host's own cells.

Small lymphocytes bearing these 'anti-self' or autoimmune receptors must either be destroyed, or their activity must be permanently suppressed, to prevent them from attacking the host's own cells. The mechanisms for achieving self-tolerance in the adaptive immune system are complex and need not concern us here, but autoimmune diseases (such as rheumatoid arthritis and multiple sclerosis in humans) are the price paid when anti-self lymphocytes escape. When vertebrates evolved a more acute strategy for detecting pathogens on the basis of tiny differences in their amino acid patterns, they sacrificed the ability to distinguish reliably between legitimate targets and 'self'. Adaptive immunity represents one of the most striking examples of an evolutionary compromise, in which mechanisms that increase the risk of autoimmune diseases have been selected for because they also increase the effectiveness of defences against pathogens. In this trade-off, the benefit greatly outweighs the risk.

5.4.3 CO-OPERATION BETWEEN ADAPTIVE AND INNATE IMMUNITY

We began this section with a brief reference to the three main lineages of small lymphocytes, and it is high time we sketched in their separate contributions to adaptive immunity and in cooperating with innate immunity. They all require activation by binding to the epitope that 'fits' their receptors and to appropriate cytokines before clonal expansion can take place, as described above. Activated **helper T cells** synthesize and release several cytokines that enhance the mechanisms of innate immunity and activate other small lymphocytes. In fact, without fully functioning helper T cells, most other immune defences become extremely inefficient or stop altogether.

Cytotoxic T cells (like the NK cells of innate immunity) destroy host cells infected with intracellular pathogens, using very similar mechanisms of cell-mediated cytotoxicity to those already described (Section 5.2.4). The main difference is that cell-mediated cytotoxicity in the innate immune system is directed against host cells displaying the unusual but common pathogen carbohydrates which usually betray the presence of bacteria or fungi. On the other hand, cytotoxic T cells recognize and attack host cells displaying protein epitopes unique to each species or strain of pathogen, and are particularly adapted to detect viruses replicating inside the host's cells, a target that innate mechanisms might otherwise miss.

However, the mechanisms of innate immunity can be directed to attack targets which they cannot 'see' because they don't carry the appropriate receptors. They get directions from another lineage of small lymphocytes, the **B cells**. If a B cell is activated and provided with adequate nutrients, it synthesizes and releases huge quantities of its antigen receptors into the body fluids — a process which goes on for several weeks. These soluble antigen receptors are the large Y-shaped proteins known as **antibodies**, each with two identical binding sites (Figure 5.18) capable of binding only to the epitope that triggered the B cell in the first place.

When an antibody binds to a pathogen's epitope it does no direct harm, but it 'labels' the pathogen for destruction by the mechanisms of innate immunity. For example, phagocytes can 'get a grip' on pathogens coated with antibodies. Antibodies also agglutinate pathogens into clumps, focus cell-mediated cytotoxicity onto appropriate targets and trigger the complement cascade. This mechanism is another example of collaboration in vertebrates between adaptive and innate defences. Immunization with killed or altered 'safe' strains of common pathogens elicits the production of specific antibodies by B cells and generates long-lived memory cells, which may be enough to protect the animal if exposed to live pathogens in the future.

There are enough similarities in the molecular structure of antibody molecules in all animals to suggest that the genes involved have been copied and retained many times as evolutionary pathways diverged. Support for this hypothesis comes from the discovery in some insects of molecules with rudimentary structural and functional similarities to antibodies, although the insects could have stumbled independently on the same solution to threats from pathogens.

We said earlier that recognition of antigens by small lymphocytes is not by itself sufficient to induce an immune response. The cells of adaptive immunity must receive additional signals before they become activated. These signals are often induced by tissue damage or infectious agents. For example, a component of bacterial cell membranes that we mentioned earlier, lipopolysaccharide (LPS), activates phagocytes that in turn stimulate T cells. LPS also directly activates B cells, which can then make antibodies against bacterial components. In effect, the presence of the bacterial LPS acts as a danger signal, which alerts the phagocytes and B cells that an adaptive immune response is appropriate. Regulatory mechanisms such as this one ensure that animals usually generate immune responses only against antigens that genuinely signal danger by betraying the presence of pathogens.

Some of the activating cytokines produced in response to danger signals such as LPS are synthesized by phagocytes and others by helper T cells, each enhancing the activation status of the other (Figure 5.19, overleaf) in a further demonstration of cooperation between adaptive and innate immunity.

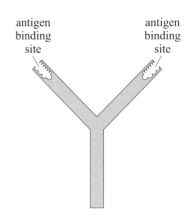

antigen binding site   antigen binding site

Figure 5.18 Diagram of an antibody molecule, showing the two identical binding sites by which it attaches to an epitope with an exactly complementary shape.

Figure 5.19 Cooperation between cells involved in innate and adaptive immunity in generating an immune response against a pathogen. The activated defensive cells undergo clonal expansion (as in Figure 5.17).

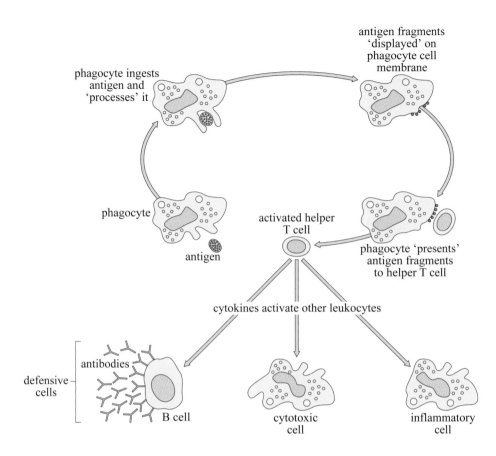

The ancient mechanisms of innate immunity have another vital role in directing adaptive immunity in vertebrates towards appropriate targets. The phagocytes act as **antigen-presenting cells**, displaying protein fragments from partially digested pathogens on their own surface membranes. This exposes pathogen epitopes that are usually buried within the organism's structure. Helper T cells can only recognize pathogen antigens which are presented to them on the surface of phagocytes, so they are 'restricted' to legitimate targets selected for them by phagocytes.

○ In what other ways could antigen presentation by phagocytes make helper T cells more efficient?

● The exposure of epitopes digested from the internal structures of pathogens maximizes the number of lymphocyte clones activated in response to an invasion.

So by detecting the threat posed by pathogens and presenting pathogen epitopes to the helper T cells, phagocytes *initiate* the adaptive immune response. And without the cytokines produced as a result of helper T cell activation, all the other defence mechanisms in the adaptive and innate immune systems are greatly reduced in their effectiveness or fail to function at all.

In the next section, we turn to a specific example of innate and adaptive immunity in action in amphibians, and speculate on the possibility that a reduction in the effectiveness of immune defences may be contributing to the worldwide decline in some amphibian species.

5.4.4 AMPHIBIAN IMMUNITY

Amphibia offer some interesting insights into fluctuations in adaptive immunity occurring at different stages of the life history and when exposed to different environmental conditions. One of the most extensively studied amphibians is the clawed frog, *Xenopus laevis* (Figure 5.20a).

(a)

thymus glands

(b)

Figure 5.20 (a) Adult *Xenopus laevis.* (b) *Xenopus laevis* tadpole. The paired thymus glands are shown.

In all vertebrates, the small lymphocytes on which adaptive immunity depends replicate in specialized structures called the lymphoid organs, which are packed with leukocytes. Amphibia are the oldest class of vertebrates to have lymphoid organs similar to those found in reptiles, birds and mammals. Adult *Xenopus* have simple lymph nodes, a pair of thymus glands (mammals have a single thymus), a spleen and bone marrow; but *Xenopus* tadpoles develop only the paired thymus glands (Figure 5.20b). Tadpoles have a much smaller antigen receptor repertoire than adult frogs and their ability to kill pathogens by cell-mediated cytotoxicity is also lower. The tadpoles' immune defences are so much less efficient than those of frogs that they accept skin grafts from other unrelated *Xenopus* tadpoles.

○ What do the differences in immune responsiveness suggest about the allocation of resources to different functions at different stages of the *Xenopus* life history?

● There seems to be a lower investment in resources that protect tadpoles from pathogens, perhaps because tadpoles are subjected to heavy predation. More resources are devoted to defence against pathogens in mature frogs, perhaps because they must survive both predators and pathogens long enough to reproduce.

The tadpole thymus glands shrink to 10% of their maximum size as the tadpole metamorphoses into a frog, re-growing rapidly thereafter, suggesting that the energy cost of metamorphosis is so great that resources are temporarily withdrawn from immune defences. The size of lymphoid organs and the effectiveness of immune responses in ectothermic vertebrates also fluctuate with the seasons, falling in *Xenopus* and many other ectotherms in the winter and rising again in spring (seasonal changes in animal metabolism were introduced in Chapter 1). A review of research from around the world on many different ectothermic vertebrates, has resulted in a model of seasonal variations in the immune system (Figure 5.21).

Figure 5.21 Model of seasonal changes affecting the structure and functions of the immune system in ectotherms (based on Zapata *et al.*, 1992). Note: this model does not apply to all ectothermic vertebrates.

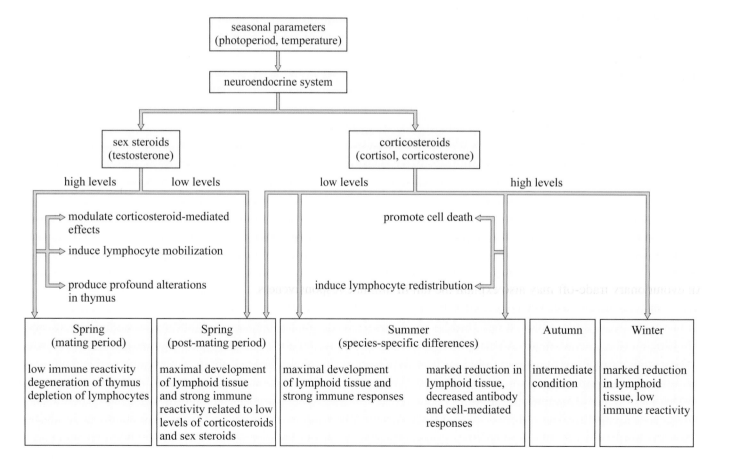

○ What factors are likely to limit pathogen-induced disease in ectothermic animals in winter, even though their immune responsiveness is low?

● The threat from pathogens falls as ambient temperature drops and many die or become dormant. Many ectotherms greatly reduce their feeding in winter and they are not seeking mates, so their exposure to pathogens also falls.

This example demonstrates a trade-off between the advantages of reducing energy expenditure in winter to the minimum necessary to sustain life, and the potential risks associated with this strategy from pathogens, predators and the cold. But ectotherms are not left undefended against pathogens. They have evolved some energy-efficient adaptations to their defence mechanisms; for example, the molecules contributing to the complement cascade in *Xenopus* are very similar to those found in mammals, but frog complement can be activated at much lower temperatures, down to 4 °C.

The key to seasonal variation in immune responsiveness in vertebrates seems to lie in fluctuations in the levels of sex hormones and the **corticosteroids** released in response to stress. Although there are species exceptions, corticosteroids generally rise in ectotherms exposed to stressors of various kinds, including temperature shock and physical handling. The rise is coupled with a fall in adaptive immunity and this effect can be reproduced artificially by injecting the animals with corticosteroids. The suppressive effect of corticosteroids on adaptive immunity in mammals is also well-known and probably underlies the increased susceptibility to infection observed in humans under stress. Corticosteroids are involved in preparing the body for 'fight or flight' by increasing the rate of metabolism and mobilizing stored sources of energy such as glucose to fuel strenuous physical activity.

○ How might a fall in immune responsiveness benefit an animal during periods of stress?

● Maintaining immune responsiveness consumes substantial amounts of energy and materials. The short-term reduction in protection against pathogens may be more than outweighed by the survival advantage of having these resources available for other functions, such as fleeing from a predator.

An evolutionary trade-off may also explain the fall in immune responsiveness as sex hormone levels rise. The energy cost of activating an immune response may be set against the energy cost of reproduction (a point we return to in Section 5.5). The corticosteroids may be involved in coordinating energy trade-offs throughout the animal kingdom. Corticosteroid-like molecules are synthesized and released by phagocytes in invertebrates, a finding that suggests a possible role for phagocytes in switching resources between defence against pathogens and other high-energy functions such as reproduction and evasion of predators.

The immunosuppressive effects of stress have been implicated as a possible contributor to the worldwide decline in some amphibian populations, which has been occurring at an accelerating rate since about the mid-1970s (Carey *et al.*, 1999). Although destruction of habitats is a major factor in some parts of the world, it cannot explain the mass mortalities of amphibians in wilderness areas and national parks. Frogs, toads and salamanders caught in habitats where the population is in sharp decline have been shown to harbour a greater number of pathogens than in areas where the populations are stable. Observations such as these have fuelled the hypothesis that the declining amphibian populations may have less effective immune defences, which leaves them vulnerable to infectious disease.

The immune responsiveness of at least some amphibian species may be adversely affected by environmental factors such as global warming, atmospheric pollution, ground-level ozone, ultra-violet radiation, heavy metal contamination or acid rain. For example, research on declining populations of the leopard frog (*Rana pipiens*) has shown that prolonged exposure to cold or to water acidification in captive populations is associated with an increased susceptibility to infection (Maniero and Carey, 1997). When the immune systems of stressed frogs were compared with those of controls, there were stress-related reductions in the numbers of leukocytes, the concentration of complement cascade molecules and the ability of phagocytes to ingest foreign particles. These differences may be enough to compromise the frogs' defences against certain pathogens.

The most significant discovery came in 1998, when a chytrid fungus (phylum Chytridiomycota) was identified in the skin of dead and dying amphibians in mass mortality locations around the world. Chytrid fungi are very common in moist soil, wetlands, rivers and pools, so the susceptibility of amphibians to fatal infections with this ubiquitous pathogen suggests that their immune defences against it have been undermined (Daszak *et al.*, 1999). This situation is comparable with the appearance of **opportunistic infections** in humans whose immune systems have been suppressed by drug treatment (e.g. to protect transplants) or by infection with the human immunodeficiency virus, HIV, which usually leads to AIDS. Opportunistic infections are due to pathogens which a fully competent immune system usually keeps under control. Some other common pathogens have also been identified in much greater concentrations in amphibian mass mortalities, including iridoviruses and some bacterial strains.

A worldwide research network — the Declining Amphibian Population Task Force (DAPTF), coordinated from the Open University in Milton Keynes — is testing these and other hypotheses. According to the Director of DAPTF, Tim Halliday, amphibians may be acting as an environmental barometer, giving us early warning of the damaging effects of environmental change on the delicate balance of cells and molecules on which the immune defences of all animals depend.

However, there is an alternative explanation which leads us back to the coevolution of hosts and their pathogens. The mass mortality events experienced by certain amphibian populations could be due to the recent emergence, through mutation, of new more virulent strains of pathogens, which the host's immune defences cannot control. In the final section of this chapter, we return to the subject of coevolution and examine some of the evidence that host–pathogen and plant–herbivore partnerships undergo mutual adaptation through many generations of interaction.

SUMMARY OF SECTION 5.4

1   Adaptive immunity is found only in vertebrates and depends on small lymphocytes, which exist in clones initially of a few hundred cells each. All members of the same clone carry identical antigen receptors with binding sites that fit a unique cluster of amino acids (sometimes with sugar molecules) called an epitope.

2   Molecules with epitopes in their structure are called antigens. The antigen receptors on small lymphocytes are highly specific and can distinguish between closely related pathogen strains on the basis of their unique epitopes.

3   In most vertebrates, large antigen receptor repertoires are generated by random somatic gene recombination. Somatic genes are not passed on from one generation to the next, so the codes for receptors that bind to epitopes on pathogens encountered during an animal's lifetime are not inherited by its offspring.

4   Phagocytes also produce activating cytokines and select appropriate targets for adaptive immunity by presenting digested fragments of pathogens to helper T cells.

5   Corticosteroids suppress immune responses and may be important in switching energy resources away from defence against pathogens to other functions such as reproduction, metamorphosis and hibernation.

6   Some amphibian populations may be declining due to increased mortality from pathogens. Increased susceptibility to opportunistic infections may be due to reduced immune responsiveness caused by environmental stressors, or to the recent emergence of more virulent pathogen strains.

5.5 COEVOLUTION OF HOST—PATHOGEN AND HOST—HERBIVORE INTERACTIONS

In this final section of the chapter we explore the coevolution of host species with their pathogens or the herbivores that feed on them. The descriptions you have read so far of the cellular and molecular defence mechanisms of animals and plants have not emphasized one very important point which is central to coevolution — the effectiveness of these defences differs between individuals. Within a population, individuals with certain genes have a greater resistance to infection, herbivory or other forms of attack than others. Similarly, there is variation between individual pathogens or herbivores in the success with which they can infect or eat their hosts.

○   How do genes for resistance spread in host populations that coexist with their pathogens or herbivores over many generations?

●   Genes that confer greater resistance to infection or herbivory increase the chance of resistant hosts surviving to reproduce and pass on their 'protective' genes. Conversely, hosts with genes that confer less protection are more likely to die before breeding. So resistance to pathogens or to herbivory should increase in the host population.

However, the Red Queen hypothesis (Chapter 4) states that no matter how fast an organism adapts to its surroundings, it cannot evolve fast enough to 'outrun' the continual changes in its environment.

○ How can the Red Queen hypothesis explain why animals and plants are unlikely ever to evolve complete resistance against all pathogens or herbivores?

● Pathogens and herbivores with genes that give them some advantage in infecting or eating their hosts, or evading their host's immune defences, are also increasing in the population, usually at a much faster rate than their hosts can match because of their shorter generation times. For example, some bacteria can divide every 20–30 minutes and some herbivorous insects can reproduce in days whereas their food plants may take years to mature.

Coevolution of hosts and their pathogens or herbivores has been likened to an 'arms race', with each side continually upgrading its offensive weapons and defensive strategies in response to the latest manoeuvre from the other side. However, this analogy is misleading. In modern arms races between nations, the end-point is weapons of mass destruction developed by both sides, but held as a deterrent. In host–pathogen or host–herbivore interactions the analogy breaks down in several ways.

Pathogens and herbivores must use their 'weapons' in order to obtain the resources for growth and reproduction from their hosts or food plants and, in doing so, expose themselves to counter-attack. Both sides suffer losses and each exerts selection pressure on the other, but the outcome *prevents* the 'arms race' from escalating towards the production of even more damaging weapons. The explanation lies in the dependence of pathogens and herbivores on their hosts. It is not in the long-term interests of any pathogen or herbivore to devote so much of its resources to attacking its hosts or food plants that it brings about *their* mass destruction, because this outcome would hasten its own extinction. So there is a theoretical optimum limit on the investment that pathogens or herbivores can make in attacking their hosts before they begin to reduce their own chances of survival.

○ Apply similar reasoning to the host's side of the interaction.

● There should also be an optimum level of investment made by hosts in their defence mechanisms. Super-defences would be so costly in energy and resources that to produce them would reduce the efficiency of other functions and adversely affect the hosts' chances of surviving and reproducing.

It is therefore in the long-term interests of both parties to the interaction *not* to escalate the 'arms race' beyond a certain optimum level which ensures the survival of both. In effect, both sides are engaged in trade-offs, which balance the costs and benefits of attack or defence against alternative uses for the energy and resources required. In the following sections we consider evidence to support this trade-off model of coevolution.

5.5.1 EVIDENCE FOR TRADE-OFFS IN HOST–PATHOGEN COEVOLUTION

The trade-off model predicts that all hosts — even the most resistant — suffer a degree of damage from pathogens because investing even more energy and resources in super-defences would reduce the hosts' fitness in other ways. This line of reasoning is compatible with the Red Queen hypothesis outlined earlier, because the speed with which pathogens can evolve new mechanisms for exploiting their hosts means that hosts would have to invest more and more resources in defence if all their pathogens were to be eliminated. The huge cost of this response would soon outweigh the benefits. So the model predicts that natural selection does not favour the persistence of either super-destructive pathogens or super-defensive hosts.

But 'super-bugs' have certainly appeared in the past and continue to emerge, causing mass mortality in the process. As described earlier, a new strain of chytrid fungus may be the major cause of amphibian population declines around the world. However, the *initial* appearance of new and lethal pathogens does not undermine the trade-off model of host–pathogen evolution. Random mutations in pathogen genomes inevitably generate lethal variants from time to time. Viruses sometimes exchange genes when two strains infect the same cell, creating an entirely new and potentially dangerous virus. Or pathogens that coevolved in one species may acquire the ability to infect a new host species, which may be far more susceptible to pathogen-induced damage.

The trade-off model accepts that destructive pathogens arise, but predicts that the level of **virulence** tends to fall over time, stabilizing around an optimum level at which both host and pathogen populations survive, even though some organisms die or suffer reduced reproductive success. Virulence is a poorly defined term which is confusingly used in different contexts. It sometimes refers to the severity of symptoms produced by a certain pathogen in its hosts (e.g. a 'virulent' strain causes particularly nasty symptoms). Virulence can also reflect the host mortality rate during an outbreak of an infection and some definitions take a long-term view of the proportion of the affected host population that survives to reproduce. Whichever definition is used, virulence should be seen as a property of the *interaction* between the pathogen and its host, which can change over time.

○ How does natural selection and the trade-off model of coevolution explain the tendency for virulence to decline from the initally high levels often seen in a new infectious outbreak?

● Virulence falls as a result of natural selection acting on genetic variations in both the host and pathogen populations. The most virulent pathogens kill their hosts too quickly and so reduce their own reproductive success, whereas less virulent pathogens have a better chance of reproducing and infecting new hosts. The most vulnerable hosts quickly die out of the population, while the proportion with better defences increases over time. As the two populations coevolve over many generations, a level of virulence should be reached in which the loss of fitness sustained by infected hosts is traded-off against the costs of devoting even more resources to defence.

This is precisely what happened when a deadly strain of the *Myxoma* virus was released into rabbits that had been introduced into Australia to control their huge population numbers. The initial very high rate of rabbit mortality gradually fell over time as the few rabbits with adequate defences against the virus survived and slowly replenished the population. But at the same time, the *Myxoma* strain was decreasing in virulence. As the rabbit population recovered after many generations, it was found that transfer of *Myxoma* from these animals to new rabbit colonies produced higher mortality than in the coevolved rabbits, but far lower mortality rates than had been the case when the virus was first introduced into Australia.

○ According to Chapter 4, what link has been postulated between the evolution of sexual reproduction in animal hosts and their exposure to increasingly diverse and rapidly evolving pathogens?

● Sexual reproduction may have evolved at least partly as a consequence of selection pressure from pathogens. The genetic diversity between host individuals that is a consequence of sexual reproduction may have been selected for because it has the potential to generate more diverse and more effective defence mechanisms.

It is worth noting that there is a price to pay for this benefit. The close contact between hitherto separate individuals during sexual reproduction, particularly where fertilization is internal, provides new opportunities for transmission of pathogens to new hosts. The costs and benefits to host animals of sexual reproduction is another example of a trade-off.

The fact that sexual reproduction is a costly and (in many animals) a seasonal activity has provided opportunities to test the predictions of the trade-off model of host–pathogen coevolution (Ebert and Hamilton, 1996; Sheldon and Verhulst, 1996; Moller *et al.*, 1999). Animals that devote more energy and resources at certain times of year to attracting mates, reproducing or raising their young, should be more susceptible to pathogens during these periods because they can devote fewer resources to defence. The most reliable evidence for this concept has come from studies of birds, where it is relatively easy to manipulate the amount of effort that parents devote to rearing their young by adding or removing eggs from the nests. Experiments of this kind have tended to show that there is a positive relationship in several species (e.g. great tits, *Parus major*) between brood size and infestation with some common avian parasites. However, there is a potential flaw in these experiments.

○ What alternative interpretation could explain the results?

● It cannot be ruled out that the greater pathogen loads in individuals who are feeding larger numbers of young are a consequence of increased exposure to pathogens during the longer periods of foraging needed to feed them.

Far more convincing have been experiments in several species of birds (e.g. barn swallows, *Hirundo rustica*) and fish (e.g. guppies, *Poecilia reticulata*) which have demonstrated an inverse relationship between the brilliance of their display colours and the strength of their immune responses. For example, male swallows display red throat patches which become more intensely coloured in the mating season. Male birds with pale throat patches were found to have higher levels of antibodies in their bloodstream.

○ How can this finding be interpreted as a trade-off?

● One interpretation is that males who are more heavily infected with pathogens have to devote more energy and resources to their immune defences (e.g. by producing more antibodies) in order to survive, but in consequence they have less available to produce brilliant display signals.

Figure 5.22 Barn swallow *Hirundo rustica*.

There is a flaw in this argument too, but it has led to an even more interesting possibility. The red colouration in the throat patches is due to pigments called carotenoids, which are widely used in colourful display ornaments in many species of birds, fish, reptiles, amphibians and insects. Carotenoids are synthesized only by plants and some bacteria and algae, so animals that use these pigments in their display signals have to acquire them in their diet. This fact undermines the notion that barn swallows with high pathogen loads have diverted so much energy and resources to their immune defences that they do not have enough left over to produce brilliant throat patches, since they are not using their *own* resources to produce the pigments. (In fact, some processing of dietary carotenoids does occur to produce the range of different colours seen in the display ornaments of many species, but the costs to the host are relatively small.)

However, a strong inverse association between carotenoid levels and the host's immune defences has been found in an increasing number of vertebrate species (Owens and Olson, 1999). For example, experiments in domestic chickens showed that carotenoid levels fell very rapidly in birds that were artificially injected with a blood parasite. Conversely, immune responses were reduced in birds fed a diet from which carotenoids were excluded. Such experiments suggest that carotenoids may have a direct role in defences against pathogens. A fall in carotenoid levels during an immune response is what you would predict for a resource that the animal cannot synthesize for itself to meet increased demand. There is a long way to go before the role of carotenoids and the proposed trade-off between sexual signals and immune defences are fully understood, so the account given here is tentative but increasingly supported by experimental evidence. Fortunately, further evidence for mutual adaptation and coevolutionary trade-offs comes from phylogenetic data.

5.5.2 EVIDENCE FOR COEVOLUTION FROM PHYLOGENETIC DATA

If coevolution has taken place then we can make some predictions about the evolutionary history of the organisms, expressed as testable hypotheses. For example, we might predict that if organisms had coevolved then the phylogenies of the hosts would match closely with those of the pathogens or herbivores which showed high levels of specificity.

Blood parasites of vertebrates and the intermediate insect hosts that act as vectors, transmitting the parasite between vertebrate hosts, are an example of phylogenies which can be used to test coevolutionary hypotheses. Have the parasites coevolved with their vertebrate hosts or their insect hosts, or both, or neither? The order Haemosporina (Apicomplexa) comprises various blood parasites of vertebrates, including *Plasmodium* (Figure 5.23a) which causes malaria and kills over one million people annually. Other species in the Haemosporina can infect birds, e.g. *Leucocytozoon* species which are a major cause of poultry loss. In all cases, the insect hosts are flies (Diptera) whilst the vertebrate hosts can be mammals, birds or reptiles. A phylogeny of the Haemosporina has been constructed based on morphology and life-cycle information from 14 species. As the phylogeny is one of many possible it is referred to as 'hypothesized evolutionary relationship' and is compared with the phylogenies of vertebrate and dipteran hosts (Figure 5.23b).

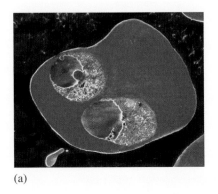

(a)

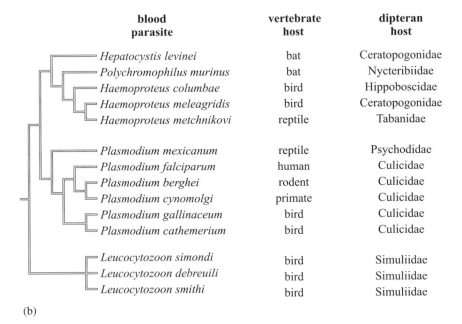

blood parasite	vertebrate host	dipteran host
Hepatocystis levinei	bat	Ceratopogonidae
Polychromophilus murinus	bat	Nycteribiidae
Haemoproteus columbae	bird	Hippoboscidae
Haemoproteus meleagridis	bird	Ceratopogonidae
Haemoproteus metchnikovi	reptile	Tabanidae
Plasmodium mexicanum	reptile	Psychodidae
Plasmodium falciparum	human	Culicidae
Plasmodium berghei	rodent	Culicidae
Plasmodium cynomolgi	primate	Culicidae
Plasmodium gallinaceum	bird	Culicidae
Plasmodium cathemerium	bird	Culicidae
Leucocytozoon simondi	bird	Simuliidae
Leucocytozoon debreuili	bird	Simuliidae
Leucocytozoon smithi	bird	Simuliidae

(b)

Figure 5.23 (a) False colour electron micrograph of two stages in the life cycle of *Plasmodium falciparum* (blue and pink) parasitizing a red blood cell (magnification approximately ×4000). (b) The hypothesized evolutionary relationships of fourteen species of Haemosporina and their associated vertebrate and dipteran (fly) hosts.

The evidence for coevolution is better for the insect hosts than the vertebrate hosts. The 14 parasite species fall into three major groups: species 1 to 5; species 6 to 11 (the *Plasmodium* species) and species 12 to 14 (the *Leucocytozoon* species). All of the *Leucocytozoon* species are transmitted by blackflies (Simuliidae) whilst all of the *Plasmodium* species bar one are transmitted by mosquitoes (Culicidae — the one exception is Psychodidae). The first group, comprising three genera of parasite, are associated with four families of fly. However, most *Haemoproteus* hosts are known to be ceratopogonid midges. In summary, there seems to be a strong link between the three parasite genera (*Plasmodium*, *Leucocytozoon* and *Haemoproteus*) and their dipteran hosts. These fly families are themselves closely related, suggesting an ancestral parasite–dipteran vector association. There is a weak association between the vertebrate hosts and the parasites. Species 12 to 14 (*Leucocytozoon*) all have bird hosts, as do two of the *Plasmodium* species. However, the other *Plasmodium* species are found in reptiles, rodents, humans and other primates. There are no clear vertebrate patterns for species 1 to 5.

5.5.3 HOW SOME HERBIVORES TURN PLANT DEFENCE TO THEIR ADVANTAGE (THE CASCADING CONSEQUENCES OF COEVOLUTION BETWEEN DEFENDER AND ATTACKER)

Here we discuss how, during plant–herbivore coevolution, some insect herbivores, having evolved mechanisms to cope with potentially toxic secondary compounds ingested when they eat the plants, have also evolved means of incorporating the toxins into their own bodies where they act as their own defence. We will consider some examples of this strategy and how it has affected the behaviour, morphology and diversity of the species involved. Initially we assume that the defences have come from the plants eaten by the herbivore. We will discuss the evidence for this assumption later in this section.

What types of herbivorous insect are likely to use plant defences? A frequent prerequisite is that the insect herbivores feed only on one or a limited range of plant species. It is intuitive that once particular herbivore species become involved in a coevolutionary interaction with plant species they may specialize more and more on a single genus or species of plant. Furthermore, many herbivore species may specialize on one particular host. For example, ragwort (*Senecio jacobaea*), a plant which is toxic to vertebrates, is eaten by many species of herbivorous fly, beetle and moth which are not found on any species outside of the genus *Senecio*. Thus coevolution may help to promote diversity in these groups of organisms.

○ To further identify the type of herbivorous insect using plant defences consider how a predator could detect that an insect herbivore has a chemical defence. (The term predator covers any natural enemy of a herbivore).

● The predator could either directly detect the chemical or respond to a signal that the toxin is present in the herbivore's body.

The herbivore with a chemical defence needs to provide a signal because otherwise it may be consumed. If the herbivore is killed then the toxin is a failure, even if it leads to death of the predator, unless closely related herbivores (e.g. siblings) can benefit from future avoidance by that predator. It may be that the herbivore can survive a small bite out of its body (e.g. on the outer part of a butterfly wing) in which case the signal could be an unpleasant taste. For potential predators hunting by sight, such as insect-feeding birds, **warning coloration** advertises that a herbivore contains a chemical defence.

○ What behaviour would reinforce the role of colours?

● The prey would show off its colours, e.g. by being active during the day and by behaving in a conspicuous manner, such as flying slowly.

We are developing a picture of the type of herbivorous organisms which might be expected to contain plant chemical defences. When we look for such organisms in nature we find a number of possible examples. The first two examples in Figure 5.24 (burnet moth, *Zygaena* sp. and cinnabar moth, *Tyria jacobaeae*) are found in Britain and mainland Europe; the second group of three are found in Central and South America. (The Ithomiinae is a subfamily of the butterfly family Nymphalidae. *Heliconius*, introduced in Chapter 3, is a genus in the subfamily Heliconiinae which is also in the Nymphalidae.)

Figure 5.24 (a) Burnet moth (*Zygaena* sp.); (b) cinnabar moth (*Tyria jacobaeae*) adult and (c) larvae; (d) *Heliconius erato*; (e) butterfly in the subfamily Ithomiinae; (f) poison arrow frog in the family Dendrobatidae.

○ Which of the organisms in Figure 5.24 is the odd one out?

● The poison arrow frog — it is obviously not an insect (!) and is not herbivorous.

We will return to these frogs at the end of the section.

All of these organisms carry warning coloration. Do the insects have any of the behavioural features that we expect? Yes, the burnet and cinnabar moths are day-flying (unlike most moths) and weak fliers; the cinnabar larvae aggregate conspicuously at the top of their host-plant ragwort; *Heliconius* and Ithomiinae butterflies fly slowly several metres above the ground in tropical forest, in full sight of insect-feeding birds. These butterflies, like the cinnabar moth, acquire their toxins as larvae. The larvae of *Heliconius* are found only on *Passiflora* species (passion-vines), with different *Heliconius* specializing on different *Passiflora*. The Ithomiinae are also restricted to plant species in two closely related families; the Solanaceae (tomato and potato family) and the Apocynaceae.

Now we should consider an important consequence of warning coloration which has implications for biological diversity.

○ If two herbivorous insect species with chemical defences had a common predator, what might be the relationship between the colours of the insect?

● It may be that selection pressures result in colours being similar so that a predator quickly recognizes a potentially toxic insect. In other words, an insect with warning colours different from those of other herbivorous insects may be attacked because a predator, such as a bird, would not recognize it as toxic.

In short, it is predicted that selection pressures could produce mimicry in potentially toxic insects (the concept of mimicry was introduced in Chapter 3). This mimicry amongst animals living in the same area can take two forms. In Mullerian mimicry, described in the text question and Chapter 3 (Section 3.3), *all* individuals are toxic and have similar markings. In other words they share a common badge, which reinforces the message of potential toxicity to predators. However, the evolution of warning coloration also produces the possibility of 'cheating', which may occur if an animal which is *not* toxic evolves warning coloration. The animal has the benefits of the warning colours without the costs of dealing with the plant defence. This situation is known as **Batesian mimicry** in which there are toxic and non-toxic species sharing the same markings. Both forms of mimicry are found in *Heliconius* and Ithomiinae butterflies and members of other butterfly and day-flying moth families in Central and South America. These two types of mimicry are named after the biologists who first studied them (Box 5.1 and Figure 5.25).

BOX 5.1   BATES AND MULLER

Henry Walter Bates (1825–1892) sailed from Liverpool for South America with his friend Alfred Russel Wallace (who later achieved fame by describing a theory of evolution similar to Charles Darwin's) on 25 April 1848. After one month they reached the mouth of the Amazon. They spent the next two years travelling together up the Amazon. On 26 March 1850 they parted company with Bates travelling along the Upper Amazon. He remained in the region for nine years, making many important observations on natural history, in particular insect life. He returned to England in 1859 with a collection of more than 8000 new species, most of which were insects.

Fritz Muller was a major early supporter of Darwin. He published widely on the life history, morphology, systematics and evolution of insects. He was one of the earliest scientists to apply mathematical arguments to evolution.

(a)   (b)

Figure 5.25   (a) H. W. Bates. (b) F. W. Müller.

We have assumed that the insect herbivores in Figure 5.24 can obtain the defence chemicals from the plant. What is the evidence for this assumption? The methods of acquisition of chemical defences have been studied in detail for one class of alkaloids — the pyrrolizidine alkaloids (more easily pronounced as PAs!). PAs are found in various plants including the genus *Senecio*. The cinnabar moth uses the PAs from its larval host-plant ragwort. Many of the Ithomiinae butterflies also use PAs. There appear to be three methods by which the Ithomiinae and other insect herbivores can obtain their PAs.

1   Larvae consume the plant, sequester the PAs and store them in the body during larval growth and pupation.

2   Adults collect the PAs from the host plants, either by nectar feeding (the nectar contains the PAs) or by probing withered leaves.

3   *De novo* biosynthesis of defensive chemicals in the animals — the chemicals from the plants (acquired through routes 1 or 2) possibly acting as precursors.

The first method has been found in several Neotropical butterfly species, including *Tithorea harmonia*, a member of the Ithomiinae, during larval feeding on PA-containing plants such as *Prestonia acutifolia*, a member of the Apocynaceae. The Ithomiinae divide into species which feed as larvae on Apocynaceae and those (the majority) which feed on Solanaceae. The second method of acquisition is well known for the Solanaceae-feeding Ithomiinae. Whilst they acquire some alkaloids (but not PAs) through larval feeding, the PAs are acquired through feeding by adult males. Tests with butterfly-eating spiders showed that freshly emerged adults (i.e. before they had started feeding) of Solanaceae-feeding Ithomiinae were not protected, in contrast to adults caught in the field, after they had been able to collect PAs. Chemical analysis confirmed that the freshly emerged adults did *not* have PAs, in contrast to the field-caught individuals.

The role of the males in the Solanaceae-feeding Ithomiinae is very interesting. It is known that the PAs can also serve as precursors to male pheromones which attract females. So it seems that males gather the PAs and females assess the alkaloid content of courting males, according to their PA-derived pheromone levels, and choose a mate with the greatest quantity. Males can then pass alkaloids to females via the sperm package.

Finally, where do poison arrow frogs fit into the picture? They represent the next link in the food chain — their skins contain alkaloids which are believed to be acquired by the consumption of insects (which themselves contain alkaloids). Thus there is the possibility that alkaloids synthesized in the plant for defence against herbivores are being used two steps up the food chain, protecting the frogs against their natural enemies!

5.5.4 AN EXPERIMENT TO DETERMINE THE COST OF DEFENCE AND ITS GENETIC BASIS (FURTHER EVIDENCE FOR COEVOLUTION)

At several points in this chapter we have alluded to the idea that chemical, cellular or physical defence may carry a cost to the organism producing it. Determining the size and nature of this cost is important because it has to be traded off against other vital functions such as reproduction. Assessment of the cost of defence is difficult for two reasons. First a suitable 'currency' has to be chosen. The proximate cost to the organism can be measured in terms of energy or nutrients. Ultimately the cost is in terms of the relative fitness of the organism so we need to determine changes in relative fitness. In practical terms that often means measuring one component of fitness such as change in survival or fecundity (Chapter 3). The second problem is to devise an experimental system within which the changes in fitness can be assessed. The aim of this section is to illustrate an experimental method using a plant–insect herbivore system. The method relies on the fact that there is variation between individuals in the extent of defence. In this case, we consider not only whether there is a cost to defence but also whether the characters have evolved in response to herbivore pressure. In short we will consider experimental evidence for plant–insect coevolution.

It is important to test the coevolution hypothesis that plant resistance characters have evolved in response to herbivory (a general version of the plant defence theory of Ehrlich and Raven for secondary compounds). This is because there is an alternative hypothesis that the characters evolved to serve other ecological or physiological plant functions, such as drought tolerance, and that the herbivores evolved in response to these characters. This hypothesis is known as the **'sequential evolution hypothesis',** in which herbivores play no role in plant evolution.

Mauricio and Rausher (1997) pointed out that the distinction between the two hypotheses 'lies in the nature of the selective agents assumed to be responsible for the evolution of resistance characters'. If the coevolution hypothesis is correct, the selective agents are herbivores, but for sequential evolution, they are not herbivores. Mauricio and Rausher suggested that the best experimental test to distinguish between the hypotheses would be to *remove* the proposed selective agent and examine the response of the plants.

○ Under the sequential evolution hypothesis, what is the expected response of plants to experimental removal of herbivores?

● There should be no response.

The plant *Arabidopsis thaliana* (Brassicaceae, cabbage family, Figure 5.26) was used because the species is known to have genetic variation for two characters that reduce damage by herbivores under natural conditions: total glucosinolate concentration and trichome density. Glucosinolates are a group of natural products found in all Brassicaceae. Trichomes are small hairs which act as a physical defence against herbivory.

If there is a fitness cost to producing these defence characters and the coevolution hypothesis is true, then removal of herbivores should result in reduction of these characters. Common herbivores of *A. thaliana* in the United States (where the study was undertaken) include two species of flea beetle in the family Chrysomelidae (the leaf beetles), the common name of flea being given because of their greatly enlarged hind legs, which allow them to jump between leaves.

Arabidopsis thaliana is mainly self-fertilizing and therefore seed from each plant forms an inbred line. Seed was collected from 144 plants, germinated and plants grown in the same environmental conditions. This procedure was repeated over three generations to ensure maternal effects (e.g. nutrients passed directly from mother plant to seed) were similar so only genetic differences remained between inbred lines. Twelve young plants from the third generation of each of the 144 inbred lines were transplanted into a field. Half of the plants were sprayed with insecticide to remove insects and the other half allowed to be infested by flea beetles.

○ What is the possible flaw in the experimental design of spraying insecticide?

● The insecticide may act directly on the plant (rather than simply removing insects). This possibility was eliminated by measuring growth in the presence and absence of insecticide.

Figure 5.26 *Arabidopsis thaliana.*

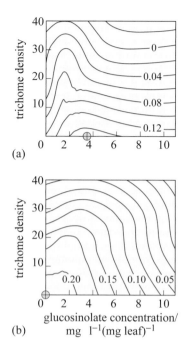

(a)

(b) glucosinolate concentration/
mg l^{-1}(mg leaf)$^{-1}$

Figure 5.27 Contour plots of change in relative fitness with glucosinolate concentration (mg l^{-1} (mg leaf)$^{-1}$) and trichome density (number of trichomes per 2.4 mm^2). Each of the red contour lines shows points of equal relative fitness. The symbol ⊕ indicates the point of maximum fitness. (a) Change in fitness in presence of herbivores (control unsprayed treatment). (b) Change in fitness in absence of herbivores (sprayed treatment) Note how the contour lines increase in value towards the bottom left corner of the graph. Based on Mauricio and Rausher (1997).

After three months a series of measurements was made on the plants. Flea beetles chew the leaves producing characteristic 'shot-gun' holes. The number of holes in the leaves was counted to give a measure of herbivory. Glucosinolate levels were measured in four leaves of each plant and trichome density was estimated in a fixed area on the upper side of each of four leaves. The total number of fruits was measured to give an estimate of fitness. As *A. thaliana* has only one bout of flowering, fruit number represents the reproductive output of a plant. Assuming no differences in survival, relative fitness can then be calculated as the total number of fruits of an individual divided by the maximum number of fruits of any individual.

Statistical analysis of the data was complex but the results were very clear. The patterns of relative fitness of plants with and without herbivores showed significant effects of total glucosinolate concentration and trichome density. In the presence of herbivores maximum fitness (indicated by the symbol ⊕) occurred at zero trichome density but at a glucosinolate concentration of 3.5 (Figure 5.27a). In the absence of herbivores, maximum relative fitness occurred at zero glucosinolate and zero trichome density (Figure 5.27b).

○ What does the pattern in the presence of herbivores suggest would be the long term consequences of herbivores on *A. thaliana*?

● In the presence of herbivores, it is predicted that individuals without trichomes and with a glucosinolate concentration of 3.5 would replace other individuals.

○ Why do *A. thaliana* individuals possess trichomes if the maximum fitness of plants occurs in the absence of the trichomes, regardless of whether herbivores are present or absent?

● Other herbivores, not present in this study, may be affected by trichomes. Under these conditions, plants with trichomes do have a higher relative fitness. It may also be that this state was ancestral, i.e. that the trichomes evolved in response to herbivores which are now extinct or very rare, so that the *A. thaliana* populations are moving towards being free of trichomes.

Overall this study strongly suggested that producing glucosinolates and trichomes has a fitness cost, so that when herbivores are not present the best strategy for the plant is to produce neither physical nor chemical defences. Thus these experiments and observations support the coevolution hypothesis as set out by Mauricio and Rausher.

SUMMARY OF SECTION 5.5

1 There are several lines of evidence to show that organisms involved in attack and defence have coevolved and that trade-offs are occurring between devoting resources to defence or to other functions such as reproduction.

2 A consequence of coevolution between hosts and their pathogens is that virulence tends towards an optimum level which ensures the survival of both the host and the pathogen species. Hosts may tolerate a greater pathogen load during periods of high reproductive effort.

3   Comparison of the phylogenies of hosts and parasites provide further evidence for coevolution. Blood parasites in the order Haemosporina seem to have coevolved with their dipteran (fly) vectors rather than their vertebrate hosts.

4   Coevolution of some plants and insect herbivores has led to the latter using the plants' defence for themselves, which in turn has contributed to the evolution of warning coloration and mimicry.

5   Experimental evidence for coevolution in plants and herbivores has come from a study in which the removal of herbivores was associated with increased fitness of plants, due to the reduced cost of defence.

REFERENCES

Beck, G. and Habicht, G. S. (1996) Immunity and the invertebrates, *Scientific American,* November, pp. 42–46.

Carey, C., Cohen, N. and Rollins-Smith, L. (1999) Amphibian declines: an immunological perspective, *Developmental and Comparative Immunology*, **23**, pp. 459–472.

Daszak, P., Berger, L., Cunningham, A. A. *et al.*, (1999) Emerging infectious diseases and amphibian population declines, *Emerging Infectious Diseases*, **5** (6), pp. 735–748.

Ebert, D. and Hamilton, W. D. (1996) Sex against virulence: the coevolution of parasitic diseases, *Trends in Evolution and Ecology*, **11** (2), pp. 79–82.

Ehrlich P. R. and Raven, P. H. (1964) Butterflies and plants: a study in coevolution. *Evolution*, **18**, 586–608.

Fearon, D. T. (1997) Seeking wisdom in innate immunity, *Nature,* **388**, pp. 323–324.

Feeny, P. P. (1976). Plant apparency and chemical defence. *Recent Advances in Phytochemistry*, **10**, 1–40.

Ganz, T. and Lehrer, R. I. (1999) Antibiotic peptides from higher eukaryotes: biology and applications, *Molecular Medicine Today*, **5** (7), pp. 292–297.

Krebs, C. J. (1994) *Ecology*. Harper Collins, New York.

Maniero, G. D. and Carey, C. (1997) Changes in selected aspects of immune function in the leopard frog, *Rana pipiens*, associated with exposure to cold, *Journal of Comparative Physiology*, **167**, pp. 256–263.

Mauricio, R. and Rausher, M. D. (1997) Experimental manipulation of putative selective agents provides evidence for the role of natural enemies in the evolution of plant defence. *Evolution*, **51**, 1435–1444.

Møller, A. P., Christe, P. and Lux, E. (1999) Parasitism, host immune function and sexual selection, *The Quarterly Review of Biology,* **74** (1), pp. 3–20.

Owens, I. and Olson, V. (1999) Costly sexual signals: are carotenoids rare, risky or required? *Trends in Ecology and Evolution*, **13** (12), pp. 510–514.

Rhoades, D. F. and Cates, R. G. (1976). Towards a general theory of plant antiherbivore chemistry. *Recent Advances in Phytochemistry*, **19**, 168–213.

Sheldon, B. C. and Verhulst, S. (1996) Ecological immunology: costly parasite defences and trade-offs in evolutionary ecology, *Trends in Evolution and Ecology*, **11** (8), pp. 317–321.

Stefano, G. B., Salzet, B. and Fricchione, G. L. (1998) Enkelytin and opioid peptide association in invertebrates and vertebrates: immune activation and pain, *Immunology Today*, **19** (6), pp. 265–268.

Zapata, A. G., Varas, A. and Torroba, M. (1992) Seasonal variations in the immune system of lower vertebrates, *Immunology Today*, **13** (4), pp. 142–147.

FURTHER READING

Carey, C., Cohen, N. and Rollins-Smith, L. (1999) Amphibian declines: an immunological perspective, *Developmental and Comparative Immunology,* **23**, 459–472. [The authors review the damaging effects of climate change and atmospheric pollution on the immune defences of amphibian populations in different geographic locations, and conclude that increased susceptibility to infection is a major contributor to amphibian population declines.]

Daszak, P., Berger, L., Cunningham, A. A. *et al.* (1999) Emerging infectious diseases and amphibian population declines, *Emerging Infectious Diseases,* **5**, 735–748. [Two emerging infectious diseases — the fungal infection chytridiomycosis and ranaviral disease — are implicated in the sharp rise in the rate of extinctions and population decline among amphibians around the world.]

Ganz, T. and Lehrer, R. I. (1999) Antibiotic peptides from higher eukaryotes: biology and applications, *Molecular Medicine Today,* **5**, pp. 292–297. [This article reviews the prospects for extracting naturally occurring antibiotics from a wide range of animal species, from moths to frogs, which may overcome the problem of bacterial resistance to antibiotics such as penicillin.]

Krebs, C. J. (1994) *Ecology*. Harper Collins, New York. [This is an important reference book for all aspects of ecology, with an excellent section on plant–herbivore interactions and plant defences.]

Ottaviani, E. and Franceschi, C. (1997) The invertebrate phagocytic immunocyte: clues to a common evolution of immune and neuroendocrine systems, *Immunology Today,* **18**, pp. 169–173. [Structural and biochemical similarities between the phagocytes of the innate immune system and cells involved in the nervous or endocrine systems of invertebrates provide evidence that these physiological systems are in constant interaction with the immune system, and that this communication is part of the fine-tuning of the immune response.]

Owens, I. and Olson, V. (1999) Costly sexual signals: are carotenoids rare, risky or required? *Trends in Ecology and Evolution,* **13**, pp. 510–514. [Research is reviewed which suggests that the carotenoid pigments used by many animals in colourful display signals may also have a central role in maintaining the immune defence system, and that trade-offs between defence against infection and attracting a mate may be occurring.]

Roitt, I., Brostoff, J. and Male, D. (1996) (4th edn), *Immunology*, Mosby, London. [This well-organized and superbly illustrated textbook is highly recommended to anyone wanting a detailed but accessible account of how the immune system develops and defends animals (including humans) from infectious organisms and parasites.]

Zapata, A. G., Varas, A. and Torroba, M. (1992) Seasonal variations in the immune system of lower vertebrates, *Immunology Today,* **13**, pp. 142–147. [This article summarizes the authors' model of how the immune responsiveness of Amphibia and other cold-blooded vertebrates fluctuates seasonally, leading to the proposition that reduction in defence against infection is a price worth paying for the advantage conferred by winter hibernation.]

LONGEVITY

6.1   INTRODUCTION

It is the fate of all sexually reproducing organisms to die, but there is enormous variation, both within and between species, in how long they can live before they do so.

Longevity is defined as the length of an organism's life. It is one component of its life history and must thus be considered along with other life history variables. Of crucial importance is the concept of a life history trade-off: to live for a long time, an organism must allocate less of its resources to other life history functions, such as reproduction and defence, and more to maintaining itself.

6.1.1   AGE AND LONGEVITY

Detailed analysis of longevity, in species other than humans, is limited by a scarcity of reliable data on how long animals and plants live in nature. The data that do exist for other species come from three sources.

One method is to mark or label individual organisms at birth and record their death. Marking individuals in the wild is a time-consuming and often difficult task and, for some groups of organisms, is not practical. The best data are for birds, which are easily fitted with leg rings before they leave the nest. Even when individuals are marked early in life, the chance of field biologists witnessing their death is very small. The recapture of live animals that were marked at a known age does, however, provide good data on the relative frequencies of different age classes in a population and thus allows us to deduce longevity, as described below.

It is also possible to determine the age of individuals directly. In seasonal habitats, trees can be aged by counting the number of growth rings in their cut trunks or, less invasively, by taking small cores from their trunks, and some molluscs can be aged by counting growth rings in their shells. A comparable technique is widely used to age ectothermic ('cold-blooded') vertebrates, such as amphibians and reptiles. In temperate habitats, these animals typically have a growth spurt in spring, when food is abundant, but show no growth during the rest of the year. This pattern is shown in cross-sections of their bones which, when appropriately stained, show alternating pale and dark rings, representing annual changes in rate of growth. These preparations can be made from a single finger or toe, so that an animal does not have to be killed to determine its age. The number of such rings thus provides a good estimate of age. A similar method can be used for some fishes, the scales of which show lines which indicate seasonal changes in growth rate.

When the age of a large sample of individuals has been determined, it is possible to plot the relative frequencies of individuals of different ages, a procedure that reveals the **age structure** of the population, as shown in Figure 6.1.

Figure 6.1 Histogram showing the age structure of a population of adult (i.e. after metamorphosis from the tadpole stage) common toads (*Bufo bufo*). Data from Gittins *et al.* (1982).

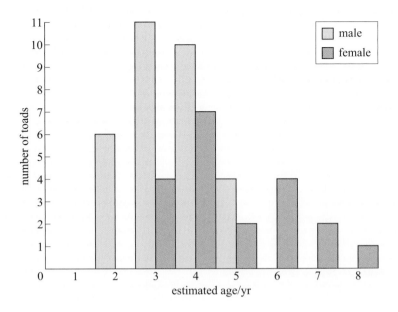

○ What is the most abundant age class of male and female toads in this population?

● Three years among males, four years among females.

These classes are called the *modal* age classes for each sex.

The ages at death of animals that die in captivity, for example in zoos, have also been recorded. Such data are of limited value because they are a poor reflection of average longevity. Animals may survive for longer in captivity than they normally do in the wild. For example, common toads have been known to live for 40 years or more in captivity, but field data suggest that they rarely live beyond ten years in the wild.

○ Why might animals live longer in captivity than in the wild?

● Captive animals do not have to find their own food, and are protected from many natural causes of mortality, such as predation and some diseases.

Once reliable data have been obtained for individuals of a given species, we need to derive some measure of age, so that data from one species can be compared with those from another. Maximum longevity is sometimes used for this purpose (see below), but is of limited value, because the maxima may be unrepresentative of age across a population. For example, a very few people have lived to be over 100 years old, but such records are clearly not representative as a measure of human longevity. Another possibility is to determine the average age of individuals in a population of a species, but this measure too is sometimes of little value.

Consider, for example, the common toad (*Bufo bufo*). A single female toad lays between 1000 and 3000 eggs in a single season. More than 99% of them fail to develop beyond the smallest tadpole stage; most are killed by frost, fungal infection, desiccation or predation by fish, newts and insect larvae. Of the tiny number of tadpoles that survive through this hazardous early stage and become toads, some, as shown in Figure 6.1, may live to be at least eight years old. The mean longevity of an entire clutch of *Bufo* eggs is a matter of days or weeks, but calculating the mean age of adult toads, which is three to four years, takes no account of the huge mortality that occurs early in life during the egg and tadpole stages.

There is no single measure that adequately summarizes the longevity of a species with a complex life cycle, like a toad. To gain a full picture of longevity in a particular species, it is necessary to take account of the fact that mortality rate (frequency of death in a population) changes with age, and to compute, for different ages, the expectation of further life. Figure 6.2 shows **survival plots** for two types of bird.

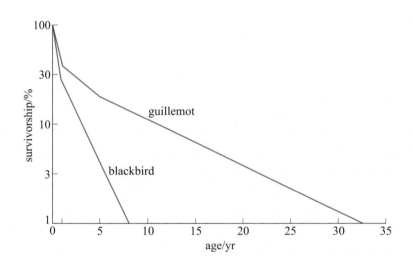

Figure 6.2   Survival plots for guillemots (a typical seabird, order Charadriiformes) and blackbirds (order Passeriformes). Note that the vertical scale is logarithmic. Data from Campbell and Lack (1985).

In both types of bird, annual mortality is very high in the first year of life. Thereafter, annual mortality is lower, especially for the seabirds. The outcome is that a few guillemots can be expected to reach the age of 32 years, while maximum longevity for most blackbirds is eight years. Table 6.1 presents data for a number of bird species and shows that, as one would expect, there is an inverse relationship between annual mortality and longevity.

Table 6.1   Annual mortality and life expectancy in some birds.

Species	Annual adult mortality/%	Expectation of further life at adulthood/yr*
small paserines	70	0.9
wood pigeon (*Columba palumbus*)	40	2.0
swift (*Apus apus*)	20	4.5
yellow-eyed penguin (*Megadyptes antipodes*)	10	9.5
royal albatross (*Diomedea epomophora*)	3	32.8

* Number of years of life beyond the point when bird reaches adulthood.

6.1.2 DIVERSITY IN LONGEVITY

Although, for the reasons given above, values for maximum longevity do not give a truly representative picture, they can be useful for illustrating the marked differences in longevity that exist between species. Plants have very wide ranges of longevities: while many small herbs are annuals, some, including *Arabidopsis thaliana*, completing their life cycle in a few weeks, most trees live for decades or centuries, and a few, including yew and bristle-cone pines, can live for millennia. Table 6.2 presents a selection of longevity data for various animals.

Table 6.2   Maximum recorded lifespans in a selection of animals.

Taxonomic group	Common name	Maximum recorded lifespan/yr
Invertebrates		
Platyhelminthes	tapeworm	35+
	planarian	6–7
Arthropoda, Crustacea	lobster	50
	barnacle	5+
Insecta, Lepidoptera	butterflies	0.2–0.75
Mollusca	scallop	22
	mussel	100+
	slug	3
	octopus	3–4
Vertebrates		
Osteichthyes (bony fish)	sea horse	1
	lake sturgeon	82
	white sturgeon	30
	cod	85
	haddock	26
Reptilia	Chinese alligator	52
	Galapagos tortoise	100+
Aves (birds)	domestic dove	30
	eagle	46
	eagle owl	68
Mammalia	house mouse	3
	sheep	20
	horse	46
Primates	rhesus monkey	29
	chimpanzee	44
	human	118

The data in Table 6.2 illustrate the enormous diversity in longevity among animals. Many insects have life cycles that last less than a year; some turtles and tortoises can live for more than 100 years. Even closely related species can have very different longevities. The lake sturgeon lives nearly three times as long as the white sturgeon, for example. In general, vertebrates live longer than invertebrates, though there are some notable exceptions; for example, some mussels live for more than 100 years.

Another general pattern that emerges from data on maximum longevity is that, among birds and mammals, larger species live longer than smaller ones (Figure 6.3). Figure 6.3 also enables us to compare different groups of animals. Birds live longer than mammals in general, but bats live much longer than both birds and other mammals of comparable body size.

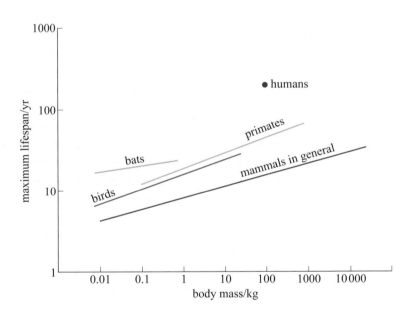

Figure 6.3 The relationship between maximum recorded lifespan and body mass in wild mammals, humans and birds. Note that humans are exceptional among mammals. Both scales are logarithmic to enable the widely ranging data to be displayed on a single graph. Data from Stearns (1992).

6.2 THE CAUSES OF DEATH

We have seen that, in general, biologists know very little about how long organisms live. For most species, they know even less about why they die, because they rarely witness the death of individuals in the wild. In some cases, *post-mortem* examination is possible, but the results are often inconclusive. Organisms die through a variety of causes, which are categorized under two headings: **intrinsic** and **extrinsic mortality factors**. Extrinsic factors are those that arise through interactions with the environment, as discussed below.

1   *Starvation.* Organisms nearly always produce many more offspring than can be sustained by the food supply. Consequently, in many species, among them the African lion, starvation early in life is a major cause of mortality. In many birds, notably birds of prey, the chicks hatch at intervals of a few days and the parents always preferentially feed the first-born, which grows rapidly, while its less frequently fed siblings often die from starvation before fledging. Among plants, many young die as a result of lack of light or space.

2 *Infections*. Animals and plants are continually exposed to infection by a wide diversity of pathogenic microbes and animal, fungal and microbial parasites. The impact that disease and parasites have on natural populations is well understood in only a few instances, for example among red grouse (*Lagopus scoticus*) living on British moorland. The general picture that emerges from such studies is that infectious diseases and parasites have little impact on life expectancy, but that they do have a marked negative effect on reproductive output and competitive ability, a point to which we will return later. Occasionally, lethal outbreaks of infection are recorded; for example, mass mortalities of amphibians were reported during the 1990s in Australia, central America and southeast England; Dutch elm disease devastated elm populations in Europe and the USA during the 1960s and 70s.

3 *Being eaten*. Plants are eaten by herbivores, herbivores by predators; nearly all animals, except many internal parasites and animals at the very top of a food chain, are subject to predation. In many species, mortality through predation is especially severe in young, small organisms and during dispersal.

4 *Accidents and random environmental events*. Before they become fully competent in coping with their environment, young animals are prone to accidental death. For example, the young of cliff-nesting birds are at risk of falling off narrow ledges. Many animals die accidentally as a result of human influences; in industrialized countries, death on the road accounts for huge numbers of frogs, snakes, hedgehogs and badgers, as well as low-flying birds such as owls. Extreme weather conditions, such as severe storms, floods and prolonged frosts and droughts, also frequently cause mass mortalities. For both plants and animals, fire of natural or human origin can have a devastating effect on a population, though many plants and animals are very well adapted to survive naturally occurring fires.

6.2.1 INTRINSIC FACTORS IN MORTALITY

'I hope I die before I get old.' (The Who)

Intrinsic factors that cause mortality underlie the phenomenon of ageing, or senescence. **Senescence** is defined as a progressive deterioration in structure and function of cells, tissues, organs, etc. with time since that function commenced. As humans, we are very familiar with the way that ageing affects us and our pets, but it is much less obvious in wild organisms, for the simple reason that most die of other causes before they become old. Furthermore, because senescence involves a decline in various life functions, ageing organisms become more susceptible to extrinsic mortality factors, such as predation.

Many arguments have been put forward to explain the evolution of ageing. Those set out below are not mutually exclusive and each may be of relevance to some species but not others. There is no single mechanism or process that causes senescence.

1 *Death is adaptive*; that is, it has been favoured by natural selection. The most common argument proposed to support this hypothesis is that, by dying, adults do not compete with their offspring and therefore enhance their

chances of surviving. This kind of argument can only apply where adults and their young are in direct competition for the same resources, such as food or light. Many animals have one or more larval stages with diets and habits partly or completely different from those of their parents. Even when development is direct (i.e. there is no larva), the generations are not in direct competition, because the adults are larger than their progeny. However, in plants, large adults (e.g. trees) often compete strongly with smaller offspring growing nearby, for light, water and soil nutrients.

Other arguments arise from the general principle that the power of natural selection declines as organisms approach their age of death.

2   *The 'genetic dustbin' hypothesis*. Natural selection eliminates genes that cause mortality prior to reproduction, but cannot eliminate 'late-acting' genes that shorten an organism's lifespan after it has reproduced. Senescence is thus due to the combined effect of harmful genes that selection has not eliminated from the gene pool.

3   *The 'disposable soma' hypothesis*. Natural selection favours individuals that invest heavily in reproduction early in life and, as a consequence, insufficient resources are invested in mechanisms that repair genes and replace defective proteins. As a result, genetic and molecular defects gradually accumulate throughout life and cause senescence after reproduction.

4   *Decline in the effectiveness of the immune system*. Perhaps as a result of the processes suggested in (2) and (3), the immune system becomes less effective with increasing age. This hypothesis is supported by the fact that, in humans, the incidence of both infectious and auto-immune diseases increases with age.

5   *Antagonistic pleiotropy*. Pleiotropy means that genes have multiple effects on the phenotype. Genes that are favoured by natural selection because they have advantageous effects early in life may have deleterious effects in later life. In female rodents, the secretion of oestrogen, essential for reproductive function early in life, has damaging effects on the hypothalamus (a part of the brain), which are manifested in later life. It has also been suggested that, in humans, oestrogen promotes fertility in early life but may later be a causal factor in breast cancer.

6   *Free-radical damage*. Highly reactive metabolites that act as oxidizing agents damage proteins, lipids and DNA. The accumulation of the products of free-radical damage leads to malfunctioning of structural tissues and aberrant metabolism.

6.2.2 TRADE-OFF BETWEEN LONGEVITY AND REPRODUCTION

A fundamental assumption in life history theory is that there is a trade-off between reproduction and longevity; that is, individuals that produce more offspring and/or nurture them more intensively or for longer have shorter lives than those that invest less heavily in reproduction. The most obvious way to test this assumption is to measure reproductive investment in many individuals of the same species and to see what kind of relationship it has with longevity.

○ What kind of relationship would you expect?

● An inverse relationship, i.e. a negative correlation.

Figures 6.4 and 6.5 show the results of two studies that have examined the correlation between reproductive effort and longevity in small, short-lived invertebrates that can be conveniently maintained in the laboratory. Rotifers are tiny, filter-feeding invertebrate animals. Under ideal laboratory conditions, they can produce parthenogenetic offspring every few hours over a lifespan of only a few days or weeks. In this study, the numbers of offspring produced during each 12 h period were measured, and from these measurements age-specific fecundity could be calculated.

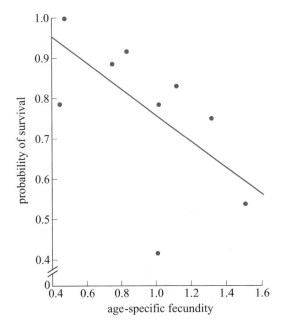

Figure 6.4   Relationship between probability of survival and current fecundity (i.e. eggs laid per female) in the rotifer *Asplancha brightwelli*. Data from Begon *et al.* (1986).

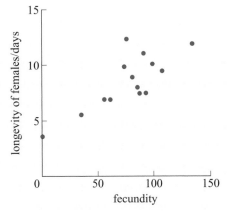

Figure 6.5   Relationship between longevity of the adult (i.e. sexual) stage and fecundity in females of the seed-eating beetle *Callosobruchus maculatus*. Beetles spend most of the life cycle as a grub-like larva, which moults several times before it develops into an adult. Data from Lessels (1991).

○ Do the data presented in Figures 6.4 and 6.5 support the prediction that longevity and reproductive effort are negatively correlated?

● The data for rotifers (Figure 6.4) do, but those for beetles (Figure 6.5) show a positive correlation, the opposite to what is predicted. Beetles that have more offspring also live longer as adults.

Many studies of this kind have been carried out, and the results are very variable. Some have yielded the expected negative correlation, many a positive correlation, and others no correlation at all. Where do these data leave the hypothesis that there is a trade-off between reproductive effort and longevity? The answer is that a failure to find a negative correlation does not represent evidence against such a trade-off, because this kind of correlation approach is not an appropriate test of the hypothesis. The argument goes as follows.

Suppose that individuals in a population differ in their ability to acquire the resources that they need to sustain both survival and reproduction. Suppose then that all individuals make an identical trade-off, allocating resources to survival and reproduction in the ratio 4 : 6, for example. Those individuals that have acquired more resources therefore allocate more resources to *both* survival and reproduction than those that have acquired less. This strategy would produce a positive correlation like that shown in Figure 6.5. Thus, because trade-offs are made at the level of the individual, and because organisms differ in their ability to acquire resources, finding correlations *between* individuals does not reveal trade-offs within a single life history.

A valid method for obtaining evidence that a trade-off exists is to conduct an experiment in which an organism is forced to invest more than it otherwise would in either survival or reproduction. If an animal, for example, is somehow made to invest more in reproduction, the trade-off hypothesis predicts that its longevity is reduced. Figure 6.6 shows the results of an experiment on the same species of beetle as that from which the data in Figure 6.5 were obtained. In this experiment, female beetles were assigned to four treatments, in which their reproductive effort was manipulated by controlling their access to males and/or to sites (beans) where they could deposit their eggs.

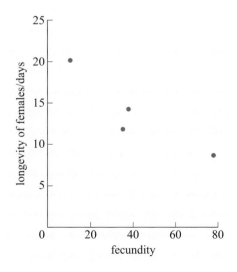

Figure 6.6 Relationship between longevity and fecundity in females of the beetle *Callosobruchus maculatus*, in an experiment in which female reproductive effort was experimentally manipulated. Data from Lessels (1991).

○ Do the data in Figure 6.6 support the hypothesis that there is a trade-off between longevity and reproductive effort?

● Yes, they do. As predicted, the correlation is negative.

Thus evidence that organisms do make a trade-off between longevity and reproduction can be obtained from experiments in which the effort that an organism invests in reproduction is manipulated. As you will see later in this chapter, the same is true of other kinds of life history trade-offs.

SUMMARY OF SECTIONS 6.1 AND 6.2

1   Longevity is difficult to measure in wild animals and values for captive specimens may not be representative.

2   Survival plots summarize the mortality pattern of a particular species. Those of closely related species can differ greatly.

3   Ageing (senescence) is an intrinsic cause of death; extrinsic factors from the environment include starvation, disease, predation and accidents.

4   Organisms that produce many offspring at an early age have shorter lives than similar species that delay reproduction, i.e. there is a trade-off between longevity and reproduction.

6.3   LONGEVITY AND REPRODUCTION

If organisms are to pass on their genes to the next generation, they must reproduce before they die. Short-lived organisms have no option but to reproduce early in life, but long-lived organisms may follow a range of different life histories. For example, they may delay reproduction until they are old and then reproduce only once; they may start breeding early and then reproduce several times during their lives, or they may delay breeding and breed more than once. A basic distinction that is made in this context is between organisms that reproduce only once, a condition called **semelparity** (Latin, 'once breeding'), and those that breed several times, called **iteroparity** (Latin, 'repeated breeding'). Organisms with these breeding strategies are called semelparous and iteroparous, respectively.

6.3.1   A GENERAL THEORY OF LIFE HISTORY EVOLUTION

Biologists seek to relate life history variables, such as longevity and pattern of reproduction, to environmental variables, to produce general theories of life history evolution. The most influential of such theories involves distinguishing between the **growth rate** of a population, and its maximum size as determined by the nature of the habitat, called its **carrying capacity**. A population such as that illustrated in Figure 6.7 increases in numbers at an initially slow, but then accelerating rate, because there is no predation or competition. At a certain population size, it reaches a maximum growth rate (indicated by the maximum gradient of the curve). As the population gets larger, it grows more slowly as a result of competition between individuals for increasingly scarce resources, and eventually reaches the carrying capacity of the habitat. Theoretically, life history characters can be divided into those that maximize population growth rate and those that maximize carrying capacity.

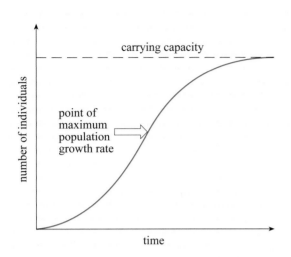

Figure 6.7 The relationship between the size of an expanding population of organisms and time, showing the point of maximum population growth rate and the carrying capacity of the habitat.

The theoretical features of organisms and of habitats which maximize the rate of population growth or carrying capacity are summarized in Table 6.3.

Table 6.3 Summary of properties of habitats and life histories that maximize carrying capacity or population growth rate.

	Maximizes carrying capacity	Maximizes population growth rate
habitat	stable, favourable to growth and survival	unstable and harsh
life history character		
development	slow	fast
adult body size	large	small
age at first reproduction	late in lifespan	early in lifespan
frequency of breeding	iteroparity	semelparity
number of progeny per breeding episode	few	many
lifespan	long	short
generation time	long	short

When it was first proposed, this very simple approach to life histories was greeted with much enthusiasm but, as researchers have studied a greater variety of organisms, the initial support has waned considerably, because most species are found to have life histories with a mixture of the properties listed in Table 6.3. For example, in comparison to other frogs and toads, the European fire-bellied toad (*Bombina variegata*) lives in unstable habitats, breeding in ephemeral ponds; it has a small adult body size and it starts to breed early in life. However, it also has a long lifespan, breeds many times during its life and, at each breeding episode, produces only a small clutch of eggs.

Figure 6.8 Giant timber bamboo (*Bambus oldhamii*).

The life history of a the giant timber bamboo, *Bambus oldhamii* (Figure 6.8) makes a similar point. This large species of the grass family flowers only once and then dies, but lives to an age of about 120 years before doing so!

Most ecologists now regard the distinctions made in Table 6.3 as being of considerable value in helping to provide a conceptual framework for thinking about life histories, but of only limited value in terms of characterizing individual species. It is best to see the two strategies as the extremes of a continuum, within which the great majority of species fall, showing a 'mosaic' of characters, like the fire-bellied toad.

6.3.2 BODY SIZE AND TIMING OF REPRODUCTION

If an organism delays reproduction, or limits its reproductive effort early in life, is it able to achieve higher reproductive success later in life? In other words, is there a trade-off between reproduction early in life and later in life? To answer this question, we have to consider another variable, which is related to both age and reproductive success, body size.

There are basically two patterns of growth during life: continuous growth and asymptotic growth (Figure 6.9). **Asymptotic growth** is typical of most insects, birds and mammals and means that growth ceases once a species-typical adult size has been reached. Animals such as most fish, amphibians and reptiles, and plants, show **continuous growth**; they grow throughout their lives, albeit at a declining rate as they get older. Typically, growth is rapid before the onset of reproduction, and is much slower thereafter, as in the frog curve in Figure 6.9.

The reason why body size becomes important in the context of longevity and reproduction is that, in many organisms, there is a positive correlation between individual body size and reproductive success. In most plants and in animals that lay eggs, female fecundity usually correlates with body size (Figure 6.10). In mammals, larger females often produce larger litters, but even in those species that produce only one young at a time, offspring survival is often positively correlated with maternal size. As a result, it is often adaptive for females to delay reproduction until they have reached a body size at which they can achieve high reproductive success.

Among males, body size is sometimes correlated with reproductive success, but for very different reasons. Body size does not normally constrain gamete production as it does in many females; even very small males can produce sufficient sperm to fertilize the eggs of many females and greater body size does not confer any advantage in this respect. Male size is, however, very important in species in which males compete aggressively with one another for females and in which larger males have an advantage in fighting, for example in red deer and elephant seals, as discussed below.

Female common toads (*Bufo bufo*) living in Britain do not breed until they are three or four years old, in contrast to males, who breed when they are two or three. This difference in breeding age between the sexes has interesting consequences. Data gathered by recording the survival of individually marked toads reveal that,

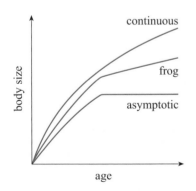

Figure 6.9 Typical continuous and asymptotic growth curves, and the growth curve of a typical frog.

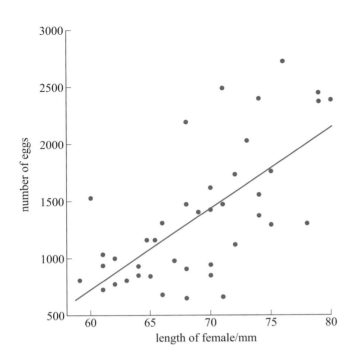

Figure 6.10 The relationship between annual fecundity (number of eggs produced) and female body length in the common toad (*Bufo bufo*). The line shown is the statistically determined best-fit to these scattered data. From Davies and Halliday (1977).

in both sexes, annual survival is around 30% in Britain, giving a survival curve like that shown in Figure 6.11: if 3000 individuals survive to one year, about 1000 live to two years, 300 to three years, etc. When we record the number of animals that come to a pond to breed, we find that, although 3000 animals of each sex reach the age of one year, about 1450 males, but only 450 females, are sexually mature and ready to breed. This imbalance arises because the majority of those females that delayed breeding for one year longer than males (i.e. until they are three or four years old) die before they have a chance to breed. A feature of toad breeding aggregations is that males outnumber females by about 3 : 1, for the reason given above. As a result, there is intense competition between males to mate with females, in which larger individuals hold an advantage.

Thus, female toads delay breeding by one or two years and thereby achieve a larger body size, which ensures them a high fecundity, but this strategy involves a trade-off with survival: the cost is a reduced probability, compared with males, of living long enough to breed at all.

At this point, there may well be a nagging question in your mind: if it is advantageous for male toads to be larger in competition for mates, why do they not also delay breeding until they are larger? The answer is that, whereas the relationship between female body size and fecundity is deterministic (small females cannot lay large numbers of eggs), that between male size and mating success is probabilistic (small males do sometimes succeed in fertilizing a female). While it is impossible for a small female to lay a large clutch, it is possible, and indeed happens in some circumstances, that small male toads acquire mates. It is therefore adaptive for males to start breeding early in life and so avoid the risk of dying before they do so.

Figure 6.11 Survival plot for a wild population of male and female common toads, based on an annual survival rate of 30%.

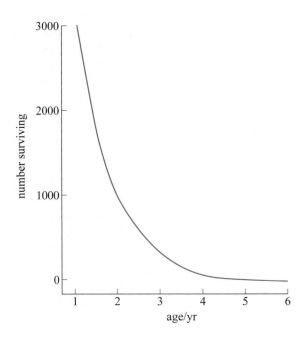

We have examined the life history of toads in some detail, because it makes an important general point. It shows how no single life history variable, such as longevity, can be understood in isolation from others, such as pattern of growth, age at first breeding, fecundity and mating success. It also makes another interesting point, that the life histories of males and females of the same species are not necessarily identical. There are many organisms in which the sexes follow very different life histories and, in consequence, have different patterns of longevity, of which two examples are discussed in the next section.

SEX DIFFERENCES IN LIFE HISTORY

The northern elephant seal (*Mirounga angustirostris*) (Figure 6.12) breeds on beaches in California and provides an extreme example of competition among males for females. Most females produce one pup per year (Figure 6.13) and become sexually receptive shortly after giving birth. Males fight to establish 'harems' of females and, unlike toads, only the largest males are successful. Male mating success is highly skewed; in any one year, only 4.4% of males inseminate 75% of females, and over their lifetime, only 10% of males get to mate at all. Figure 6.13 compares the age-specific reproductive success of male and female elephant seals.

○ The data in Figure 6.13 reveal that male elephant seals start to breed about three years later than females. Can you explain this difference between the sexes?

● Males have to delay breeding until they are large enough to compete with other males for mates.

Figure 6.12 Adult male northern elephant seals (*Mirounga angustirostris*) come ashore on Californian beaches a few days earlier than the females and establish territories. During the breeding season, mating and territory defence occupy most of their time; they eat little, living off their large fat reserves.

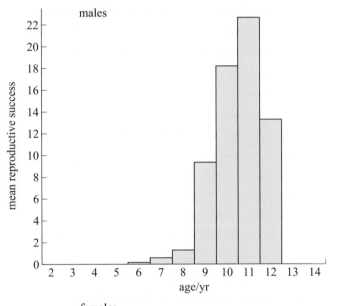

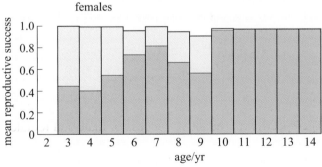

Figure 6.13 The mean reproductive success of male (top) and female (bottom) northern elephant seals as a function of age. For males, reproductive success is measured as the number of females inseminated, for females as number of pups born. The deeper red areas in the lower histogram represent the number of pups that survive to weaning. Data from Le Boeuf and Reiter (1998).

In the elephant seal, the distribution of reproduction over an individual's lifetime is very different for males and females. As Figure 6.13 shows, females start to breed at three years old and produce one pup per year, their success in weaning them increasing with age. Males do not start to breed until they are six or seven years old, and then, if they are successful in mate competition, enjoy only three or four years as 'harem masters', before dying at a younger age than females.

A similar, though less extreme pattern is seen in the red deer (*Cervus elephas*) breeding on the Scottish island of Rhum (Figure 6.14), Again, males compete for females and are reproductively active for a shorter period.

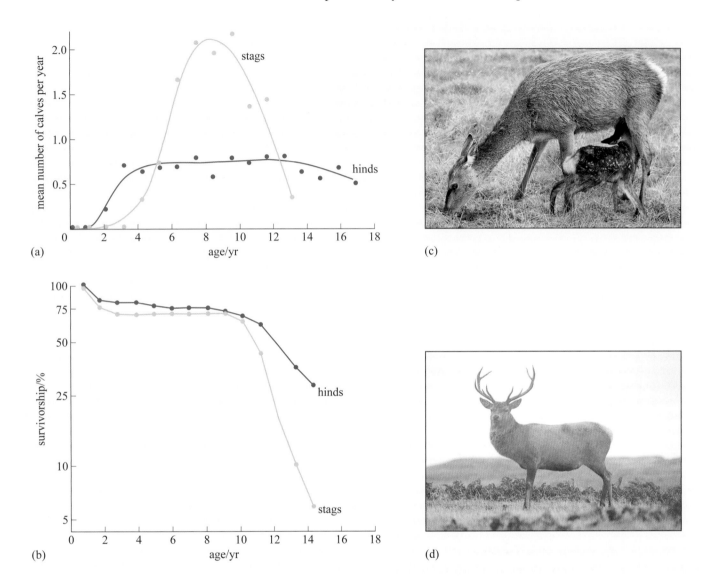

Figure 6.14 (a) The mean reproductive success of male (stags) and female (hinds) red deer as a function of age, measured as the number of calves reared per parent each year. (b) Male and female red deer survival on the island of Rhum as a function of age. Data from Clutton-Brock *et al.* (1988) (c) A red deer hind with her calf. (d) A red deer stag.

○ From the data in Figure 6.14a and b, what can you deduce about the relative longevity of red deer stags and hinds?

● Hinds and stags show similar survival rates up to the age of about nine. Thereafter, stags are much less likely to survive than hinds.

6.3.3 REPRODUCTION AND SURVIVAL

Evidence that there is a trade-off between reproduction and survival comes from a study of Antarctic fur seals (*Arctocephalus gazella*). Female seals can live for more than 15 years and start to reproduce at age two to six, with most females producing their first pups when three or four years old. Among female seals, between 40% and 50% of all recorded deaths occur during pregnancy. As a consequence, less fecund females live longer (Figure 6.15).

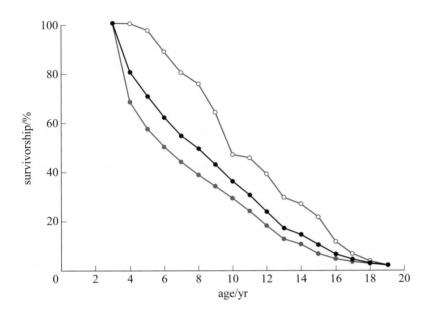

Figure 6.15 Survival plots for female Antarctic fur seals. The lower red line with filled symbols is for females that pupped every year; the upper red line with open symbols is for females that never pupped; the middle black line is for the whole female population. Data from Boyd *et al.* (1995).

○ From the data in Figure 6.15, determine (a) what proportion of female fur seals survive to the age of ten years, and (b) how the probability of survival to age ten differs between females that pup every year and those that do not pup at all.

● (a) Approximately 35%. (b) The figure is just under 30% for females that pup every year and about 47% for those that do not pup at all.

The data for fur seals strongly suggest that there is a trade-off between reproduction and survival, but are not conclusive proof that animals that invest more in reproduction impair their own prospects of survival. It may be, for example, that female seals die in pregnancy from a disease that does not affect non-breeders. As emphasized earlier in this chapter, experiments provide the best evidence for life history trade-offs.

EXPERIMENTAL MANIPULATION OF CLUTCH SIZE

The greatest number of experimental studies of the trade-off between reproduction and survival has involved clutch size in birds. Such studies use iteroparous species and involve adding or subtracting eggs from the clutch of breeding birds and then determining their subsequent survival and reproductive success.

○ If there is a trade-off between reproductive effort and survival, what would you expect to happen to birds whose clutch is reduced in size?

● They should live longer than birds with unaltered or enlarged clutches.

A field study of the California gull (*Larus californicus*) provides an example of a 'natural experiment', i.e. one that did not involve human intervention. California gulls are iteroparous and breed from age four to 23 years, nesting in dense colonies. In 1984 part of the colony being studied was flooded, with the result that birds affected had to abandon their nests while incubating their eggs. The flood occurred too late for them to lay a replacement clutch. The probability of survival of birds from the flooded area to the next year was 92%, whereas that of birds from unflooded areas was 72%.

Another experimental study essentially replicated the effect observed in the California gull. Its aim was to assess how the survival and longevity change if the birds do not breed at all. Most experimental studies of the cost of reproduction involve making birds invest more in breeding, for example by increasing their clutch size. However, this approach may not tell us much about what the survival costs of reproduction are for birds that breed 'normally'. Entire clutches were removed from the nests of 149 randomly selected pairs of black-legged kittiwakes (*Rissa tridactyla*), a species that lives for about 20 years and starts to breed at age four or five. Adult males and females from unmanipulated nests had a probability of surviving to the next breeding season of 89.8%, those from manipulated nests 95.3%. This difference seems small but proved to be statistically significant.

○ Why was it necessary to manipulate so many nests to reach these conclusions?

● Because the effect that they were trying to measure, a change in annual survival, is so small that a large sample is necessary to demonstrate its statistical significance.

More importantly, however, when a calculation is made to determine how this annual cost of reproduction affects the longevity of this long-lived species, it turns out that birds that never breed would have a life expectancy of 27.3 years, whereas those that breed every year would live for no more than 12.3 years. In other words, reproduction in this species reduces longevity by 55%. From a large number of studies involving manipulation of clutch size that have been carried out, an effect on survival is found to be a relatively rare consequence. In most studies, birds have responded in other ways, such as:

(a) producing lighter or heavier offspring at fledging during the current breeding attempt;

(b) laying a smaller or larger clutch at their next breeding attempt; or

(c) delaying their next breeding attempt.

These results do not support the hypothesis that there is always a trade-off between reproduction and survival. However, they do not refute the basic concept of life history trade-offs, but suggest that birds can make a variety of different trade-offs.

○ On the basis of results (a)–(c) can you suggest what these different trade-offs might be?

● Result (a) suggests that birds make a trade-off between the number of their progeny and the amount of effort that they allocate to feeding each offspring. Results (b) and (c) suggest that they make a trade-off between current and future reproduction.

Before we leave the topic of the relationship between survival and reproduction, there is one important factor that we have still to consider. As you saw for female elephant seals (Figure 6.13), age has effects on an animal's reproductive performance that are largely independent of survival. The most important of these effects are experience and senescence, as indicated in Figure 6.16.

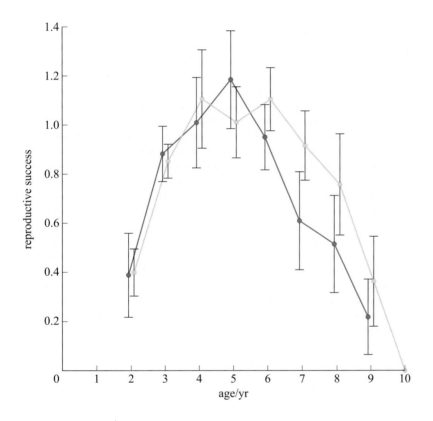

Figure 6.16 The relationship between reproductive success (measured as number of young leaving the nest) and age in the Seychelles warbler (*Acrocephalus sechellensis*) on Cousin Island over a 14-year period. Red = females; blue = males. Data from Komdeur (1996).

○ How does the reproductive success of Seychelles warblers change with age?

● It increases from age two to five years and then declines thereafter.

The first effect is due to experience; rearing young is a skill and, with successive breeding episodes, birds get better at it. This effect has been found in most iteroparous birds that have been studied in detail. An important aspect of experience is an improvement with age in birds' ability to gather food for themselves and their young.

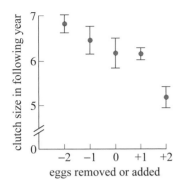

Figure 6.17 Mean clutch sizes of pairs of collared flycatchers (*Muscicapa albicollis*) in the year following manipulation of their clutch size, either egg removal (−) or addition (+). Data from Lessels (1991).

The second effect is due to reproductive senescence; as birds get older, their fertility tends to decline. This effect is more extreme in the Seychelles warbler than it is in most birds; in this species, it is due to failure of eggs to hatch.

If experience and reproductive senescence have strong effects on the reproductive success of animals, they both favour individuals that start to breed early in life. Earlier breeders acquire breeding experience earlier in life and achieve higher reproductive success before senescence becomes an important factor. Experience and senescence thus tend to counter other factors, such as growth, which tend to favour a late start to breeding.

Another prediction of life history theory is that, because future life expectancy declines in later life, individual iteroparous organisms should invest more in reproduction with each successive reproductive episode. This prediction is borne out by a number of studies. For example, as red deer get older, pregnant hinds allocate a greater proportion of lipids stored in adipose tissue to supporting their unborn calves, as opposed to their own bodies, and older California gulls feed their chicks (rather than swallow their prey themselves) more often than younger birds.

These studies suggest that organisms may make a trade-off between current and future reproduction. This hypothesis is also amenable to experimental testing using clutch-size manipulation, as shown in Figure 6.17.

○ Do the data presented in Figure 6.17 support the hypothesis that there is a trade-off between current and future reproduction?

● Yes, they do. Pairs of birds whose clutches were increased by two eggs in the first year had a mean clutch size of just over five eggs in the next year; birds whose clutches were reduced by two eggs had a mean clutch size of nearly seven in the next year.

SUMMARY OF SECTION 6.3

1 Life histories can be characterized as mixtures of properties that maximize population growth rate or carrying capacity.

2 Theory predicts that long-lived iteroparous organisms can increase their fitness by limiting or delaying reproduction in early life. In species in which reproductive success is strongly correlated with body size, breeding may be delayed until large body size has been achieved.

3 A cost of delayed breeding is a reduced probability of surviving to breed at all. In some species, these effects have led to marked differences in the life history and longevity of males and females.

4 Observational and experimental evidence reveal a trade-off between survival and reproduction: the energetic and other costs of reproduction reduce annual survival and thus longevity.

5 As individual animals get older, they acquire skills that increase their reproductive success, and they invest more in reproduction; however, in older individuals these effects are countered by reproductive senescence.

6 Within their lifespan, organisms may limit their reproductive effort in one year and so increase their reproductive success in subsequent years.

6.4 WITHIN-SPECIES VARIATION IN LIFE HISTORY AND LONGEVITY

The previous sections in this chapter illustrated some of the enormous diversity among plant and animal life histories. Differences between species in life history variables are generally explained as evolutionary adaptations to particular environments, so that the diversity of organisms reflects environmental diversity. For example, in the dichotomy summarized in Table 6.3, stable environments select for a longer life. Figure 6.2 shows that seabirds, such as guillemots and kittiwakes, live much longer than passerine birds, most of which live in forests, fields and moors. In a comparative approach to the evolutionary basis of life histories in birds, we might find evidence that marine habitats are more stable than inland ones. Differences between species may be due to adaptation to different habitats, but they may also reflect their different ancestry. For example, kittiwakes may be long-lived, to a smaller or greater degree, because they are descended from long-lived ancestors.

This problem can be resolved by comparing the life histories of populations *within* a single species that live in different habitats. Differences in life histories can only be due to adaptation (or to genetic drift, described in Chapter 3), since populations within a species have the same ancestry.

Impatiens pallida is an annual woodland herb that has been studied in Illinois over a period of six years. Individual plants growing in the interior of a wood start to flower several weeks earlier than those growing at the edge of woods. This difference might appear to be due to individual plants responding to some environmental cue, such as light intensity, that differs between the two sites, but experimental studies showed that this explanation is wrong. When plants from wood interior and edge habitats were grown together in a greenhouse, there was a marked difference in the time at which they flowered (Figure 6.18a).

The differences in survivorship between the plants in the two kinds of habitat are due to the activities of a particular species of beetle which, during June and July, consumes plants growing within a wood, but not those growing at the edge. As a result, edge plants live over two months longer than inner-wood plants (Figure 6.18b).

Confirmation that these life history differences are adaptive comes from a reciprocal transplant experiment. Plants transplanted from edge to interior had reduced fitness (measured as number of seeds produced) in comparison to interior plants, because they got eaten before they could flower. Those taken from interior to edge had reduced fitness compared to edge plants because they did not flower for as long.

The North American wood frog (*Rana sylvatica*) has an extensive range that encompasses considerable variation in altitude. The data from a comparison of life history variables of frogs from highland and lowland populations are summarized in Table 6.4.

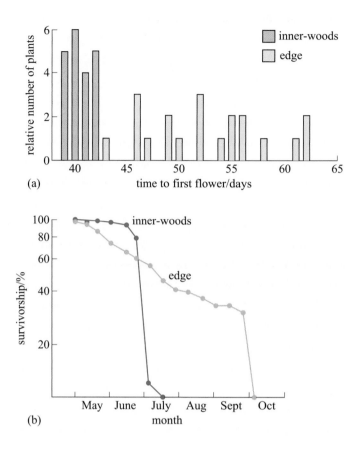

(a)

(b)

Figure 6.18 (a) The distribution of dates of first flowering in a greenhouse for *Impatiens pallida* collected from the interior and the edge of woods. (b) Survival plots of natural populations at the two sites. Data from Silvertown and Lovett Doust (1993).

Table 6.4　Life history variables of highland and lowland populations of the North American wood frog (*Rana sylvatica*).

Variable	Highland populations (7 ponds)	Lowland populations (2 ponds)
altitude	865–1100 m	43 m
mean duration of breeding season	121 days (May–September)	177 days (April–October)
mean body length		
males	55.3 mm	41.7 mm
females	64.4 mm	47.7 mm
age at first breeding		
males	95% begin at 3 years	86% begin at 1 year
females	62% begin at 4 years	99% begin at 2 years

Among females from both habitats, body size is positively correlated with fecundity (number of eggs) and egg size. Egg number and size are both characters that confer higher fitness (the latter, because tadpoles that hatch from large eggs are more likely to survive). It appears at first sight, therefore, that highland frogs are considerably fitter than lowland frogs.

○ Why is this conclusion incorrect? (Study the data in Table 6.4 and refer back to the account of toad life history in Section 6.3.2.)

● The apparent fitness advantage of the larger highland frogs is offset by their much later age at first reproduction. Highland frogs are less likely to survive to first breeding than lowland frogs.

The adaptive basis of the life history differences between high- and low-altitude wood frogs is not clear. It is likely to be due to the fact that, at high altitudes, frogs experience lower temperatures and a shorter growth season than those at low altitude. Consequently, if high-altitude frogs started to breed as early in life as lowland frogs, they would be very small and vulnerable to predation, and would have very low fecundity. Unfortunately, measuring the fitness of individual frogs is not easy. In fact, the focus of this study was not on the adaptive basis of life history variation in wood frogs but on whether it has a genetic basis.

The differences in breeding habits between lowland and highland wood frogs could be genetic, selection having favoured alternative alleles in the two habitats. On the other hand, the differences could be environmental, the two kinds of frog having similar genotypes but responding differently to their different habitats. One way to resolve this question is by carrying out a reciprocal transfer experiment. If the differences are genetic, then juvenile highland frogs moved to a lowland pond should follow the life history pattern of highland, not of naturally lowland frogs.

○ If the differences are environmental, what result would you expect from an experimental translocation?

● The life histories of translocated frogs would be characteristic of their new habitat, not of their original one.

Just such an experiment was carried out in the USA: frogs caught in highland habitats were marked, and released into lowland areas, and the converse. Their longevity and body size were recorded over several years. All the translocated frogs retained some traits characteristic of their site of origin, but also showed evidence of adapting their growth and longevity to their new habitat.

Thus, in wood frogs life history differences between highland and lowland populations are partly determined by genetic differences and partly by individuals responding to their environment during their development.

Another kind of within-species variation is **polymorphism**, in which individuals that follow different life histories live side by side in the same population. Salamanders provide many examples of polymorphic life histories. The point of interest for biologists is how to explain the coexistence of alternative life histories in animals that are apparently subject to similar selection pressures.

All salamander larvae are predators, feeding on insects and other invertebrates. In the North American mole salamander (*Ambystoma talpoideum*), some larvae in some populations become cannibalistic, feeding on salamander eggs and, as they get larger, on smaller larvae. Cannibalistic larvae (known as cannibal morphs) develop a distinctive head shape, with more powerful jaws than normal larvae, and grow much faster. How can normal and cannibalistic larvae coexist? Why don't the cannibals wipe out the normal larvae?

Although the cannibal life history confers the advantage of a faster growth rate, such larvae have a higher food requirement and use more energy pursuing prey which take evasive action. As a result, the cannibal morph only arises in ponds where the density of salamander larvae is high. Moreover, some pathogens and parasites of salamanders are more efficiently transferred by cannibalism than by transmission through intermediate hosts. As a result, cannibalistic larvae have higher parasite loads and infection rates than normal larvae.

Many salamanders, including several species of *Ambystoma*, have a life history polymorphism that has important evolutionary implications. In the typical life history, larvae grow to a certain size and then undergo metamorphosis, changing shape and physiology, and become terrestrial (Figure 6.19). But some populations are **paedomorphic** (meaning 'in the form of the child'): they retain many features of the typical larva, such as external gills and a wide head, and remain fully aquatic, although they eventually mature sexually and reproduce as efficiently as normal adults. Paedomorphosis can be genetic or facultative, i.e. occurring in response to specific environmental conditions, such as living in ponds that do not dry up during the year. The evolutionary significance lies in the fact that the paedomorphic life history has become the norm in a few species, notably the axolotl (*Ambystoma mexicanum*) (Figure 6.20).

Figure 6.20 The axolotl (*Ambystoma mexicanum*) is a fully aquatic salamander that eats large invertebrates, tadpoles and small fish in warm, shallow lakes.

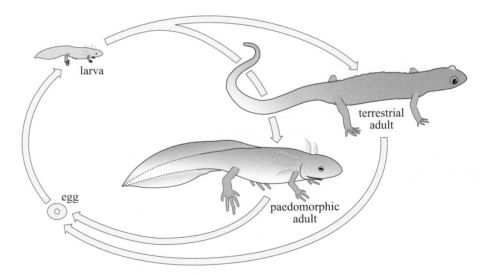

larva

terrestrial adult

egg

paedomorphic adult

Figure 6.19 Normal and paedomorphic life histories in *Ambystoma*.

6.5   LABORATORY STUDIES OF LONGEVITY

Laboratory studies can enable us to investigate hypotheses about organisms that we cannot hope to assess by studying them in nature.

6.5.1   GENES FOR A LONGER LIFE

A crucial question that is much better addressed in the laboratory than in the field is whether longevity is determined by selectable genes. There is no *a priori* reason to suppose that it does; death could simply be an inevitable consequence of the wear and tear of life. A first step to determining the genetic basis of a character is to select for it artificially. Artificial selection is a procedure in which, over many generations, only the offspring of individuals with a particular phenotypic character are allowed to breed. Artificial selection for longevity has produced longer-lived strains in a variety of organisms, including the nematode *Caenorhabditis elegans* and the fruit-fly, *Drosophila*. Once a longer-lived strain has been produced, it becomes possible to identify the alleles that determine its longevity, and to examine in detail how they act.

Artificial selection for longevity in *C. elegans* has yielded strains that live for up to 70% longer than wild worms. Interestingly, a characteristic of these strains is that they mature sexually later than wild strains. Moreover, strains selected for late maturity also live longer.

○   Is this result unexpected?

●   No, it's not. From earlier sections in this chapter, we would expect individuals that delay reproduction to live longer.

In one long-lived strain of *C. elegans*, researchers have found that an enzyme that protects cells from free radicals is more active than it is in wild worms. This finding supports the hypothesis that senescence is caused by the cumulative effect of damage caused by free radicals (Section 6.2.1).

Some artificially bred strains of fruit-flies (*Drosophila*) live, at least in captivity, for up to twice as long as wild flies. These long-lived flies seem to be superior in a number of ways. They can fly for longer under a wide range of temperatures and humidity levels; they carry more fat and so are more resistant to starvation; and they are less prone to dehydration. As in *C. elegans*, the activity of enzymes that counter the effects of free radicals is higher. These experiments support the hypothesis that genes influence longevity.

6.5.2   ENVIRONMENTS FOR A LONGER LIFE

Laboratory studies can also address the question of whether different environments or 'lifestyles' can affect longevity. On the principle that 'we are what we eat', one obvious environmental influence is diet. Food restriction studies have been carried out on a variety of animals, including fruit-flies, mice and rats. The term 'food restriction' does not mean that subjects suffer malnutrition. Laboratory animals such as rats are usually allowed to eat *ad libitum*, meaning that food is always available to them. Once it has been established how much they eat each day on an *ad libitum* regime, their diet can be restricted by a specified small amount which does not affect their health. Indeed, food-restricted rats that weigh 25–30% less than *ad libitum* controls are normal in most respects, but live for longer. Similar results have been obtained for fruit-flies and mice. Several hypotheses that explain why food restriction promotes longevity are currently under investigation.

The life history of the Mediterranean fruit-fly (*Ceratitis capitata*), also known in California as the medfly, includes two physiological modes which result in different patterns of reproduction and longevity. They are a waiting mode, in which both mortality and reproduction are low, and a reproductive mode, in which mortality is very low at the onset of egg-laying but accelerates as eggs are laid. If adult medflies are fed only on sugar, they remain in the waiting mode, but if they are switched to a protein diet they go into reproductive mode. In their natural environment, sugar is abundant but accessible protein is scarce. Paradoxically, medflies that are switched from the waiting to the reproductive mode by being provided with protein live for longer than those kept constantly in either mode.

This result is puzzling because it cannot be accounted for by the general principle that longevity is shortened by reproduction. Were that so, the medflies kept permanently in the waiting mode would have lived longer than those that were switched to the reproductive mode. It appears that medflies make some kind of physiological switch when they start breeding that enables them to both reproduce and to delay death. Whatever this mechanism is, it appears to be an adaptation to the rapidly fluctuating environment in which medflies live, one in which opportunities for breeding are highly unpredictable.

6.5.3 SEX AND A LONGER LIFE

Evidence presented in earlier sections supports the hypothesis that organisms make a trade-off between survival and reproduction. Individuals that engage in less reproductive activity should therefore live longer. This effect could simply be due to the fact that reproduction requires organisms to divert energy and other resources away from survival. Laboratory studies, however, have revealed that other mechanisms are involved.

Most individuals of the nematode *C. elegans* are hermaphrodites that can either fertilize their eggs with their own sperm or use sperm from males. In many aquatic animals, the eggs are fertilized externally, without the parents coming into contact with each other. But since gametes cannot survive for long except in water, most terrestrial animals copulate, with sperm being transferred into the body of the female (or hermaphrodite). Mating with males is found to reduce the longevity of hermaphrodites in comparison to those that fertilized themselves (Figure 6.21a). In contrast, the longevity of males is not reduced by mating (Figure 6.21b). Self-fertilized hermaphrodites produce as many gametes as those that were fertilized by males.

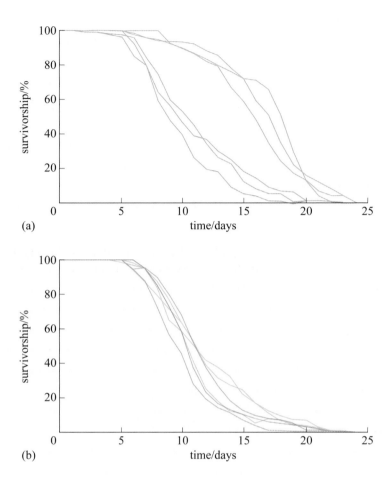

(a)

(b)

Figure 6.21 Survival plots for (a) hermaphrodite and (b) male *C. elegans* in laboratory cultures. The orange curves are data for individuals that that did not mate and the purple (a) and blue (b) curves are the data for animals that did mate. Each group of animals was replicated three times. Data from Gems and Riddle (1996).

○   Can the reduced longevity of hermaphrodites fertilized by males be attributed to their putting more resources into reproduction and less into body maintenance?

●   No. It suggests that there is some survival cost to the act of mating.

The nature of this cost is not clear but Gems and Riddle have made some suggestions. It could be stress induced by copulation or it could be that there is something in seminal fluid that reduces the longevity of its recipients. This latter possibility has been investigated extensively in fruit-flies.

By controlling how much females were exposed to males, researchers found that female fruit-flies that mate frequently die younger than those that mate only occasionally (Figure 6.22). By scoring the number of eggs that females produced, they eliminated the obvious possibility that the reduced longevity of the 'high-mating' flies could be the result of their producing more eggs. 'High-mating' and 'low-mating' females laid similar numbers of eggs and there was no difference in their hatchability.

Figure 6.22 Survival plots for 'high-mating' and 'low-mating' female fruit-flies. Data from Fowler and Partridge (1989).

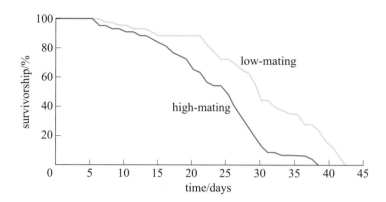

During mating, male fruit-flies pass to females in their seminal fluid a secretion produced by the accessory glands associated with their genitalia. It is this secretion which reduces female longevity; females that mate at high frequency with males whose accessory glands have been experimentally destroyed do not show reduced longevity (Figure 6.23).

Figure 6.23 Survival plots for female adult fruit-flies exposed to males whose accessory glands have been totally destroyed, partially destroyed or left intact. The control groups of flies were not exposed to males. Data from Chapman *et al.* (1995).

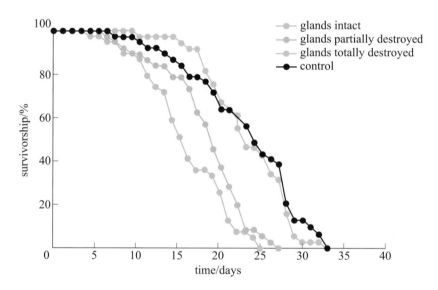

Why should males pass to females a substance that reduces female longevity? To answer this question, we have to consider some fundamental aspects of sexual reproduction. Because males produce much larger numbers of gametes than females, there is inherent rivalry among males for access to females. It may take the form of male aggression, as in elephant seals (Section 6.3.2), or as competition to be attractive to females, as in *Drosophila*, peafowl and birds of paradise.

Male competition also takes the form of behavioural or physiological mechanisms by which males control or influence the availability of females, or their eggs, to other males. For example, males of many species guard females with whom they have mated and keep their rivals away. In some snakes, males cover females with whom they have mated with 'anti-aphrodisiac' secretions which make them sexually unattractive.

A common form of male rivalry is sperm competition; within the female, the ejaculate of one male competes with that of one or more others to fertilize her eggs. The secretion that a male fruit-fly passes to a female has at least three effects that are advantageous to the male. It accelerates egg-laying and thus reduces the time during which other males might mate with the female; it reduces her receptivity to other males; and it helps to destroy the sperm of other males. In essence, the genital tracts of female fruit-flies are part of the 'battleground' on which males compete, but their activities may impair female survival. For terrestrial animals, mating may be essential for sexual reproduction, which provides many long-term advantages (see Chapter 4) but, like eating (see Chapter 2), it carries physiological costs that may reduce longevity.

This brief overview of some laboratory studies of longevity shows how powerful they can be in revealing the mechanisms of ageing, and how varied, complex and unexpected they can be. They also suggest that longevity is a very labile character, which can be altered considerably by both selective breeding and environmental manipulations. The implications of these findings for the study of ageing and longevity in humans are profound.

SUMMARY OF SECTIONS 6.4 AND 6.5

1 Longevity and reproductive strategy vary within a species as well as differing between species. Some of the differences are genetic.

2 Artificial selection for longevity in short-lived laboratory animals increases mean lifespan by as much as twofold.

3 Frequent experience of internal fertilization *per se*, as well as the trade-off between body maintenance and egg production, reduce the lifespan of females that breed.

6.6 SOME PHYSIOLOGICAL ASPECTS OF LONGEVITY

In this section, we consider the interactions between reproductive behaviour and some processes that contribute to ageing and death.

In many semelparous insects, for example mayflies and some butterflies, the adults lack mouthparts and do not feed. All the storage lipids and other resources they acquired as larvae are expended in reproduction and then, exhausted, they die. *Antechinus stuartii*, a small insectivorous marsupial from Australia is an unusual example of semelparity and post-reproductive death. In this species, pregnancy lasts about a month, during which time all the adult males die. Anaemia, haemorrhages, elevated hormone levels and suppression of the immune system have all been implicated as causes of death within three weeks of mating. During the short breeding season, males become extremely active; they no longer sleep and engage in frequent aggressive interactions with other males and mate with females. Males caught before the breeding season and prevented from fighting or mating live for a few months longer than wild males, but do not survive until the next breeding season. The females, in contrast, occasionally live for a second, even a third breeding season.

The **immunocompetence hypothesis** makes a link between reproductive hormones, parasites and pathogens, the development of **secondary sexual characters** and body condition. Secondary sexual characters are characters in which males and females differ, excluding the reproductive organs; they include colourful plumage in male birds and beards in men. Body condition is an index of 'well-being' in which a measure of size, such as length, is divided by weight; individuals in good condition are relatively heavy for their size. The following points support the immunocompetence hypothesis:

1   The male reproductive hormone testosterone suppresses the immune system of males.

2   The development of male secondary sexual characters and habits requires both high levels of testosterone in the blood and that a male be in good condition.

3   Infection by a parasite or pathogen reduces testosterone level and body condition.

4   Males with poorly developed secondary sexual characters are less attractive to females and/or are less successful in competition with rival males.

The immunocompetence hypothesis predicts that reproduction reduces male viability. To compete successfully for mates, males must have high levels of testosterone, but the hormone increases the risk of infection, and infection reduces condition. Animals that end a breeding season in poor condition are less likely to survive to the next.

Some aspects of the immunocompetence hypothesis are well supported by empirical data. In many birds, for example, males are more susceptible to infection than females. There is some evidence that parasites have a negative effect on the development of male secondary sexual characters. In birds, there is a good correlation between age and parasite loads. However, much of the evidence for links between hormones, parasites and the immune system is not convincing and, while high levels of testosterone are commonly associated with male aggression, the link with secondary sexual characters is often weak. Finally, there is increasing scepticism in the concept of general immunocompetence which protects against all parasites and pathogens. Individuals certainly differ in the effectiveness of their immune response to specific pathogens or parasites, but any one individual is resistant to some, and susceptible to others.

The **corticosteroids** are hormones synthesized in the adrenal glands and are produced at times of stress, such as during aggression.

○   What does the immunocompetence theory predict would be the long-term consequence of dosing free-living, wild animals with extra corticosteroids?

●   The treated animals would acquire more parasites and pathogens than the controls.

The negative effect that reproduction generally has on longevity may be due to elevated corticosteroid levels making animals more susceptible to parasites and pathogens.

There have been very few studies that have documented the negative effects of parasites on the survival of their hosts under natural conditions. In one study, deermice (*Peromyscus maniculatus*) were infected with different levels of a protoctist parasite, *Eimeria arizonensis*, and released into field enclosures. Infected males were less likely to survive over winter than uninfected controls.

○ Why is it necessary to infect animals experimentally with parasites, rather than measure the survival of hosts that differ naturally in their parasite levels?

● Natural variation in parasite levels is likely to reflect general health, and animals may fail to survive the winter because they are in poor condition, not because they are carrying more parasites.

This possibility can be tested by experimentally infecting with parasites animals that are in both good and poor condition.

Alternative life histories within species (Section 6.4) provide excellent opportunities to study mechanisms that affect longevity. Salmon breed in streams and rivers; their young remain there for at least a year and then go to sea for several years, before returning to freshwater to breed. Some species of salmon are semelparous; the adults die after spawning. Male Coho salmon (*Oncorhynchus kisutch*) in the eastern Pacific have two alternative life histories. In common with females, some males, called 'hooknoses' because of their prominent snout and large teeth, do not breed until they are three years old. Other males, called 'jacks', breed at two years old, having grown to only 30% of the size of hooknoses, and lacking both the distinctive snout and the bright red breeding coloration of the larger morph. Hooknoses compete aggressively with one another for access to females. Jacks don't fight but instead adopt a 'sneaky' mating behaviour, rushing between a mating male and female and ejaculating onto the emerging eggs. The difference between hooknoses and jacks is genetically determined but, in other salmon species, life history polymorphisms are determined by non-genetic mechanisms.

In the Atlantic salmon (*Salmo salar*) (Figure 6.24), which is bred in large numbers in Scottish fish farms, young fish, called parr, differ in the age at which they leave their natural breeding habitats and go to sea, where they become smolts. Many, called S1 smolts, do so at one year old; S2 smolts delay the transition by a year. Figure 6.25 shows the growth patterns of S1 and S2 fish. Note that there is a clear difference in the size of S1 and S2 parr by November of their first year, when they are six months old.

Detailed studies of the behaviour of salmon parr have revealed differences between S1 and S2 fish that are apparent before a difference in size can be detected. Parr are aggressive, especially when they are living at high densities: dominant fish win more of their aggressive encounters (most of which are over food) and spend more time feeding, so they grow faster and eventually become S1 fish. Subordinates eat less and grow more slowly, to become S2 fish. Biologists in Glasgow found that young fish destined to become S1 parr have a higher standard metabolic rate (SMR) than those destined to become S2 parr. These differences (shown in Figure 6.26) can be detected before the development of aggressive behaviour. These results suggest that very early in life, small metabolic differences between individuals form the basis of a dichotomy, 'amplified' by social interactions, between S1 and S2 fish. Unfortunately, it is not known if S1 and S2 fish differ in their longevity.

Figure 6.24 An Atlantic salmon (*Salmo salar*).

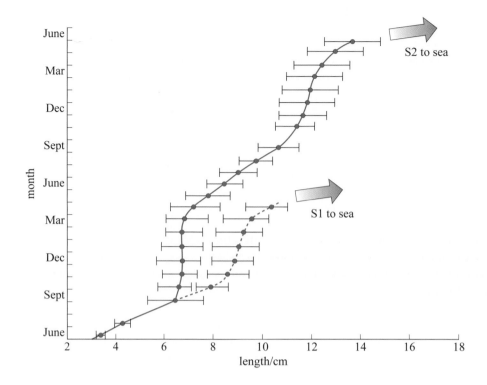

Figure 6.25 Changes in the size of Atlantic salmon parr over the first two years of life. Data from Metcalfe *et al.* (1992).

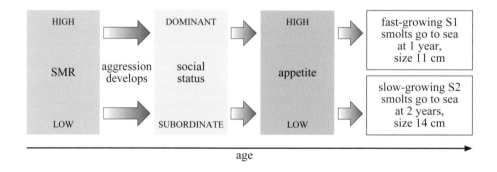

Figure 6.26 Development pathway leading to the life history difference between S1 and S2 smolts of Atlantic salmon. SMR (standard metabolic rate) is the metabolic rate of an organism measured under a standard set of conditions.

6.7 SOME CONSEQUENCES OF A LONGER LIFE

As mentioned earlier, there is considerable evidence that, especially for iteroparous birds and mammals that have prolonged, complex parental care, reproductive success increases with age. This effect has two principal causes: first, individuals allocate a greater proportion of their time and/or resources to reproduction as they get older and, secondly, experience of breeding makes individuals more skilled and efficient.

Many long-lived birds, such as kittiwakes and albatrosses, normally form breeding pairs for life. If a bird's mate dies, it generally finds a new one. Following such a change of mate, the breeding success of most adults drops immediately, suggesting that increasing reproductive success with age is related to the performance of birds as pairs, not just as individuals. A corollary of this situation is the phenomenon of 'divorce' in birds. Long-term studies of several species that are normally monogamous have shown that pairs that have low breeding success in their first year together often split up and seek new mates for the following year.

6.7.1 MENOPAUSE

In women, menstruation and fertility cease at the age of about 50, many years before death is likely, a phenomenon called **menopause**. It used to be thought that menopause is unique to humans but long-term studies of mammals reveal that it is not. Reproduction ends in females some years before death in baboons, Japanese macaques, elephants, lions and pilot and killer whales, for example. In baboons at Gombe in Tanzania, females stop breeding, on average, at age 20 but some live until 27; for Serengeti lions the equivalent figures are 13 and 17 years. There are currently five hypotheses to account for the evolution of menopause in mammals:

1   Menopause is an artefact of a life abnormally extended by a benign environment. Normally, individuals die from predation, starvation or other natural cause while still capable of breeding. This argument is supported by the fact that female pets and zoo animals commonly live on for some years after reproduction has ceased whereas their wild counterparts do not.

2   Both death and reproductive cessation are due to senescence, caused by deterioration which cannot be prevented by natural selection (Section 6.2.1), but reproductive senescence and ageing occur at different rates in some species.

3   Menopause prevents females producing offspring with serious chromosomal defects, which tend to become more frequent with age.

4   The 'good mother' hypothesis proposes that in mammals in which the young are dependent on parental care for a long time, menopause ensures that mothers do not divert their reproductive effort from their existing progeny to new ones.

5   Continued life after reproduction has ceased enables older females to give care to young other than their own — the 'useful granny' hypothesis.

○ How do hypotheses 1 and 2 differ from hypotheses 3–5?

● Hypotheses 1 and 2 both argue that menopause is a consequence or by-product of other processes; they do not argue that it is adaptive. In contrast, hypotheses 3, 4 and 5 are adaptive explanations, arguing that menopause is favoured by natural selection.

Hypotheses 1–5 are not mutually exclusive; in any one species, one or more of them may be relevant. There are conceptual problems with most of them. For example, only hypothesis 4 addresses the question of why menopause should occur in females but not in males. Hypothesis 3 invokes 'the good of the species' but theorists insist that natural selection acts on *individuals*, favouring those that leave more descendants in subsequent generations, not on species. As discussed in Section 6.2.1, natural selection cannot prevent late-acting deleterious alleles being passed on to progeny. Hypothesis 5 may appear to have the same fault, but can be explained by **kin selection**, an extension of natural selection which argues that selection favours individuals that allocate reproductive effort to juveniles other than their own, provided that those young are genetically related to them. For most of these hypotheses, there is a lack of data that would make it possible to test them thoroughly.

○ What sort of observations would support the 'useful granny' hypothesis?

● Demonstrating that post-menopausal females play a role in rearing their grandchildren and that the care they provide enhances the reproductive success of their daughters.

The 'useful granny' hypothesis has been tested by examining data from Gombe baboons and Serengeti lions (Figure 6.27). Although females of both species care for their grandchildren, no role for baboon grandmothers was detected. In contrast, lion 'grandmothers' enhance the survival of their daughters' cubs, but only if they themselves are still breeding. These observations reveal no contribution of non-reproductive grandmothers to the survival of their daughters' offspring.

There are numerous ideas about why menopause has evolved but, from these and similar studies, it is clear that we are a long way from knowing whether it has been favoured by natural selection because it contributes to reproduction, or whether it is simply the by-product of selection acting on other aspects of animals' life histories.

SUMMARY OF SECTIONS 6.6 AND 6.7

1 In some animals, there is a trade-off between reproductive success and immune function.

2 Secondary sexual characters may indicate a male's capacity to resist parasites and pathogens.

3 Salmon have two alternative life histories determined in part by genes but also by growth and social status early in life.

4 A few other long-lived mammals as well as humans undergo menopause, a post-reproductive state about whose adaptive significance several hypotheses have been proposed.

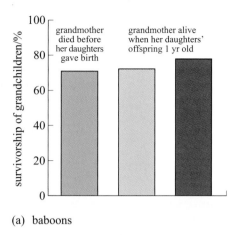

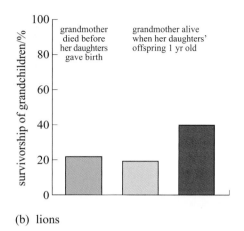

(a) baboons

(b) lions

6.8 CONCLUSION

This chapter has shown that longevity is a character that cannot sensibly be considered in isolation from other life history variables, such as growth, age at first breeding and lifetime schedule of reproduction. The complex interdependence of one life history variable with others arises because, during their lives, organisms make numerous trade-offs between life history components.

Why is it important to understand the life histories of animals and plants? Developed human societies are grappling with the social, medical and economic problems raised by the fact that average longevity is now greater than ever before. It is important to understand the biological determinants of longevity, not least because they influence the nature and quality of a life extended into old age.

We live at a time when biodiversity on Earth is undergoing an unprecedented decline, with species disappearing at an alarming rate. If we are to understand why particular species become extinct, and if we are to intervene effectively to conserve them, it is vital that we understand their life histories. Broadly speaking, individual species decline for one or a combination of two reasons: an increased mortality rate or a reduced reproductive rate, or a combination of both. These processes require very different counter-measures to reverse them and effective conservation must be informed by a thorough understanding of what factors are affecting which of numerous life history variables.

There is increasing awareness that organisms have not evolved in isolation, but are the product of coevolution. For example, most pathogens and parasites have life histories that are very different from their hosts', but which are intimately adapted to them. The biological importance of pathogens and parasites should not be underestimated. Some biologists have calculated that parasitic species outnumber non-parasites by 5 : 1; infectious diseases kill more humans annually than any other factor. It is vital to efforts to control or prevent disease that we understand the life histories of hosts and of parasites and how they have coevolved.

Like all the life processes discussed in this book, longevity is determined by genes and other intracellular mechanisms, and by the ability of hormones and other intercellular messengers to coordinate the function of the body as a whole.

Figure 6.27 The effects of the survival and reproductive status of grandmothers on the survivorship of their daughters' offspring in (a) baboons and (b) lions. Data from Packer *et al.* (1998).

REFERENCES

Begon, M., Harper, J. L. and Townsend, C. R. (1986) *Ecology*, Blackwell Scientific Publications, p. 509.

Boyd, I. L., Croxall, J. P., Lunn, N. J. and Reid, K. (1995) Population demography of Antarctic fur seals: the costs of reproduction and implications for life-histories, *Journal of Animal Ecology*, **64**, pp. 505–518.

Campbell, B. and Lack, E. (eds) (1985) *A Dictionary of Birds*, Poyser, p. 6.

Chapman, T., Liddle, L. F., Kaib, J. M., Wolfner, M. F. and Partridge, L. (1995) Cost of mating in *Drosophila melanogaster* females is mediated by male accessory gland products, *Nature*, **373**, pp. 241–244.

Clutton-Brock, T. H., Albon, S. D. and Guinness, F. E. (1988) Reproductive success in male and female red deer, in *Reproductive Success*, T. H. Clutton-Brock (ed.), Chicago University Press, pp. 325–343.

Davies, N. B. and Halliday, T. R. (1977) Optimal mate selection in the toad *Bufo bufo*, *Nature*, **269**, pp. 56–58.

Fowler, K. and Partridge, L. (1989) A cost of mating in female fruit-flies, *Nature*, **338**, pp. 760–761.

Gems, D. and Riddle, D. L. (1996) Longevity in *Caenorhabditis elegans* reduced by mating but not gamete production, *Nature*, **379**, pp. 723–725.

Gittins, S. P., Steeds, J. E. and Williams, R. (1982) Population age-structure of the common toad (*Bufo bufo*) at a lake in mid-Wales determined from annual growth rings in the phalanges, *British Journal of Herpetology*, **6**, pp. 249–252.

Komdeur, J. (1996) Influence of age on reproductive performance in the Seychelles warbler, *Behavioural Ecology*, **7**, pp. 417–425.

Le Boeuf, B. J. and Reiter, J. (1998) Lifetime reproductive success in northern elephant seals, in *Reproductive Success*, T. H. Clutton-Brock (ed.), Chicago University Press, pp. 344–362.

Lessels, C. M. (1991) The evolution of life histories, in *Behavioural Ecology*, 3rd edn, J. R. Krebs and N. B. Davies (eds), Blackwell Scientific Publications, pp. 32–68.

Metcalfe, N. B., Huntingford, F. A. and Thorpe, J. E. (1992) Social effects on appetite and development in Atlantic salmon, *World Aquaculture Workshops, No. 2*, pp. 29–40.

Packer, C., Tatar, M. and Collins, A. (1998) Reproductive cessation in female mammals, *Nature*, **392**, pp. 807–811.

Silvertown, J. W. and Lovett Doust, J. (1993) *Introduction to Plant Population Biology*, Blackwell Science, Oxford, p. 160.

Stearns, S. C. (1992) *The Evolution of Life Histories*, Oxford University Press, pp. 184, 186.

FURTHER READING

Stearns, S.C. (1992) *The Evolution of Life Histories*, Oxford University Press. [Although intended for post-graduate students, this book provides a comprehensive introduction to theory about the evolution of life histories.]

ACKNOWLEDGEMENTS

Grateful acknowledgement is made to the following sources for permission to reproduce material in this book:

CHAPTER 1

FIGURES

Figure 1.3: Bronson, F.H. (1987) 'Environmental regulation of reproduction in rodents', in Crews, D. (ed.) *Psychobiology of Reproductive Behavior*, p. 209, Prentice-Hall Inc., a Pearson Education Company; *Figures 1.6, 1.9*: Adapted from Irving, L. (1966) 'Adaptations to cold', *Scientific American*, **214** (1), p. 96, by permission of the Executrix of the Estate of Bunji Tagawa; *Figure 1.7*: Adapted from *A Dictionary of Birds* (1985) p. 207, T. & A. D. Poyser Limited, by permission of Academic Press (London) Limited, © The British Ornithologists' Union, 1985; *Figure 1.8*: Pough, F. H., Heiser, J. B. and McFarland, W. N. (1996) *Vertebrate Life*, 4th edn, © 1996 by Prentice-Hall, Inc. Simon and Schuster/A Viacom Company, Upper Saddle River, NJ; *Figure 1.11*: Halliday, T. (1980) *Sexual Strategy*, Oxford University Press; *Figure 1.12*: From *Biology of Plants* by P. Raven, R. F. Evert and S. E. Eichhorn, © 1999 by W. H. Freeman and Company/Worth Publishers. Used with permission; *Figure 1.14*: Pinder, A. W., Storey, K. B. and Ultsch, G. R. (1992) 'Estivation and hibernation', in Feder, M. E. and Burggren, W. W. (eds) *Environmental Physiology of Amphibians*, The University of Chicago Press, © 1992 by The University of Chicago. All rights reserved; *Figure 1.15*: From L. C. H. Wang (1978) *Strategies in Cold: Natural Torpidity and Thermogenesis*, L. C. H. Wang and J. W. Hudson (eds), Academic, New York; *Figure 1.16*: Nunes, S. *et al.* (1998) 'Body fat and time of year interact to mediate dispersal behaviour in ground squirrels', *Animal Behaviour*, **55** (3), p. 612, Academic Press (London) Limited; *Figure 1.17a and b*: Illustration by Adolph E. Brotman in Emlen, S. T. (1975) 'The stellar-orientation system of a migratory bird', *Scientific American*, August 1975; *Figure 1.17c and d*: Emlen, S. T. (1975) 'The stellar-orientation system of a migratory bird', *Scientific American*, August 1975.

CHAPTER 2

FIGURES

Figure 2.1: © Saffrey; *Figures 2.2, 2.5, 2.7d, 2.13, 2.14, 2.17*: © Caroline M. Pond; *Figure 2.3b*: Photograph of a crayfish foregut showing structure of the teeth, © D. M. Holdich and T. Smith; *Figure 2.6b*: © Dr Daniel Janzen; *Figure 2.9*: Bertsch, A. (1984) 'Foraging in male bumblebees (*Bombus lucorum* L.): maximizing energy or minimizing water load?', *Oecologia,* **62** (3), p. 328, Figure 3. © Springer-Verlag Berlin Heidelberg 2000, Springer-Verlag GmbH & Co. KG, Berlin, Germany; *Figure 2.10a*: Pat Morris; *Figure 2.10b*: Heather Angel; *Figures 2.11a, c and 2.12a*: Stevens, C. E. (1977) 'Comparative physiology of the digestive system', in Swenson, M. J. (ed.) *Duke's Physiology of Domestic Animals*, 9th edn, Cornell University Press; *Figure 2.11d*: Stevens, C. E. (1983)

'Comparative anatomy and physiology of the herbivore digestive tract', *Proceedings of the Second Annual Dr Scholl Conference on the Nutrition of Captive Wild Animals*, Lincoln Park Zoological Society, Chicago; *Figure 2.12b, c, e*: Stevens, C. E. and Hume, I. D. (1995) *Comparative Physiology of the Vertebrate Digestive System*, 2nd edn, Cambridge University Press; *Figure 2.12d*: Clemens, E. T. and Maloiy, G. M. O. (1977) 'The digestive physiology of three East African herbivores: the elephant, rhinoceros and hippopotamus', *Journal of Zoology*, **198**, Cambridge University Press; *Figures 2.15 and 2.16*: Adapted from Diamond, J. M. and Buddington, R. K. (1987) 'Intestinal nutrient absorption in herbivores and carnivores', in Dejours, P. *et al.* (eds) *Comparative Physiology: Life in Water and on Land*, p. 198 and p. 200, Fidia Research Series, IX-Liviana Press, Padova © 1987, Springer-Verlag GmbH & Co. KG; *Figures 2.19a, b, c*: Baumann, P. *et al.* (1995*)* 'Genetics, physiology and evolutionary relationships of the genus *Buchnera*: Intracellular symbionts of aphids', *Annual Review of Microbiology,* **49**, p. 59, © 1995 by Annual Reviews (www.AnnualReviews.org); *Figure 2.20*: Adapted from Ferraris, R. P. and Diamond, J. M. (1993) 'Crypt/ villus site of substrate-dependent regulation of mouse intestinal glucose transporters', *Proceedings of the National Academy of Sciences,* **90**, p. 5871, National Academy of Sciences; *Figure 2.21a*: B. Pomfret; *Figure 2.21b–d:* Adapted from Secor, S. M. and Diamond, J. (1995) 'Adaptive responses to feeding in Burmese pythons: Pay before pumping', *Journal of Experimental Biology*, **198**, p. 1318, The Company of Biologists Limited; *Figure 2.22a*: Hamner, W. M. and Jenssen, R. M. (1974) 'Growth, degrowth, and irreversible cell differentiation in *Aurelia aurita*', *American Zoologist*, **14**, p. 843, American Society of Zoologists; *Figure 2.22b*: © Pat Morris; *Figure 2.23*: By courtesy of Dr M. J. Cullen, Muscular Dystrophy Group Research Laboratories, Newcastle General Hospital, Newcastle Upon Tyne.

CHAPTER 3

FIGURE

Figure 3.11: Darlington, C. D. (1971) 'The evolution of polymorphic systems', *Ecological Genetics and Evolution*, pp. 1–19, Creed, E. R. (ed.), Blackwell, Oxford.

CHAPTER 4

FIGURES

Figure 4.2: Heather Angel/Biophoto; *Figure 4.12*: Reprinted with permission from Keller, L. F. *et al.*, 'Selection against inbred song sparrows during a natural population bottleneck', *Nature*, **372**. Copyright 1994 Macmillan Magazines Ltd; *Figure 4.13*: Adapted from Johnston, M. O. (1992) 'Effects of cross and self-fertilization on progeny fitness in *Lobelia cardinalis* and *L. siphilitica*', *Evolution*, **46** (3), Society for the Study of Evolution; *Figure 4.18*: Freeman, S. and Herron, J. C. (1998) *Evolutionary Analysis*, Prentice-Hall, Inc., Simon and Schuster/A Viacom Company; *Figures 4.20, 4.21*: Adapted from Antonovics, J. and Ellstrand, N. C. (1984) 'Experimental studies of the evolutionary significance of sexual reproduction. I. A test of the frequency-dependent selection hypothesis', *Evolution*,

38 (1), Society for the Study of Evolution; *Figure 4.22*: Lively, C. M. (1992) 'Parthenogenesis in a freshwater snail: reproductive assurance versus parasitic release', *Evolution*, **46** (4), Society for the Study of Evolution; *Figure 4.23*: Reprinted with permission from Clutton-Brock, T. H., Albon, S. D. and Guinness, F. E. (1984) 'Maternal dominance, breeding success and birth sex ratios in red deer', *Nature*, **308**. Copyright 1984 Macmillan Magazines Ltd; *Figure 4.24*: Bull, J. J. (1983) *Evolution of Sex Determining Mechanisms*, Benjamin/Cummings; *Figure 4.25*: Adapted from Krebs, J. R. and Davies, N. B. (1984) *Behavioural Ecology, An Evolutionary Approach*, 2nd edn, Blackwell Science Ltd; *Figure 4.26*: Adapted from *Sexual Selection* by J. L. Gould and C. G. Gould, © 1989 by Scientific American Library. Used with the permission of W. H. Freeman and Company; *Figure 4.27*: Adapted from Silvertown, J. W. and Doust, J. L. (1993) *Introduction to Plant Population Biology*, Blackwell Science Ltd.

TABLE

Table 4.1: Pieau, C. *et al*. (1994) 'Environmental control of gonadal differentiation', in Short, R. V. and Balaban, E. (eds) *The Differences Between the Sexes*, Cambridge University Press.

CHAPTER 5

FIGURES

Figures 5.1, 5.4: Professor Robert Dourmashkin (St Barts, Royal London and QMW School of Medicine); *Figure 5.2a–d, Figure 5.12a*: © Pat Morris; *Figures 5.2e, 5.20a:* © Caroline Pond; *Figure 5.5b*: Roitt, I. *et al*., *Immunology*, 5th edn, p. 210, © 1998 Mosby, an imprint of Times International Publishers Ltd; *Figure 5.6a*: Reprinted from Roitt, I. *et al*. (1996) *Immunology*, 4th edn, fig.15.6, courtesy of Dr A. F. Rowley by permission of Mosby, an imprint of Times International Publishers Ltd; *Figure 5.6b*: Juergen Berger, Max-Planck Institute/Science Photo Library; *Figure 5.6c*: Professor S. Gordan, Sir William Dunn School of Pathology; *Figures 5.7, 5.20b*: Reprinted from Roitt, I. *et al*. (1996) *Immunology*, 4th edn, fig. 15.9, by permission of Mosby, an imprint of Times International Publishers Ltd; *Figure 5.8a*: NIBSC/Science Photo Library; *Figures 5.8b, 5.23*: CNRI/Science Photo Library; *Figure 5.9*: Reprinted from Roitt, I. *et al*. (1996) *Immunology*, 4th edn, fig. 15.12, courtesy of Dr W. H. Hildemann by permission of Mosby, an imprint of Times International Publishers Ltd; *Figure 5.10*: Brian Rogers/Biofotos; *Figure 5.11*: Harland, W. B. *et al*. (1989) 'A Geologic Time Scale', Cambridge University Press; *Figures 5.12b, 5.24e*: © Mike Dodd; *Figure 5.13*: Reprinted with permission from Whittaker, R. H. and Feeny, P. P. 'Allelochemics, chemical interactions between species', *Science*, **171**, p. 757, Copyright 1971, American Association for the Advancement of Science; *Figure 5.14*: Adapted with permission from Rhoades, D. F. and Cates, R. G. (1976) 'Toward a general theory of plant antiherbivore chemistry', *Recent Advances in Phytochemistry*, **10**, pp. 168–213, Kluwer Academic/Plenum Publishers; *Figure 5.22*: Stan Osolinski/OSF; *Figure 5.23a*: CNRI/Science Photo Library; *Figure 5.23b*: Carreno, R. A. *et al*. (1997) 'Phylogenetic analysis of haemosporinid parasites (apicomplexa: haemosporina) and their coevolution with vectors and intermediate hosts', Archiv für protisten kunde, **148**, pp. 245–252, Urban and Fischer Verlag Niederlassung Jena;

CHAPTER 6

FIGURES

INDEX

Note: Entries in **bold** are key terms. Page numbers referring to information that is given only in a figure or caption are printed in *italics*.